W9-CUW-575

BLACKWATER LOCALITY NO. 1

A Stratified, Early Man Site in Eastern New Mexico

BY JAMES J. HESTER
with sections by
ERNEST L. LUNDELIUS, JR.
and
ROALD FRYXELL

Fort Burgwin Research Center
Southern Methodist University

This report on Blackwater Locality No. 1 is one of a series of publications dealing with the results of research on the history and ecology of New Mexico and adjacent areas, which are issued by the Fort Burgwin Research Center, a non-profit foundation created at the instance of the late Ralph M. Rounds for scientific and educational purposes and administered by Southern Methodist University. The publications, numbered consecutively, appear at irregular intervals.

The preparation of this publication was assisted by a grant-in-aid from the Wenner-Gren Foundation, and part of the initial research was supported by a National Science Foundation Grant to the Research Center.

© 1972 By Fort Burgwin Research Center, Inc.
Southern Methodist University

Fort Burgwin Research Center
Ranchos de Taos, New Mexico

Publication of the Fort Burgwin Research Center, No. 8

This work is dedicated to

all who have worked at

Blackwater Locality No. 1.

a--Johannes Iverson and Fred Wendorf collecting pollen samples, March 1956; b--excavations at El Llano Dig 1, Jesse Collins, unidentified laborer, Sam Sanders; c--1949-50 excavations of the Texas Memorial Museum, Hal Story, Glen Evans, and E.H. Sellards examining strata, East Wall, North Pit; d--F.E. Green seated left and unidentified companion salvaging mammoth, Aug. 1962; e--J. Hester excavating mammoth tooth, Locality 5, Sept. 1962; f--E.B. Howard with mammoth tusk, Anderson Basin, ca. 1932; g--Frank Hibben and Tom Bolack, governor of New Mexico, examining finds at El Llano Dig 1, Jan. 1963; h--excavations by Arthur Jelinek, 1957, Gary Ashby, Gordon Brown, Arthur Jelinek, Pete Brechemin; i--tents protecting finds at El Llano Dig 1, Jan. 1963; j--participants in the Palynology of the Pleistocene of the Southwest field trip, International Conference on Palynology, April 1962; k--James Warnica clearing mammoth limb bones at base of Gray Sand, 1956 or 1957; l--Portales businessmen discuss preservation of a portion of the site with Sam Sanders, Johannes Iverson, and Fred Wendorf, March 1956; m--Erik Reed excavating bison bones, probably North Pit, 1940; n--aerial view of El Llano Dig 1, Jan. 1963; o--Oscar Shay clearing mammoth bones, 1956; p--installation of the gravel mining dredge, 1954; q--photographing the El Llano Dig 1 with aid of the telephone company truck, Feb. 1963; r--Governor Jack Campbell with his children examining strata in the North Bank, El Llano Dig 1, 1963; s--members of the International Geological Congress with members of the California Institute of Technology excavating party, Mr. Prall, Dr. Victor Von Straelen, Mr. Peter Anderson, Lady Smith Woodward, Sir A. Smith Woodward, Dr. Chester Stock, Dr. John C. Merriam, Mr. Jake McGee, Mr. R.W. Wilson, Mr. Ridgley, Dr. E.B. Howard, and either F.D. Bode or H.D. Curry, Aug. 1933; t--Edwin Meachem, Governor of New Mexico, Sam Sanders, and Tom Bolack, Lt. Governor, 1962; u--Eastern New Mexico University students excavating mammoth, Nov. 1961. (All identifications of individuals read left to right.)

PREFACE

The significance of the finds of Paleo-Indian artifacts associated with extinct vertebrates in Blackwater Draw is known to all students of American Archaeology. Unfortunately, the exact nature of these finds has been only briefly summarized in various publications (Howard, 1935; Cotter, 1938a, 1938b; Wormington 1957; Sellards, 1952), with no comprehensive site report having been prepared to date. As a result, while the general nature of the finds is known, much of the detailed information from the site has never been published. The magnitude of this unreported material has been unknown to the general public. At least twenty field parties from nine different institutions have excavated at the site since 1932. The total excavation time expended is between 1,000 and 2,000 man-days. Yet the total published material from this work consists of less than 100 pages. Because of a fortunate series of events, much of the unpublished information from the site has been gathered together and is reported in this volume.

In the fall of 1961, I was conducting excavations at the Blackwater Draw gravel pit as part of the research on the High Plains Ecology Project sponsored by a National Science Foundation grant to the Fort Burgwin Research Center with Fred Wendorf as principal investigator. At that time, we decided to expand our knowledge of the site by consulting the material on file at the Texas Memorial Museum. This research revealed much original data recorded by E.H. Sellards and Glen L. Evans between 1949 and 1957. Dr. W.W. Newcomb, director of the Texas Memorial Museum, wished to have this material better known to the scientific public and suggested that it be described and assembled for publication. Dr. Newcomb made available all of that institution's collections and records pertaining to the site. In addition, because of the scattered nature of the reports on other work done at the pit we felt it would be appropriate to combine information on prior and recent research into one monograph. Consequently, additional information was requested from institutions and individuals who had

participated in the research. The response was extremely gratifying. Those contacted cooperated to the fullest extent, furnishing field notes, photographs, maps, etc. With this material on hand the American Philosophical Society provided a grant (Grant No. 3168 from the Penrose fund) to support the preparation of a manuscript. After this volume was partially completed major new finds at the site nearly doubled the quantity of material to be reported. Therefore, a second grant to aid manuscript preparation was obtained from the Wenner Gren Foundation for Anthropological Research. Excavations conducted by the author were funded by a portion of the NSF grant to the Fort Burgwin Research Center for the High Plains Ecology project and a grant from the State of New Mexico.

This volume, therefore, represents the efforts of a great many people whose contributions are hereby gratefully acknowledged. Cooperating institutions include: the California Institute of Technology, Eastern New Mexico University, El Llano Archaeological Society, The University of Pennsylvania Museum, The Philadelphia Academy of Natural Sciences, Portales News Tribune, The Texas Memorial Museum, the University Research Institute of The University of Texas, University of Texas Radiocarbon Laboratory, and The U.S. National Park Service. Persons who responded with information include: Joe Charboneau, Kathryn H. Clisby, E. Mott Davis, Carolyn Disker, Jerry Durett, Jeremiah Epstein, Gordon Greaves, Mrs. E.B. Howard, A.V. Kidder II, Willard Libby, Donald Moyer, W.W. Newcomb, Sam Sanders, Linton Satterthwaite, Albert H. Schroeder, Dee Ann Suhm, and H.M. Wormington.

The principal group of individuals contributing to this volume are those who excavated at the site over the years (see frontispiece). While many of these individuals have been forgotten, there are records of the following having worked there: George Agogino, A.W. Anderson, Ernst Antevs, Harry A. Bliss, F.D. Bode, Ted Bohannon, Alexander B. Brock, Gordon Brown,

Kirk Bryan, Malcom Bull, Bill Burnett, George Cheston, William T. Clark Jr., Robert Coffin, Jesse Collins, J.L. Cotter, Ambrose C. Crer III, Jack Cunningham, D. Curry, Frederika de Laguna, A.E. Dittert Jr., Ben Donathan, Glen L. Evans, Lincoln Godfrey, F.E. Green, Ray Griffin, Louis Griffith, Charles Harrison, Alton Hayes, Herbert Hemphill Jr., E.B. Howard, Arthur J. Jelinek, William E. King, Clyde Kluckhohn, Don Krieble, Dennis Lomas, Grayson E. Meade, Charles E. Mear, J. McGee, Clifton C. McGehee, Carl Moore, George Murname, J.D. Murray, Stuart A. Northrup, R.C. Pendergraft, Hollis Peter, Erik K. Reed, Paul Reiter, F.N. Richat, George O. Roberts, C.N. Russell, Howard Schmied, Otto Schoen, E.H. Sellards, Oscar Shay, Robert R. Solenberger, Chester Stock, Hal M. Story, James Vick, J.M. Warnica, Fred Wendorf, John White, R. Whiteman, R.W. Wilson, Adolf H. Witte, and Burton Yin.

I wish to express my appreciation to a number of people who have aided in the preparation of this manuscript through typing, drafting, and the printing of photographs. These individuals include: Mary Alexander, Marc Applebaum, Hugh Calkins, Anne R. Clark, Donna DeLozier, Maria Jorrin Driscoll, Audrey Hobler, Philip M. Hobler, Phyllis Hughes, Dick Leonard, Lois Leopold, Virginia Martin, Marcia McGee, Marilyn Miller, Francis Ortiz, Terry Resnick, Darwin Simnacher, Alice Wesche, Mrs. W. Klapp, and Mrs. G. Merriam. The text was typed for reproduction by Eve Dubus.

Compilation of the material for study included: the borrowing of artifacts from amateur archaeologists in the Portales area; the collection of photographs, letters, and notes from all persons and institutions engaged in work at the site; the correlation of this material by internal cross-checking; and the supplementation of the information by interviewing all of the principals involved, drawing upon their memory for additional facts and verification of data obtained through other means.

In effect, the research was historical in nature as some of the principals were deceased, and field notes and records were frequently inadequate. In contrast to typical archaeological site reports the major problem was the securing of adequate provenience data on the individual excavations and the specimens recovered in these excavations.

In retrospect, this has been a fascinating scientific jigsaw puzzle, one that has been continually stimulating and intellectually satisfying.

CONTENTS

CONTENTS

ILLUSTRATIONS

Frontispiece

TABLES

INTRODUCTION

Blackwater Draw consists of an extinct river bed in the headwaters of the Brazos River (Bryan, 1938; Price, 1944). At some time prior to the advent of man in the area, this stream was beheaded by the headward cutting of the Pecos River (Antevs, 1936, p. 304) with the result that since that time the water supply has been limited to local runoff. This condition led to the development of a series of small shallow ponds along the draw. These ponds have a history of fluctuating water levels associated with lacustrine deposition, interspersed with periods of erosion which alternately eroded the pond sediments or covered them with aeolian deposits. One such pond, located at the edge of the draw is Blackwater Locality No. 1. The specific location is in the SE 1/4 Section 25, TIN, R 34E, Roosevelt County, New Mexico (Fig. 1). This pond is unique in being situated at an elevation some 50 feet above the floor of the draw. The geological causes of this perched pond are yet to be fully explained. However, it is evident that there was present a fairly stable water supply through time which recent findings suggest was provided by a series of springs (Haynes and Agogino, 1966). The pond was oval in shape, approximately 100 yards east-west and 250 yards north-south. There was an outlet channel 50 yards in width at the south end of the pond which drained into the main body of the draw. The pond was probably never more than a few feet in depth. Between approximately 15,000 years ago and 8,000 years ago, when the pond dried up, a maximum of 12 to 15 feet of pond sediments were deposited. These strata differ strikingly in character and in included artifacts and fossils.

A brief summary of the geological evidence indicates that the pond sediments from early to late include (1) a fine grained light tan sand, termed the Gray Sand, (2) a massive medium sized brown sand, the Brown Sand Wedge, (3) a massive diatomaceous silt--the Diatomite, and (4) a massive organic stained fine grained silt--the Carbonaceous Silt. There is evidence that between each of these units the pond dried up. Following the deposition of the Carbonaceous Silt, the water table dropped below the surface and aeolian deposits record the geological history of the most recent 8,000 years at the site. Extinct animals are present in quantity in the Gray Sand unit, in association with Clovis artifacts. The overlying Brown Sand Wedge included a few extinct forms, primarily Bison and Folsom artifacts. The Diatomite contained the extinct Bison antiquus associated with Folsom culture artifacts. The Carbonaceous Silt contained bones of Bison (probably the recent species) associated with artifacts of the Parallel Flaked Horizon. The differing character of the pond sediments indicate that the pond varied through time in depth, clarity, salinity, vegetal growth, and freshwater faunas. The significance of these fluctuations is primarily climatological and is discussed in detail by Wendorf and Hester (n.d.).

Following the initial discovery of the site in 1932, major excavations were carried out by the following institutions: Philadelphia Academy of Natural Sciences and the University of Pennsylvania Museum, 1932-37; California Institute of Technology, 1933; Texas Memorial Museum, 1949-50, 1953-57; Museum of New Mexico, 1956, 1961-63; University of Chicago, 1956-57; Fort Burgwin Research Center, 1961-63; Texas Technological College, 1958, 1962, 1963; and Eastern New Mexico University, 1961. Finds by Eastern New Mexico University after March 1963 are reported elsewhere by Agogino and Hester (n.d.).

As the development of these studies is a complex matter we will consider their history at some length in the section to follow.

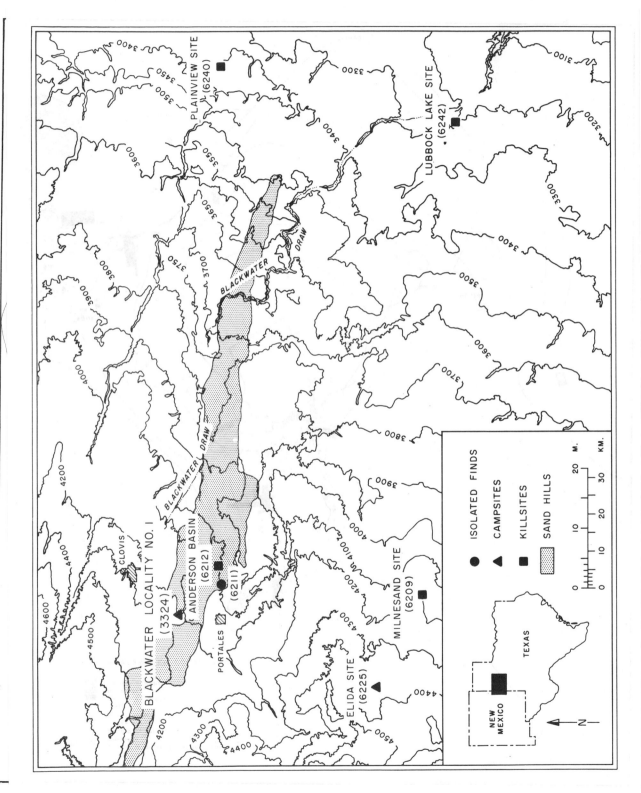

Fig. 1. Map of gravel pit vicinity. All site numbers are in the Laboratory of Anthropology system, Santa Fe, New Mexico.

HISTORY OF INVESTIGATIONS

University of Pennsylvania—Philadelphia Academy Expeditions

During the summer of 1932, A.W. Anderson of Clovis, New Mexico, called E.B. Howard's attention to a Folsom point that he had found in a blowout in Blackwater Draw. As a result, Howard (who had been digging at Burnet Cave) went to Clovis to investigate the site prior to returning to his post at the University Museum in Philadelphia. With Anderson and George Roberts, Howard visited several blowouts in the area. He then returned to Philadelphia with the intention of revisiting the Clovis area the following spring. A few months later, a pit was opened in Blackwater Draw by the New Mexico State Highway Department to supply gravel for the road being constructed between Clovis and Portales. During these operations quantities of animal bones in the "blue" layer were encountered. Early reports used the terms "blue" or "blue sands" to refer to the beds later designated "Brown Sand Wedge, Diatomite, and Carbonaceous Silt." The engineer in charge, Walter Burns, communicated with George Roberts, who relayed the information to Howard. This resulted in a revisit to the gravel pit by Howard in November 1932. At the same time, interested personnel on the staff of the Portales newspaper notified Stuart A. Northup, Clyde Kluckholn, and Paul Reiter of the University of New Mexico of the finds. On their visit to the pit December 22, 1932, they were unable to determine if the artifacts present were in direct association with the extinct vertebrates. However, a number of bones were collected and sent to the U.S. National Museum in January 1933. These bones were identified by C.W. Gilmore and C.L. Gazin as those of mammoth, bison, camel, and horse. In addition, artifacts were borrowed from local collectors which, with bones and a stratigraphic model of the site, were placed on exhibit in the library of the University of New Mexico.

The following summer Howard directed a joint University of Pennsylvania Museum-Academy of Natural Sciences of Philadelphia

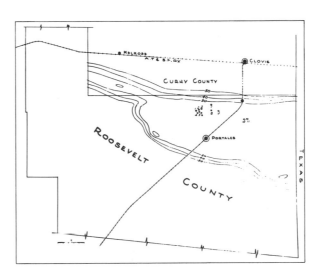

Fig. 2. Map of blowout sites in Blackwater Draw, from Howard (1935, Pl. XVII).

project with J. McGee and R. Whiteman participating. Investigations were made at the gravel pit and at ten blowouts (wind deflation basins) in Blackwater Draw (Fig. 2). The most important of the localities studied were the gravel pit (#7), Anderson Lakes (#10,11), and Beck Forest Lake (#3). Early in the season John C. Merriam, President of the Carnegie Institution of Washington, visited the site. He, in turn, made it possible for Chester Stock to organize a party from the California Institute of Technology (Howard, 1935, pp. 81-2).

Research conducted by the Howard party consisted of the study of the stratigraphy of the gravel pit and blowouts, the location of artifacts and vertebrate fossils, and the collection of molluscs, diatoms, and soil specimens for study. The California Institute of Technology party specialized in the recovery of the vertebrate fossils.

Fig. 3. View to the northwest of the South Pit 1933. Note mapping station in right center of photograph; this station is also located on the map (Fig. 26). Photo taken July 15, 1933, by F.D. Bode. Courtesy California Institute of Technology.

The following season, 1934, Howard returned to the gravel pit and continued archaeological excavations. Ernst Antevs, supported by a grant from the Carnegie Institution of Washington, was the member of the party responsible for a geological study of the sediments (Antevs, 1936).

In 1935 research at the pit was limited, and no full scale excavation was attempted. However, there is a newspaper article to the effect that on July 25, Harry A. Bliss, a paleontologist from the University of New Mexico, with three assistants, Robert Coffin, Hollis Peter, and Alton Hayes, visited the pit.

A field party under the direction of Howard and J.L. Cotter returned to the gravel pit July 1, 1936. The project was again jointly sponsored by the University of Pennsylvania Museum and the Academy of Natural Sciences of Philadelphia with financial assistance from the Carnegie Institution of Washington. The research was directed primarily toward the recovery of artifacts and fossils in association through detailed excavations (Cotter, 1938a).

Late in 1936 the finds began to receive national publicity. Popular articles describing the association of human artifacts with extinct animals appeared in the New Mexico Magazine and in the Literary Digest (Wallis, 1936; Anonymous, 1936). In March 1937, the Academy of Natural Sciences of Philadelphia sponsored an International Symposium on Early Man celebrating the 125th anniversary of the founding of the Academy. One of the special events at this symposium was the opening of a Hall of Early Man exhibits. Among the exhibits was a two-ton block of bones with artifacts in place from the Clovis site exhibited in a reconstructed pit.

The final field party under the direction of Howard and Cotter worked at the gravel pit from June 13 to August 13, 1937. The work consisted of an extension of the area excavated in 1936 (Fig. 30). An additional aspect of the research was the collecting of invertebrates by William T. Clarke Jr. (Clarke, 1938).

Following the end of the 1937 season the site was abandoned for a number of years. In

1940, Erik K. Reed of the U.S. National Park Service visited the site in order to determine if the pit was of sufficient importance to be preserved as a site of national historic interest. His report of January 27, 1941, states:

> The Clovis site is certainly worth doing something about, however; my idea would be to add it to Eastern New Mexico State Park, of which it would then become a major feature-- Designation as a National Historic Site certainly would be justifiable and desirable.

Reed quotes from a letter of November 28, 1940, from J.L. Cotter as follows:

> Here you have a fossil and artifact-- bearing stratum extending literally four square miles along the ancient lacustrine area. This deposit has been excavated on a massive scale at least three times, tons of invaluable evidence of human and fossil associations have been tossed up and not once was any effort made to make an intelligent record or to conserve material in situ, consider the chance of

the State of New Mexico when they were developing Eastern New Mexico State Park with CCC labor. They actually excavated by slow strip operations an artificial lake bed going right through the blue clay and sand zone. Countless mammoth and bison bones and many artifacts were encountered . . . .

> As you know, there is probably no other fossil bed in the country which lends itself so perfectly to in situ demonstration. After the 1937 field party for the Academy of Natural Sciences, we crated and moved several tons of fossil material to Philadelphia, where we erected a complete reproduction of 200 square feet of the most concentrated fossil finds replacing the mammoth and bison bones in their exact original positions as recorded by original triangulation charts and photographs. Half a dozen artifacts, including the two bone shaft portions, were also placed in replica, where they had been found among the bones. One exhibit was designed as a feature of the Hall of Man during the Symposium on Early Man in 1936, but remained for some time afterward because of the interest shown in it by visitors. It has always been my dream that such an exhibit could be made in situ over the exact spot,

Fig. 4. View of the east side of the pit showing concrete foundations of gravel sifter utilized by New Mexico State Highway Department. Photo taken July 15, 1933, by F.D. Bode. Courtesy of California Institute of Technology

with a permanent structure erected over it,
after the manner of the splendid museum at
Moundville, Alabama, constructed by CCC
labor over "in situ" mound cemetery excavation . . . If it were possible for the State of
New Mexico to extend its park area five miles
west to include the gravel pit sites and erect

such facilities it would be an ideal . . . I
know full well the improbability of such a pro-
gram being carried out . . . .

        As we know, these efforts to preserve the
site as an outdoor museum were unsuccessful.

Texas Memorial Museum Excavations

        Between 1940 and 1949, interest in the
pit lapsed with the only visitors being amateur
archaeologists interested in augmenting their
collections. This fact is attested to in the
field notes of A.H. Witte who was studying
early man sites in the High Plains for the Texas
Memorial Museum during the summer of 1946.
He visited amateur collectors in the area and
noted artifacts from the dumps of the gravel pit
in the collections of twenty-five or thirty different persons.

        Witte continued to conduct surveys and
excavations of early man sites in the High
Plains and in July of 1949, at the request of
E.H. Sellards, began testing the deposits of
the gravel pit which was termed by Sellards,
Blackwater Locality, No. 1 (Fig. 5). Almost
immediately Witte began making finds of artifacts and vertebrate fossils in situ. His excavations with two assistants totaled thirty
man-days in July and twenty-six man-days in
August. During August, Glen Evans visited

the site, and plans were made to continue the
excavations. On November 16, Witte returned
to the site with three assistants and began
cleaning the exposed banks preparatory to detailed stratigraphic studies. After these cuts
were prepared, Glen Evans returned to the site
and prepared the maps and stratigraphic sections presented in this volume (Figs. 35, 36,
38, 39, 44). In addition he worked out the
geologic descriptions of the various units.
This description became the type section for
the site (Fig. 37).

        In early December 1949, E.H. Sellards
made his first visit to the site which was to be
followed by many other trips over the following
decade. Later that month excavations were
discontinued for the winter.

        The 1950 field season began in May, again
under the field direction of Witte and Evans with
one assistant. In June, the crew increased to
eleven with Sellards and Grayson Meade participating. This crew excavated until the end
of July. During this season, research was
concentrated on the geologic and stratigraphic
studies with much effort being expended in the
location of artifacts and fossils in situ (Fig. 5).
A total of 584 man-days were spent digging between July 1949, and July 1950.

        Following the 1950 season, work at the
pit was discontinued until August 1953. During this interval, Glen Evans left the employ of
the Texas Memorial Museum. As a result, all
Sellard's work done after 1953 was to suffer
from the lack of Evans' precise knowledge of
the stratigraphy of the site. A second factor
of importance was the resumption, in 1952, of
gravel mining at the pit by a private firm headed
by Sam Sanders.

        In August of 1953, Sellards began an as-
sociation with amateur archaeologists in

Fig. 5. Texas Memorial Museum excavations in 1949. The location is probably
the west side of the South Pit, Station E.
Texas Memorial Museum photo.

Fig. 6. Sellards excavating at the gravel pit, 1955. Probably the south edge of the North Pit, Station A. Courtesy Texas Memorial Museum.

Portales which was to last until 1957. During this interval, two amateurs, Oscar Shay and James M. Warnica, were part-time employees of the Texas Memorial Museum. They worked on a part-time basis at the pit in practically every month between August, 1953, and October, 1957. They excavated at the site with Sellards and also in his absence. Finds were given field catalog numbers and shipped to the Texas Memorial Museum. Sellards also made periodic trips to the pit to continue excavations during this interval. He worked at the pit in April and May 1954; in June, August, and November 1955; and May 1956 (correspondence and Sellards' field notes) (Fig. 6).

A primary emphasis during the 1953-1957 field seasons was on the salvage of specimens as they were uncovered by the gravel mining. An additional concern was the securing of samples for radiocarbon dating.

Between 1957 and his death on February 4, 1961, Sellards concentrated on the analysis of materials from the pit. He shipped bones to specialists for C-14 dating, uranium, and fluorine content analyses. He also hired Robert Pendergraft to make maps of the site recording strata and locations of excavations (Fig. 15). Unfortunately, Sellards' untimely death prevented him from assembling these materials for publication. However, his unflagging interest in the site compelled him to continue excavations until he was past 80 years of age, a devotion to science difficult to surpass.

Other Research

Concurrently with the Texas Memorial Museum excavations of 1956 and 1957, excavations were conducted by other research parties. In 1953 after the excavations at the Midland Site, Glen Evans informed Fred Wendorf of the importance of the Blackwater Site and of its impending destruction through gravel mining. As a result, Wendorf contacted New Mexico State officials and local officials in Portales in an attempt to have part of the site set aside as a scientific preserve. By May of 1956 it had become apparent that no such preserve would be established and the site would continue to be destroyed. At this time Fred Wendorf and A.E. Dittert Jr., of the Museum of New Mexico, decided to salvage what information they could from the site. Excavations were conducted May 21-26, 1956 (Dittert, 1957, Fig. 7). Results included the finding of vertebrate remains and stratigraphic details of the beds at one margin of the former pond.

During the summers of 1956 and 1957, Arthur J. Jelinek, at that time of the University

Fig. 7. Dittert and Wendorf excavations, 1956. Arrow indicates point where Sellards and Warnica obtained charred and uncharred bones dated by Humble Oil.

Fig. 8. Excavations directed by Arthur Jelinek, 1957.

Fig. 9. Excavations in Folsom age campsite debris, Locality 4, west side of pit. Recorders are James J. Hester and James M. Warnica, September 1962.

of Chicago, conducted excavations at the site. He located a partially articulated mammoth in the Brown Sand Wedge unit and collected specimens for radioactivity analyses (Fig. 8).

Between 1958 and 1961, little research was accomplished at the site. In November 1958, Fred Wendorf and F.E. Green visited the site as part of their investigations on the High Plains Ecology Project (Wendorf, 1961), a project sponsored at that time by Texas Technological College and supported by the National Science Foundation. Research at the pit included the location of a Folsom point in situ and the collecting of samples for pollen analysis. Unfortunately, no pollen was recovered from the samples.

The High Plains Ecology Project was resumed in August 1961, with sponsorship now provided by the Fort Burgwin Research Center aided by a new grant from the National Science Foundation. Personnel on the project included Fred Wendorf, Jerry Harbour, and James J. Hester. The destruction of the site through gravel mining by this date was nearly complete. As a result, the original stratigraphy was preserved in only a few small sections. Research focused on the collection of samples for pollen analysis, C-14 dating, radioactivity tests, and the identification of invertebrates. Excavation of archaeological materials by Hester revealed several Folsom age bison kills, fragments of a Parallel Flaked Horizon bison kill, and Folsom age campsite debris (Fig. 9). Field work was resumed in June 1962, with Hester and Vance Haynes reexamining the stratigraphy and collecting more samples (Fig. 10). In August 1962, Bob Slaughter began washing sediments of the Brown Sand Wedge unit for micro-vertebrates (Fig. 11). A final type of salvage was the removal of soil profiles by Roald Fryxell as permanent study and exhibit specimens (Fig. 12).

Beginning in September 1962, a series of major finds were made along the northwest border of the pit in an extensive area being stripped preparatory to gravel mining. Between September 1962, and the summer of 1964, salvage excavations were carried out by the Museum of New Mexico, Eastern New Mexico University, Texas Technological College, and the El Llano Archaeological Society of Portales.

Fig. 10. Vance Haynes correlating pollen samples with stratigraphy, south wall South Pit, High Plains Ecology Project, 1962.

Fig. 11. Bob Slaughter washing samples from the Brown Sand Wedge for microvertebrates, south wall South Pit. High Plains Ecology Project, 1962.

As the pit operator held a lease on the privately owned property he had complete control of permission to excavate. Owing to the intense local and regional interest generated, local pressure groups were extremely influential. The result was that no one institution remained in favor with the gravel pit operator for any length of time. Because of the importance of the site, as soon as one group of excavators became personna non grata, another group moved in. The ensuing excavations became scientific chaos. The major excavations during this period are as follows: September 1962, Hester excavations (Localities 4 & 5) for the Museum of New Mexico and the Fort Burgwin Research Center as part of the High Plains Ecology project. September 1962, F.E. Green of Texas Technological College and amateurs of Portales continued excavation of the cut opened by Hester. A few days later

Fig. 12. Roald Fryxell removing a soil profile from the North Bank, El Llano Dig 1, 1963.

Fig. 13. Aerial view, toward the northeast, of El Llano Dig 1, January 1963. The excavated mammoths are visible as is the bulldozer-cut North Bank. At upper left, men are standing near a former campsite on the caliche bedrock. The white squares and rectangles are plastic sheets used to protect the bones.

J.D. Murray of Portales, who operates the mining dredge, located a hot spot of artifacts near the area that had just been excavated and recovered about 50 artifacts in two hours of digging. As soon as this fact became known locally, a party of students from Eastern New Mexico University was sent to the spot and over 200 artifacts were recovered in two days

digging. When Hester learned of these finds he returned to the site and opened another cut (Locality 6) which failed to produce much of scientific value.

A short time later, on November 29, 1962, another major find was made of mammoth bones in association with artifacts. Excavations were begun immediately by the newly organized El Llano Archaeological Society under the direction of James M. Warnica. A week later, Hester learned of the finds and returned to the site. A joint project was formed by the Museum of New Mexico and the El Llano Society, and excavations continued until January 1963. By that time a total of five mammoths had been found in association with more than 100 artifacts of Clovis age (Figs. 13, 14). Adjacent to the mammoth killsite was a 12 foot high stratigraphic cut with superimposed Folsom, Parallel Flaked, and Archaic artifacts. At the termination of this excavation, it was decided to limit the material reported in this volume to that obtained prior to February 1963. Subsequent to this decision, additional excavations have been conducted at the site by Eastern New Mexico University under the direction of George A. Agogino. Results of this work are to be published in a separate volume (Agogino and Hester, n.d.).

Correlation of Excavations

A major problem impeding the compilation of information presented in this volume was due to the fact that no base map had been prepared on which the location of the various excavations could be plotted. This problem arose because the progressive gravel mining removed all temporary benchmarks so that each excavating party utilized different vertical and horizontal datum points. However, in spite of these difficulties, it has been possible to compile the base map presented in Figure 15. In order to understand the reliability of the locations plotted, the method of construction of the maps will be discussed.

A map was prepared by Glen Evans in December 1949, consisting of the outline of the North and South Pits with areas excavated in 1949-50, plus a series of contours which

delineated the natural depression in which these pits lay. This map of Evans' has been utilized as a base on which additional information has been plotted.

Correlation of the finds of Howard and Cotter were then possible as their excavations were plotted in reference to the outlines of the south pit. Fortunately, the outline of the pit walls had changed little between 1932 and 1949.

Following excavations in November 1955, and again on October 26, 1957, Sellards hired a surveyor in Portales, Robert Pendergraft, to make a map of his recent finds, the outline of the gravel pit, and the elevation of the strata exposed at that time. These maps consisted of a series of stations which were unfortunately

Fig. 14. General view of excavations, El Llano Dig 1. In the foreground is Mammoth No. 2, Mammoth No. 1 is in the middleground, and the North Bank in the background.

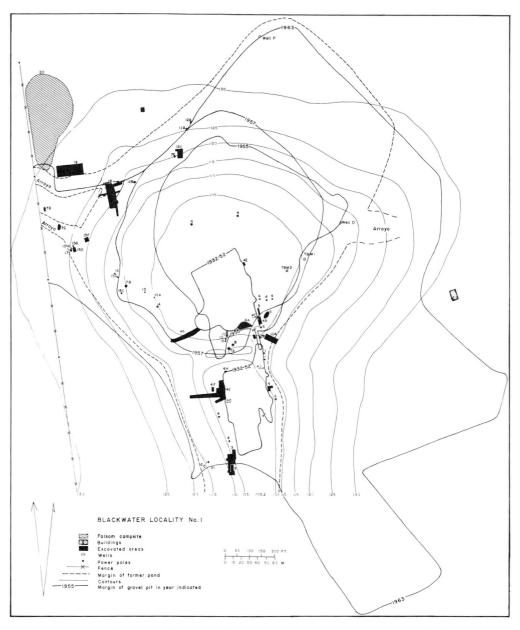

Fig. 15. Master map of all excavations at the gravel pit prior to February 1963. 1, E.B. Howard 1932-34; 2, J.L. Cotter 1936; 3, J.L. Cotter 1937; 4, TMM excavations 1949-50; 5, Sellards Locality B 1954; 6, Warnica and Shay 1954; 7, Sellards 1955 (7A, Clovis Bison Dig; 7B, Pit 1; 7C, Pit 2; 7D, Pit 3; 7E, elephant locality; 8, Warnica and Brown 1955; 9, Shay mammoth dig 1956; 10, Wendorf and Dittert 1956; 11, Jelinek 1957; 11A, Wendorf and Green 1958; 12, Hester 1961 (12A, Locality 1; 12B, Locality 2; 12C, Locality 3); 13, ENMU mammoth, 1961; 14, Green 1962; 15, Hester 1962; (15A, Mammoth Jan. 31, 1962; 15B, Pollen samples June 1962; 15C, Diatomite C-14 sample, 1962; 15D, Mammoth Aug. 8, 1962; 15E, Locality 4 Sept. 1962; 15F, Locality 5 Sept. 1962; 15G, Locality 6; 15H, Jess Collins dig 1962); 16, Warnica Agate Basin Locality Aug. 1962; 17, ENMU Spring Conduit Sept. 1962; 18, El Llano Dig 1 Dec. 1962 – March 1963; 19, Hester Jan. 1963.

keyed to a temporary bench mark on a power pole. This power pole was later moved and the area in which it had been located removed in the process of gravel mining. As the finds plotted were of importance (locating much of Sellards' work between 1955 and 1957), all the maps were shown to Pendergraft in 1962. He succeeded in establishing a horizontal correlation for all maps made between 1955 and 1957. This was accomplished by triangulation from points in common on all maps--in this case, the fence line, power poles along the fence line, the main gravel plant building, and a temporary powder house. These maps were correlated with Evans' 1949 base map by the overlap of stations on the 1955 map with Station A of the 1949-50 excavation.

In January 1963, Pendergraft and Hester revisited the site and mapped, with a theodolite, the outline of the gravel pit at that time and the position of El Llano Dig 1 and several areas excavated by Hester in 1962.

A final portion of map correlation was the plotting on the base map of the excavations of Hester, 1961; Green, 1962; Warnica and Collins, 1962; and Eastern New Mexico University, 1962. This was accomplished by correlation of points on location maps prepared by Hester at the time of these respective excavations with the position of these reference points on the base map. While these location maps were prepared with use of a Brunton compass, it is assumed that they are reasonably accurate.

Correlation of Profiles

Elevations of beds exposed in the walls of the North and South pits were recorded by Evans in 1949. These elevations are taken from an arbitrary datum which was also used as the datum for the contours of the depression surrounding the pits (Fig. 15).

Elevations taken by Sellards in 1955 were also taken from an arbitrary vertical datum. However, one of his stations coincides with a point on the pit wall which had been recorded by Evans. As a result, it has been possible to apply a correlation factor to Sellards 1955 readings which permits them to be plotted with reference to Evans' arbitrary datum. Some error is probable in this correlation as both measurements were made on the unconformities between beds. In addition, the exact points cannot be established with a

horizontal accuracy of less than 10 feet. Thus, we are assuming in this correlation that the position of the unconformities between the beds was clear at the times of measurement and that these unconformities were relatively level. Bearing these considerations in mind, we assume the degree of error in the correlation is approximately plus or minus six inches.

Vertical correlation of the beds exposed at El Llano Dig 1 was accomplished by locating the point at which Evans' 130-foot contour crossed the fence line. A mapping station was established there through triangulation with a theodolite. Again it is assumed the probable error is within six inches. Unfortunately, some of the other excavations were never tied into a vertical datum and cannot be correlated.

Summary

It has been more than thirty years since the first finds of extinct animals in association with human artifacts were made at the Blackwater Draw gravel pit. During this interval there has been scientific research at the site for twenty-two of these years, of which ten seasons were characterized by extensive excavations. A total of nine institutions have sponsored research with a multitude of scien-

tists participating. The results of this research has been of extreme importance in the study of early man in North America. These findings are described in detail in Chapter IV, Results of Research. Before we discuss these results, it is necessary to review how the site has been altered through time by progressive gravel mining.

HISTORY OF GRAVEL MINING

In the spring of 1932, the New Mexico State Highway Department began explorations for gravel in the Clovis-Portales area preparatory to the building of a road between the two cities. They located a major deposit seven miles north of Portales on the north side of Blackwater Draw in May. The contract for the highway was let September 22, and excavations were begun to secure gravel. A North Pit and a South Pit were excavated to a depth of twenty feet with the aid of trucks and teams with slips (Fig. 16). Gravel was mined until December, 1932, at which time the pits were abandoned.

The two pits opened in 1932 remained essentially unchanged in the following two decades. During this interval, extensive archaeological and paleontological researches were carried out. As a result, we have detailed data on the nature of the strata exposed in the pit walls at that time.

The land on which the pit is located is privately owned. In the 1930's the land was part of the Anderson Carter Ranch. By 1952, the land had been purchased by Charlie Baxter of Texico, New Mexico. In May of that year, Sam Sanders of Portales obtained a lease on the mineral rights, and a few months later began mining sand and gravel with a drag line (Fig. 17). There was a ready market for the sand and gravel as this was the only pit in operation for a radius of seventy-five to one hundred miles. The gravel operation expanded rapidly with the drag line being replaced in September 1954, with a hydraulic suction pump mounted on a dredge (Figs. 18, 20). The hydraulic mining included the use of giant bulldozers and earth moving carryalls to remove the overburden and transport the gravel to the dredge. Another destructive element in the hydraulic mining was the breaking up of the gravel by blasting (Fig. 19). The final step was the transport of the sand and gravel through steel pipes by water pressure to the series of conveyor belts and screens which sorted and piled them. The result was the complete destruction of the strata and the

Fig. 16. The initial gravel mining in 1932. Courtesy Mrs. E.B. Howard.

Fig. 17. Gravel mining with a drag line, 1952-54. Photo courtesy Gordon Greaves.

pulverizing of the included fossils. As the fossiliferous strata overlay the commercial deposits, it was impossible to mine the gravel and at the same time preserve the overlying sediments with their included scientific specimens.

By March of 1956, destruction of the site had proceeded to such a degree that various archaeologists and palynologists concerned over the loss of prehistoric materials decided to attempt to have a portion of the site set aside as a scientific preserve. On March 24,

Fig. 18. Gravel dredge in operation, 1962. Photo courtesy Gordon Greaves.

Fig. 19. Blasting at the gravel pit, 1954. Photo courtesy Gordon Greaves.

Fig. 20. Aerial view to the east of the North Pit in 1954 at the time of installation of the dredge. Photo courtesy Gordon Greaves.

Johannes Iverson, Kathryn Clisby, and Fred Wendorf visited the site with influential members of the Portales community. On April 2, E.H. Sellards also visited the site and discussed its preservation with local citizens. During these visits, a plan was devised whereby the city of Portales would raise a fund to purchase five acres of the site to be set aside as a scientific preserve (Fig. 21). However, this plan failed. Those responsible for the gravel mining were not willing to accept the plan because, it seems, they believed <u>any</u> <u>area</u> set aside would interfere with the removal of the gravel and, therefore, increase their costs. As a result, the plan was abandoned.

Since 1956, the mining has continued with a normal working crew of ten to twenty men operating two bulldozers, two carryalls, two payloaders, (Fig. 22) a fleet of trucks, and the dredge. The total quantity of earth-moving accomplished has been enormous with 100 to 200 cubic yards of sand and gravel and an equal amount of overburden being moved daily.

By 1961, the area mined out corresponded closely to the original limits of the prehistoric pond. Only scattered sections at the extreme edges of the former pond remained as examples of the original stratigraphy. In December of that year, a series of sixty core-drilled tests were made to map the gravel deposits. These tests extended across the 640-acre section to the south of the gravel pit and for 2,000 feet to the northwest of the pit. The results of these tests indicated a negative correlation between the thickness of the gravel deposit and the presence of the overlying fossiliferous pond deposits. Unfortunately, this information was obtained too late to help preserve much of scientific value as the locations of all the original finds had been destroyed (Fig. 23).

Fig. 21. View of south end of North Pit looking west. The photo shows the visit of Katherine Clisby, Johannes Iverson, Fred Wendorf, and Portales businessmen to select an area to be set aside as a scientific preserve, March 24, 1956. The scientific preserve is outlined in black. Locations of specific excavations are shown by number as follows: (1) Wendorf and Dittert Trench A, (2) Wendorf and Dittert Trench B, (3) Sellards' Clovis Bison Dig, (4) Brown and Warnica Peccary Dig, (5) Jelinek Dig, (6) Shay mammoth excavation. The excavations by Sellards in May 1955 were in the ditch immediately behind the group. Identification of locations of above excavations provided by James M. Warnica and Don Krieble. Photo courtesy Gordon Greaves.

Fig. 22. Stripping of pond sediments to reach underlying gravel, west side of pit, 1962. Bulldozer at upper left is on sediments overlying Locality 5. Photo courtesy Gordon Greaves.

Fig. 23. Aerial view to northeast of entire gravel pit, January 1963. Cars in upper left-hand corner are parked at the site of El Llano Dig 1.

RESULTS OF RESEARCH

As the research was accomplished by different parties at different times, it is necessary to summarize separately the results of each excavation. In addition, we must bear in mind the fact that over the past thirty-five years, research techniques have changed; consequently we are not attempting a critique of the results of each research party, but are only interested in reporting what was found. Another complicating factor is that the gravel mining beginning in 1952 revealed new stratigraphic sections differing slightly from those exposed earlier. The findings of the various expeditions reported in this section will be described in chronological order beginning with Howard's work.

University of Pennsylvania—Philadelphia Academy Finds

Investigations at the site were carried out under the overall supervision of E.B. Howard from 1932 through 1937. The efforts were centered on the gravel pit, but numerous other blowout sites along Blackwater Draw were also examined. At the gravel pit the work included stratigraphic studies, sampling for identification of fossils-diatoms, snails, and pollen grains; and the excavation of bones and artifacts from the various pond units. The findings of each of these efforts are described below.

STRATIGRAPHY

Geologic studies by Ernst Antevs in 1934 are summarized in two reports describing the stratigraphy (Antevs, 1936, 1949). As the stratigraphic profiles reported differ in content, both will be reproduced here.

The 1936 stratigraphic description (Table I) is keyed to a photograph shown as Figure 24 below. Owing to differences in nomenclature, modern bed designations have been appended to Antev's description as an aid in correlation of finds of the 1932-37 expeditions with those of later parties. These correlations are the responsibility of the current author (Hester).

TABLE I

STRATIGRAPHIC BED DESCRIPTIONS
(AFTER ANTEVS, 1936)

(Probable Modern Designation-Jointed Sand)

"(d) At top, several feet red-brown, wind-blown sand.

(Carbonaceous Silt)

Bed 3   3 feet (average exposure of 1933, 17 inches) light blue-gray clay. Bones of mammoth and bison, artifacts. Sharp limit.

(Diatomite)

Bed 2   (c) 15 inches dark blue-gray clay grading into underlying bed. Bones of mammoth and bison.

(Brown Sand Wedge)

Bed 1   2 feet (average in 1933, 18 inches) medium light blue-gray clay. Bones of bison, and, in upper part, of mammoth. Sharp limit.

(Gray Sand)

(b) 2 1/2 feet silty clay, cream-colored with gray or pink spots. Sharp limit.

(Red Gravel)

(a) 5 feet red-brown sand with some gravel . ."

Fig. 24. Stratigraphy of beds exposed on the east side of the pit during the summer of 1934 (after Antevs, 1936 Pl. 17). Modern bed designations are shown on the left.

The stratigraphy published by Antevs in 1949 gives a more detailed description of the beds and included fossils. In addition, a new series of designations is given to the described strata. The profile is then correlated with one from Anderson Basin (Fig. 25).

TABLE II

STRATIGRAPHIC BED DESCRIPTIONS
(AFTER ANTEVS, 1949)

(Probable Modern Designation-Jointed Sand)

Bed 6   (= bed e in Anderson Basin) at top. Several feet of brown to red-brown wind-blown sand. Contains bison bones up to 1.5 feet above the base (Cotter 1938a pp. 8, 10). Break and some erosion, followed by deposition of a different character--disconformity.

(Carbonaceous Silt, Diatomite)

Bed 5   (= d and c) Two to six feet of blue-gray silt-clay, silt, and sand, mixed or in layers, with silt predominating; the "blue clay" = "blue silt" or "blue sand." Locally the middle part of the bed is distinctly darker than the lower and upper part of the blue-gray color may be caused, at least in part, by organic matter and by reduced iron due to poor aeration and drainage.

Bison (Bison taylori) [Bison antiquus] is represented by large numbers of skull and skeletal remains throughout the bed, elephant or mammoth by tusks, skulls, and bones up to within six inches of the top (Stock and Bode 1938, pp. 225, 239; Cotter 1938a, pp. 8, 10; Cotter 1938b, p. 116).

Diatoms are distributed throughout the bed being most frequent near the base where they locally form almost pure diatomite. The diatom flora changes gradually from a fresh water type at the bottom of the bed to a relatively saline type at the top (K.E. Lohman in Howard 1935, pp. 88; Patrick 1938).

Mollusks occur in the lowest part of the bed in the southeast corner of the gravel pit. Eleven species have been identified, mostly forms found under debris of flood plains and in lakes (Clarke 1938).

Artifacts have been found sparsely throughout the blue-gray silt. Several were associated with bison and mammoth (Howard 1935, pp. 95, 93; Stock and Bode 1937, pp. 225; Cotter 1938a, pp. 11, 12; 1938b, pp. 116).

(Gray Sand)

Bed 4   Two and one-half feet of white sand speckled with particles of magnatite, the speckled sand. Observed only on the west side of the gravel pit.

Bison and mammoth bones have been found in the topmost foot, while horse occurs throughout the bed and most frequently in the lower part (Cotter 1938a, pp. 10, 11; 1938b, p. 166).

Diatoms are lacking in the lower part, but are present near the top, and there indicate a lake or pond with slightly brackish water (Patrick 1938, p. 21).

Artifacts of bone and chalcedony have been found in association with mammoth and bison in the upper 12 inches of the bed (Cotter 1938a, pp. 11, 12; 1938b, pp. 117). Disconformity, a long break, marked especially by caliche formation (see below).

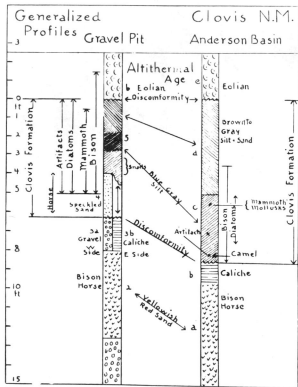

Fig. 25. Stratigraphic profiles from the gravel pit and Anderson Basin (after Antevs, 1949, p. 186).

(Brown Sand Wedge)

Bed 3b   (= b) On the east side of the gravel pit the blue-gray silt, bed 5, is underlaid by six inches to three feet of cream-colored calcareous clay with gray or pink spots--soft soil level, previous to the deposition of the overlying beds (Sellards 1940, pp. 398).

(Lag Gravel at Base of Gray Sand)

[Not designated as a separate bed by other researchers]

Bed 3a   On the west side of the pit the speckled sand is underlaid by three inches to two feet of gravel (Cotter 1938a, pp. 8). Absent on the east side, this gravel may be the correlative of the caliche. Each is underlaid by the yellowish-red sand, bed 2. Caliche forms in warm, arid, and semiarid regions; and the gravel may be a residue (channel deposit) of dry-climate erosion.

(Red Gravel)

Bed 2   (= a) Three to six feet of yellowish-red sand, the so called "pink sand", "red sand", or "yellow sand". It contains bones of bison and horse (Howard, 1935, pp. 91; Stock and Bode, 1938, pp. 225, 237).

(Red Gravel)

Bed 1   More than nine feet of reddish gravel with clay nodules (Howard, 1935, pp. 84). No fossils reported (Antevs 1949, p. 187).

The primary difference between Antevs efforts and later research is that he reported mammoth remains in the upper part of the "blue sands" (the Carbonaceous Silt). This occurrence has not been validated by subsequent research and is here assumed by the author to be an error in bed identification.

A stratigraphic profile is also presented by Stock and Bode (1938, p. 223) as follows:

TABLE III

STRATIGRAPHIC BED DESCRIPTIONS
(STOCK AND BODE 1938)

(Probable Modern Designation)

1. Wind-blown sand and dump materials excavated from the pit during quarrying operations.

(Carbonaceous Silt, Diatomite)

2. Six feet of blue-gray sandstone, the Blue Sand, of medium to fine-grained texture, containing most of the mammalian materials as well as artifacts.

(Brown Sand Wedge)

3. Two feet of white, yellow, green, or reddish clay, the Caliche, occurring as lenses immediately below the Blue Sand on the eastern side of the Gravel Pit. Absent on west side.

(Gray Sand)

4. Two feet of an almost pure white sand speckled with numerous particles of magnatite, the Speckled Sand, absent on east side but possibly the correlative of the Caliche.

(Red Gravel)

5. Five to six feet of yellow and red medium to coarse grained sandstone containing pebble conglomerate lenses, the Yellow Sand.

(Red Gravel)

6. A pebble conglomerate containing sand and clay concretions, the gravel, exposed in lower part of the sides and in the bottom of the pit.

The vertical and horizontal exposure of these beds were plotted and published (Stock and Bode, 1938, Figs. 1,3). These figures are reproduced below (Figs. 26, 27, and 28).

ENVIRONMENTAL RESEARCH

Numerous types of environmental studies were carried out on samples collected by the University Museum--Philadelphia Academy expeditions.

Diatoms: Six samples, as follows, were collected from the pit by Howard for

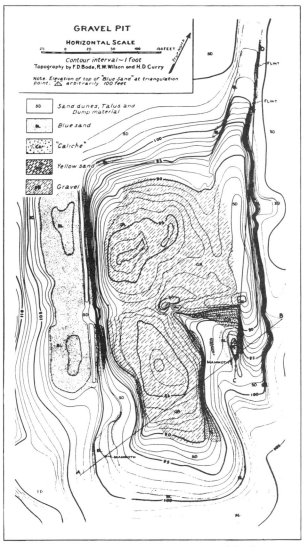

Fig. 26. Map showing exposures of beds in 1933. Flints and mammoths are those recorded by Howard (1935). Profile lines are keyed to profiles in Figure 27. Map from Stock and Bode (1938, Fig. 1).

TABLE IV

LOCATION OF DIATOM SAMPLES COLLECTED BY HOWARD

Sample No.	Probable Modern Bed Designation
1.	(Carbonaceous Silt)--Pit, east side, top of blue sand
2.	(Diatomite)--Pit, east side, middle of blue sand
3.	(Brown Sand Wedge)--Pit, east side, bottom of blue sand
4.	(Carbonaceous Silt)--Pit, west side, top of blue sand
5.	(Diatomite)--Pit, west side, middle of blue sand
6.	(Diatomite)--Pit, west side, bottom of blue sand

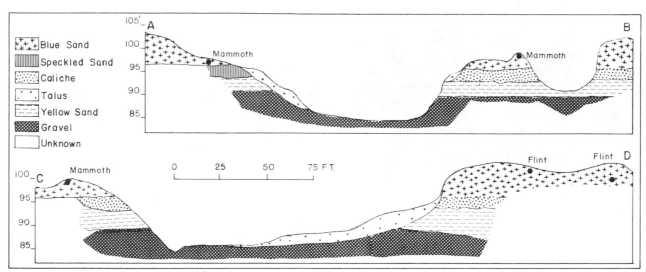

Fig. 27. Cross-sections of beds studied by California Institute of Technology field party, summer of 1933. The profiles are keyed to the site map, Figure 26. Vertical elevations are keyed to those on the site base map, Figure 15.

study. Identifications were accomplished by Kenneth E. Lohman.

Lohman identified a total of 89 species and varieties of diatoms, of which 68 are living at present in fresh water lakes and streams, and 21 are living sparingly in freshwater lakes, but more frequently in saline lakes and brackish estuaries (Howard, 1935, p. 87). Unfortunately, these species are not listed. Another difficulty is that a total of 18 samples were collected from five sites of which the gravel pit was one. From Howard's report it is not possible to determine which species were identified at each site. On the basis of the diatoms, Howard concludes that there was an increase in salinity of the lake during the period of deposition of the blue sand, an inference which is substantiated by the geological evidence for increasing aridity during this interval.

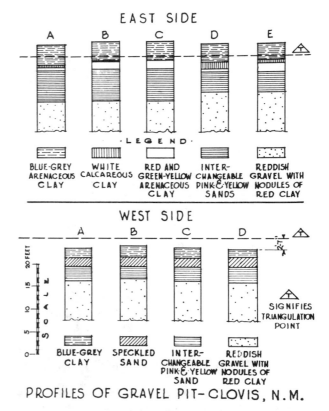

PROFILES OF GRAVEL PIT-CLOVIS, N.M.

Fig. 28. Profiles of the gravel pit drawn the summer of 1933, by the California Institute of Technology party. Probable modern bed designations are as follows; Reddish gravel with nodules of red clay = Red Gravel, Interchangeable pink and yellow sand = late facies of Red Gravel, Speckled Sand = Gray Sand, Red and green-yellow arenaceous clay = probably the Brown Sand Wedge, White calcareous clay = Diatomite, Blue-grey arenaceous clay = Carbonaceous Silt, Blue-grey clay = the Diatomite and Carbonaceous Silt combined.

Diatom samples were also collected by Howard during the 1936 season from the exposed west wall of the Mammoth Pit excavations (Fig. 29). The samples were submitted to the Academy of Natural Sciences of Philadelphia where they were identified by Ruth Patrick (1938, pp. 17-20). Specimens were abundant in the speckled sand and blue sand (Cotter's units B, D, F, and G, Fig. 29). Species identified by Patrick are listed in Table V. Ecological interpretations made by her are as follows: The flora in the speckled sand was fresh to brackish in type; and the flora of the blue clay [sand] was a fresh water type near the bottom of the bed changing to a more saline type toward the top. There was no diatom flora in the overlying brown sand unit [Jointed Sand].

The location of the samples collected and a description of the methodology used in Table V are quoted below.

Sample No. 9.	Yellow sand from the lowest part of the speckled sand. (Nos. 3101-3109)
Sample No. 2.	Speckled sand from below blue clay. (Nos. 3111-18)
Sample No. 10.	Lowest part of blue clay. Specimens taken from near mammoth bones. (Nos. 3121-3130)
Sample No. 1.	Bluish sandy silt from about lower jaw of mammoth. (Nos. 3131-3140)
Sample No. 3.	Bluish gray silt, middle level where bison bones were thickest. (Nos. 3141-3150)
Sample No. 4.	Bluish sandy silt, top of blue clay layer. (Nos. 3151-3158)
Sample No. 5.	Lowest part of brown dune sand. (Nos. 3161-3166)
Sample No. 6.	Middle part of brown dune sand. (Nos. 3171-3180)

In the following table a series of letters is used to represent the relative abundance of a species throughout the various strata; A is abundant, C is common, F is frequent, and R is rare. The relative abundance of the diatoms within a given layer is discussed at the end of the paper. Only those species are discussed which occur in sufficient numbers to make up a considerable part of the association. In many cases, particularly in rare forms, the R, as well as indicating the distribution of a species from layer to layer, coincides with its abundance as compared with other species within a single layer. However, it must be remembered that the letter represents the distribution of the species from layer to layer and only secondarily is for comparison between species in a given layer.

The column labeled habitat indicates the type of water in which a species is usually found: F is fresh, B is brackish, M is marine, and E is euryhaline.

(Patrick, 1938, p. 17f)

TABLE V

DIATOM SPECIES COLLECTED FROM THE WEST WALL
OF THE MAMMOTH PIT, 1936

Identification by Patrick (1938)

| Sample No. | 6 | 5 | 4 | 3 | 1 | 10 | 2 | 9 | Habitat |
Stratum	A	A	B	D	F	F	G	I	
Achnanthes exigua Grun.	—	—	—	R	—	R	—	—	F
A. lanceolata (Breb.) Grun.	—	—	—	F	R	R	R	—	F
A. lanceolata v. elliptica Cl.	—	—	—	—	—	—	R	—	F
A. Linearis (W. Sm.) Grun.	—	—	—	R	—	—	—	—	F
Amphora ovalis Kutz.	—	—	R	R	F	R	C	—	F
A. ovalis v. pediculus (Kutz.) V.H.	—	—	—	—	—	—	A	—	F B
A. veneta Kutz.	—	—	R	—	—	—	—	—	F B
Anomoeoneis sphaerophora (Kutz.) Pfitz.	—	—	F	F	—	—	C	—	F B
A. sphaerophora v. sculpta (Ehr.) Mull.	—	—	—	—	—	—	R	—	F B
Caloneis bacillum (Ehr.) Cl.	—	—	R	—	—	R	—	—	F B
C. silicula (Ehr.) Cl.	—	—	R	—	R	R	R	—	F
C. trinoidis (Lewis) Boyer	—	—	—	—	—	R	R	—	F B
Cocconeis disculus (Schum.) Cl.	—	—	—	—	—	F	C	—	F B
C. placentula Ehr.	—	—	F	R	F	F	—	—	E
C. placentula v. euglypta Ehr.	—	—	R	R	—	R	R	—	F
cf. C. thumensis Mayer	—	—	—	—	—	A	—	—	F
Cyclotella meneghiana Kutz.	—	—	—	—	F	—	—	—	F B
C. striata (Kutz.) Grun.	—	—	—	R	R	—	R	—	B M
Cymatopleura solea (Breb.) W. Sm.	—	—	—	—	F	R	—	—	F
C. elliptica (Breb.) W. Sm.	—	—	—	—	—	—	R	—	F B
Cymbella affinis Kutz.	—	—	—	—	R	C	—	—	F
C. amphicephala Naeg.	—	—	—	—	R	—	—	—	F
C. aspera (Ehr.) Cl.	—	—	R	R	F	—	F	—	F
C. austriaca Grun.	—	—	—	—	—	—	R	—	F
C. cistula (Hemp.) Kirchn.	—	—	C	C	A	F	—	—	F B
C. cymbiformis (Kutz.) Breb.	—	—	R	F	F	—	F	—	F
C. delicatula Kutz.	—	—	—	—	C	F	—	—	F
C. ehrenbergii Kutz.	—	—	—	—	R	C	R	—	F
C. helvetica Kutz.	—	—	—	—	—	R	—	—	F
C. lanceolata (Ehr.) Kirchn.	—	—	—	—	R	R	F	—	F B
C. leptoceras (Ehr.) Rabh.	—	—	—	—	F	R	R	—	F
C. microcephala Grun.	—	—	—	—	—	F	—	—	F
C. parva (W. Sm.) Cl.	—	—	—	—	F	—	—	—	F
C. triangulum v. gracilis Hustedt	—	—	—	—	—	—	R	—	F
C. tumida (Breb.) V.H.	—	—	—	—	—	—	R	—	F
C. turgida Greg.	—	—	—	—	F	—	F	—	F
C. ventricosa Agardh	—	—	F	F	F	A	F	—	F B
Denticula elegans Kutz	R	—	C	F	—	—	—	—	F
D. elegans v. kittoniana Grun	—	—	C	F	—	—	R	—	F
D. lauta Bail	—	—	—	R	—	—	—	—	F
D. tenuis Kutz.	—	—	—	R	—	—	—	—	F
D. tenuis v. inflata (W. Sm.) Grun.	—	—	—	—	—	—	R	—	F
D. tenuis v. intermedia Grun.	—	—	—	—	—	—	R	—	F
D. thermalis Kutz.	—	—	—	R	—	—	—	—	F
Diploneis elliptica (Kutz.) Cl.	—	—	C	F	—	—	—	—	F B
D. ovalis (Hilse) Cl.	R	—	F	—	—	R	F	—	F B
D. ovalis v. oblongella (Naeg.) Cl.	—	—	—	—	R	—	—	—	F B
Epithemia argus Kutz.	—	—	C	—	F	—	R	—	E
E. argus v. alpestris (W. Sm.) Grun.	—	—	A	—	R	—	—	—	E
E. muelleri Fricke	—	—	F	R	—	—	—	—	F
E. musculus Kutz.	—	—	R	—	—	—	—	—	B M
E. turgida (Ehr.) Kutz.	—	—	—	F	—	R	F	—	E
E. turgida v. granulata (Ehr.) Brun.	—	—	—	—	—	—	R	—	E
E. turgida v. vertagus (Kutz.) Grun.	—	—	R	—	R	—	—	—	F
E. zebra (Ehr.) Kutz.	—	—	F	F	—	—	—	—	F B
E. zebra v. porcellus (Kutz.) Grun.	—	—	R	—	—	—	—	—	B
E. zebra v. saxonica (Kutz.) Grun.	—	—	A	F	R	—	R	—	F B
E. cocconeis flexella (Kutz.) Cl.	—	—	—	—	R	—	R	—	F
Eunotia arcus Ehr.	—	—	—	—	C	—	—	—	F
E. arcus v. fallax Hustedt	—	—	—	—	R	—	—	—	F
E. lunaris (Ehr.) Grun.	—	—	—	R	R	F	F	—	F
E. lunaris v. minor Schum.	—	—	—	—	—	R	—	—	F
E. pectinalis (Kutz.) Rabh.	—	—	—	R	F	R	—	—	F

Sample No. Stratum	6 A	5 A	4 B	3 D	1 F	10 F	2 G	9 I	Habitat
E. valida Hustedt	—	—	—	—	—	F	—	—	F
Fragilaria brevistriata Grun.	—	—	—	—	—	A	F	—	F
F. brevistriata v. inflata (Pant.) Hustedt	—	—	—	—	F	R	—	—	F
F. construens (Ehr.) Grun.	—	—	—	R	—	R	C	—	F
F. leptostauron (Ehr.) Hustedt	—	—	—	R	—	F	F	F	F
Gomphonema acuminatum Ehr.	—	—	—	—	F	—	—	R	—	F
G. acuminatum f. brebissonii (Kutz.) Cl.	—	—	—	—	—	—	R	—	F
G. acuminatum v. coronatum (Ehr.) W. Sm.	—	—	—	C	C	F	R	—	F
G. acuminatum v. elongatum W. Sm.	—	—	—	—	F	—	—	—	F
G. angustatum Kutz.	—	—	—	R	—	—	—	—	F
G. augustatum v. producta Grun.	—	—	—	—	F	—	—	—	F
G. constrictum Ehr.	—	—	—	—	—	—	F	—	F
G. gracilis v. dichotomum (Kutz.) V.H.	—	—	—	—	F	—	—	—	F
G. intricatum Kutz.	—	—	—	—	F	F	R	—	F
G. intricatum v. vibrio (Ehr.) Cl.	—	—	—	—	R	—	R	—	F
G. lanceolatum Ehr.	—	—	—	—	R	—	—	—	F
G. lanceolatum v. insignis (Greg.) Cl.	—	—	—	—	R	—	—	—	F
G. parvulum Kutz.	—	—	—	R	C	—	R	—	F
G. parvulum v. micropus (Kutz.) Cl.	—	—	—	C	C	—	—	—	F
G. sphaerophorum Ehr.	—	—	—	—	—	—	R	—	F
G. subclavatum Grun.	—	—	—	R	R	—	—	—	F
Gyrosigma attenuatum (Kutz.) Rabh.	—	—	—	—	—	—	R	F	F B
Hantzschia amphioxys (Ehr.) Grun.	—	—	—	—	—	—	R	F	F B
Mastogloia elliptica v. Dansei (Thw.) Grun	—	—	R	—	—	—	—	—	E
M. grevillei W. Sm.	—	—	—	—	F	—	—	—	F B
M. smithii v. lacustris Grun.	—	—	—	—	F	—	—	—	F
Melosira crenulata v. levis (Ehr.) Grun.	—	—	—	R	R	—	—	—	F B
M. granulata v. tenuis Freng.	—	—	—	R	R	—	—	—	F
M. italica Kutz.	—	—	—	R	R	—	—	—	F
Meridion circulare (Grev.) Agardh	—	—	—	—	F	R	R	—	F
M. circulare v. constricta (Ralfs) V.H.	—	—	R	R	—	—	—	—	F
Navicula bacilium Ehr.	—	—	—	R	R	—	—	—	F
N. braziliana Cl.	—	—	—	R	—	—	—	—	F
N. cuspidata Kutz.	—	—	—	—	—	—	F	—	F
N. cuspidata v. ambigua (Ehr.) Cl.	—	—	—	R	—	R	—	—	F
N. dicephala Ehr.	—	—	—	R	R	R	C	—	F
N. exigua (Greg.) Mull.	—	—	—	—	—	—	R	R	F B
N. mutica Kutz.	—	—	—	R	—	—	—	—	B M
N. mutica v. cohnii (Hilse) Grun.	—	—	—	R	—	—	—	—	B
N. oblonga Kutz.	—	—	—	—	C	F	F	R	F B
N. pupula Kutz.	—	—	—	—	R	—	R	—	F
N. radiosa Kutz.	—	—	—	F	R	—	R	—	F
N. rhynchocephala v. amphiceros (Kutz.) Grun.	—	—	—	R	—	—	—	—	B
Neidium amphigomphus (Ehr.) Pfitz.	—	—	—	—	—	R	—	—	F
Neidium iridis (Ehr.) Cl.	—	—	—	R	C	F	R	—	F
N. iridis v. vernalis Reichelt	—	—	—	—	R	—	—	—	F
Nitzschia amphibia Grun.	—	—	—	R	F	R	—	—	F
N. commutata Grun.	—	—	—	—	R	—	—	—	F B
N. denticula Grun.	—	—	—	—	—	—	C	F	F
N. thermalis v. minor Hilse	—	—	—	—	R	—	—	—	F B
N. tryblionella v. salinarum Grun.	—	—	—	—	R	—	—	—	B
Pinnularia borealis Ehr.	—	—	—	—	R	—	—	—	F
P. brebissonii (Kutz.) Rabh.	—	—	—	F	F	F	R	—	F
P. brebissonii v. diminuta (Grun.) Cl.	—	—	—	R	R	—	—	—	F
P. dactylus Ehr.	—	—	—	—	—	—	R	—	F
P. leptosoma (Grun.) Cl.	—	—	—	R	R	—	—	—	F
P. major (Kutz.) Rabh.	—	—	—	—	R	F	R	—	F
P. major v. linearis Cl.	—	—	—	—	R	—	—	—	F
P. nobilis Ehr.	—	—	—	—	R	—	—	—	F
P. viridis (Nitzsch.) Ehr.	—	—	—	R	R	C	R	—	F
P. viridis v. intermedia Cl.	—	—	—	—	R	F	—	—	F
Rhoicosphenia curvata (Kutz.) Grun.	—	—	—	—	—	—	R	—	F B
Rhopalodia gibba (Ehr.) Mull.	R	—	A	C	R	—	F	—	F B
R. gibberula (Ehr.) Mull.	R	—	A	C	—	—	—	—	B M
R. gibberula v. protracta (Grun.) Mull.	—	—	R	—	—	—	—	—	F B
R. gibberula v. producta (Grun.) Mull.	—	—	A	—	—	—	F	—	F B
R. parallela (Grun.) Mull.	—	—	R	—	—	—	—	—	F
Stauroneis anceps v. gracilis (Ehr.) Cl.	—	—	—	—	—	—	R	—	F B

Sample No. Stratum	6 A	5 A	4 B	3 D	1 F	10 F	2 G	9 I	Habitat
S. phoenicenteron (Nitzsch.) Ehr.	—	—	—	F	C	F	F	R	F
S. smithii Grun.	—	—	—	F	R	F	R	R	F
Surirella robusta v. splendida (Ehr.) V.H.	—	—	—	R	R	—	—	—	F B
S. spiralis Kutz.	—	—	—	—	—	—	C	—	F
Synedra capitata Ehr.	—	—	—	—	—	—	R	—	F
S. ulna (Nitzsch.) Ehr.	—	—	—	—	R	C	C	F	F
S. ulna v. biceps (Kutz.) Schonfeldt	—	—	—	—	C	C	—	—	F
S. ulna v. danica (Kutz.) Grun.	—	—	—	—	—	F	—	—	F
S. vaucheriae Kutz.	—	—	—	—	—	F	—	—	F

Samples were also submitted to Paul B. Sears for pollen analysis. He concluded that the stray grains of pine and amaranth present might have drifted in from considerable distance, thus their presence did not necessarily indicate that these plants were growing around the margin of the pond.

Molluscan shells collected by Howard were submitted to Henry A. Pilsbry for identification. In this case, the provenience given is not specific being "lake bed southwest of Clovis, Roosevelt County, New Mexico" (Howard, 1935, p. 89). The lake bed sampled is presumably the gravel pit. Pilsbry's report on the shells is duplicated in Table VI.

TABLE VI

MOLLUSCS IDENTIFIED BY HENRY A. PILSBRY

"1. *Lymnaea palustris nuttalliana* Lea.

Large, well-developed specimens, up to 40 mm. long, abundant.

2. *Helisoma trivolis* (Say)

Also large for species, up to 28 mm. diameter.

3. *Helisoma anceps* (Mke.)

Up to 7 x 13 mm., cavity of left side wider than in the living New Mexican form.

4. *Gyraulus parvus* (Say)

Only three quite young specimens washed out of mud in the large shells.

5. *Physa*, undetermined

One very young shell, with the preceding species.

6. *Sphaerium*, species probably new.

Valves of the rather large species, length up to 15 mm., near S. modestum Prime, but apparently distinct from that or from any species I have seen from New Mexico and neighboring states. Probably undescribed. The same species was found in a deposit containing mammoth bones, on Salt Creek, Culberson Co., Texas.

7. *Pisidium*, species not determined.

Three minute valves, 1 to 2 mm. long, were washed out of the mud in larger shells. They are too young to be determined" (Howard, 1935, p. 89).

During the summer of 1937, William T. Clarke collected molluscs from the site. According to Antevs (1949, p. 186), these snails were obtained from the lower portion of bed 5 (presumably the bed termed "Diatomite" by later investigators) at the southeast corner of the gravel pit. Clarke (1938, p. 119) lists the species identified according to their modern habitat.

A mechanical analysis of the blue sands was made by A.W. Postel who reported the sands were composed of approximately 50 per cent clay and 50 per cent fine sand and silt with silt predominating. The grains were subangular, and appeared to be primarily water deposited although some were frosted suggesting wind erosion (Howard, 1935, pp. 86).

TABLE VII

MOLLUSCS FROM THE DIATOMITE IDENTIFIED
BY WILLIAM T. CLARKE

Species	Habitat
Gastrocopta armifera (Say)	
Gastrocopta procera (Gld.)	
Strobilops texasiana (Pils.)	Under debris
Hawaiia minusculus (Binn.)	
Vallonia gracilicosta (Reinh.)	
Pupoides marginatus (Say)	Flood plains
Retinella ellectina (Gld.)	
Gyraulus parvus (Say)	
Lymnaea obrussa (Say)	Inland lakes
Physa gyrina (Say)	Small streams with mud flats

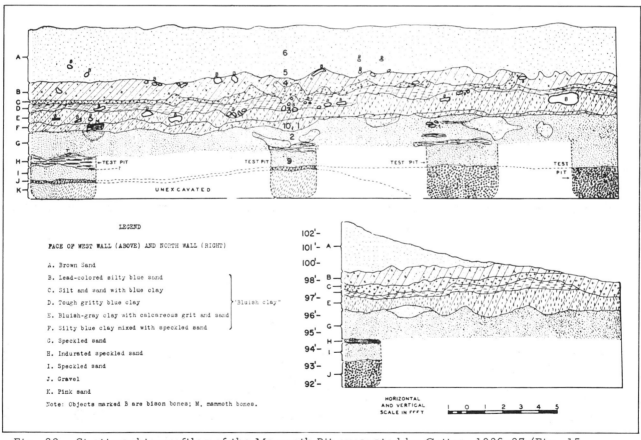

LEGEND

FACE OF WEST WALL (ABOVE) AND NORTH WALL (RIGHT)

A. Brown Sand

B. Lead-colored silty blue sand

C. Silt and sand with blue clay

D. Tough gritty blue clay   ⎫
                                    ⎬ "Bluish clay"
E. Bluish-gray clay with calcareous grit and sand

F. Silty blue clay mixed with speckled sand ⎭

G. Speckled sand

H. Indurated speckled sand

I. Speckled sand

J. Gravel

K. Pink sand

Note: Objects marked B are bison bones; M, mammoth bones.

HORIZONTAL
AND VERTICAL
SCALE IN FEET

Fig. 29. Stratigraphic profiles of the Mammoth Pit excavated by Cotter, 1936-37 (Fig. 15 location 2, after Cotter, 1938). The mammoth bone in bed F correlates stratigraphically with mammoth remains in the Brown Sand Wedge found by Jelinek in 1956. Numbers refer to diatom samples listed in Table V. The vertical scale is correlated to Evans 1949 datum. Probable correlation with Evans bed designation: A--Jointed Sand, B-C--Carbonaceous Silt, D-E--Diatomite, F-Brown Sand Wedge or Brown Sand facies of Diatomite, G-I--Gray Sand, J-K--Red Gravel.

In addition, to the formal geological studies, stratigraphic sections of two sides of the mammoth pit excavated in 1936 are presented by Cotter (1938a). These diagrams, reproduced in Figure 29, record in detail positions of vertebrates in the various beds.

ARCHAEOLOGY

The archaeological investigations demonstrated without doubt the association of artifacts with extinct vertebrates. In addition, the position and nature of these artifacts with the bones indicated that humans had been killing both mammoth and bison at the pond with the remains of two mammoth and five bison being recovered. The positions of some of the artifacts recovered by Cotter are plotted on Figures 30 and 31. The artifacts are summarized by type in Table VIII. According to modern terminology the points with the mammoths are of Clovis type while those with the bison remains of Folsom type.

The artifacts recovered in situ from the 1936 mammoth pit excavations associated with the mammoth bones included (1) 9-7 (catalog number) subtriangular flake, (2) 9-4 point, (3) 9-22 point, (4) 9-21 point fragment, (5) 9-9 bone foreshaft, (6) 9-10 bone foreshaft, (7)

9-8 retouched flake, (8) 9-27 flake, (9) 9-14 retouched flake, (10) 9-26 flake, (11) 9-33 a point not recovered in situ but thought to have been associated with the left scapula of mammoth 2 (see Figure 30).

TABLE VIII

ARTIFACTS RECOVERED BY THE UNIVERSITY
MUSEUM-PHILADELPHIA ACADEMY, 1932-1937, BY TYPE

Type		Bed					
	Undifferentiated Blue Sands	CS	D	GS	Dump	NIP	Total
Clovis point				4	2	1	7
Folsom point	2		1		2		5
Point fragment	1			1	1		3
Yuma point					1	1	2
Side-scraper	1		1		2		4
Flake knife or Point fragment				1			1
Flake				3			3
Scraper			1				1
Bifacial knife	1						1
Knife-like-scraper	2						2
Flake knife or Scraper	1						1
Bone points				2			2
Knife		?			1		2
Total	8	1	3	11	9	2	34

The above tally includes the following finds by season and provenience:

1932-34 seasons--5 artifacts in situ in "Blue Sands."
1936 season--12 artifacts in situ in the mammoth pit.

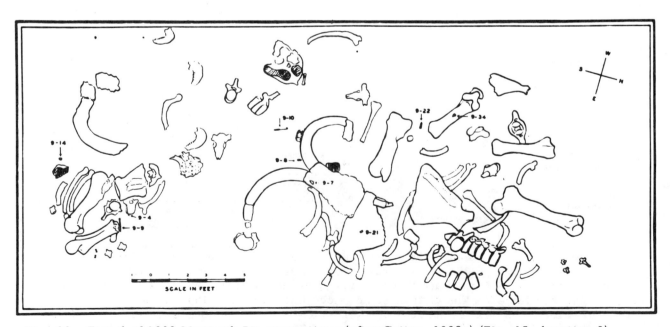

Fig. 30. Detail of 1936 Mammoth Pit excavations (after Cotter, 1938a) (Fig. 15, location 2).

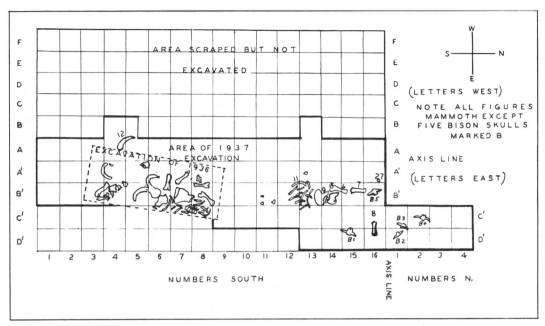

Fig. 31. Plan of 1937 Mammoth Pit excavations (after Cotter, 1938b) (Fig. 15, location 2).

--2 artifacts *in situ* in the pit walls ("Blue Sands").
--9 artifacts from the dump.
1937 season--3 artifacts *in situ*, one from mammoth pit.
--2 artifacts, found Not in Place.

All points labeled "True Folsom Points" by Cotter (1938a, 1938b) are here termed "Clovis Points" as those illustrated by Cotter would now be classified in that category.

These associations left no doubt that the two mammoths had been killed at this spot by peoples utilizing Clovis points. Some of their spears were also equipped with bone foreshafts or points. Following these kills they were butchered on the spot. Implements utilized in butchering would appear to have been the associated flakes and retouched flakes.

The bones of Mammoth 1 were quite scattered and included three vertebrae, a humerus and ulna with several associated foot bones,

Fig. 32. View to northwest of the Mammoth Pit during excavation (after Cotter, 1938a, Pl. 5, No. 5). (Fig. 15, location 2.)

Fig. 33. Artifact *in situ* recovered by the Philadelphia Academy of Natural Sciences expedition, summer of 1936, (after Cotter, 1938a, Pl. 6, No. 3).

one scapula, one large right tusk, a partial mandible, an isolated tooth and two ribs.

Mammoth 2 was in better condition and somewhat more articulated. Bones present were both tusks in a remnant of the skull with maxilla, atlas, both scapula, a femur, a tibia, ulna, humerus, radius, fibula, mandible, approximately 16 ribs, 3 articulated vertebrae, 5 articulated vertebrae, and 6 caudal vertebrae.

A horse scapula and leg bone were found at a depth of 13 inches below the Gray Sand-Diatomite contact.

A third mammoth was reported to Cotter by amateur archaeologists from Portales (Clifton McGehee and Ben Donathan) who excavated part of the mammoth in 1935. The specimen lay at the south side of the south pit. There is no record of any artifacts being associated with the bones (field notes of J.L. Cotter, 1936).

Other vertebrates from the mammoth pit excavations included bison bones, primarily from the Diatomite and Carbonaceous Silt levels, and a carnivore canine tooth listed by Cotter (1936 field notes) as possibly being that of a cat.

The 1937 excavations (June 13 to August 13) by Cotter consisted of the enlargement of the mammoth pit toward the north (Fig. 31). Major finds included the butchered remains of five bison at the contact of the Gray Sand and Diatomite. One articulated bison skeleton was found. Mammoth remains located were a femur, two tibiae, a pelvis, fibula, several vertebrae, and numerous ribs and foot bones (Cotter, 1938b, p. 116). The geographical separation between these mammoth remains and those of Mammoth 2 in the 1936 excavations is such that it is possible that the 1937 finds represent a third mammoth. This is the view now held by Cotter (personal communication).

The artifacts found in situ were two Folsom points from the blue clay, one in definite association with a bison atlas. A third artifact found in situ was a gray chalcedony knife found one inch below the brown sand-blue clay contact (probably from the bed now termed Carbonaceous Silt). A Folsom point

and a "Yuma" point were found on the dump. A final artifact find was a point termed "a small, crudely-made Folsom" located one foot below the top of the Gray Sand.

A primary concern of the archaeological work of Howard and Cotter was the documentation of artifacts recovered in situ. This was accomplished by the taking of photographs of finds in situ (Fig. 33) and the removal of blocks of matrix with bones and artifacts in association. Some of the latter are still on exhibit in Philadelphia (Fig. 34).

Fig. 34. Exhibit prepared from finds at the gravel pit, 1936-37, Philadelphia Academy of Natural Sciences. Photo courtesy that institution.

VERTEBRATE REMAINS

The collection and identification of vertebrate fossils was the responsibility of the California Institute of Technology party. Consequently, the report of Stock and Bode (1938) presents most of the specific information on the occurrence of vertebrates. During subsequent excavations, Howard and Cotter also located vertebrates in situ. These occurrences are summarized in Table IX and itemized in detail in Appendix 3.

SUMMARY

The University Museum-Academy of Natural Sciences research was a major effort concentrating on early man remains and the associated fossils. Their work represents one of the most comprehensive research programs on remains of this time period ever attempted in North America. The results clearly demonstrated the association of man and extinct vertebrates and in addition defined the nature of the environment at the time the association occurred. A major criticism of the work is that the investigators believed similar deposits at the various sites were contemporaneous. This belief led to a lumping of the finds from the various sites which makes it difficult to determine today which site is represented by which specimens. Another difficulty is that the "Blue Sands" from the gravel pit actually contained several units of differing ages separated by erosional unconformities. Nonetheless,

TABLE IX

VERTEBRATE SPECIES COLLECTED BY THE CALIFORNIA INSTITUTE OF TECHNOLOGY-PHILADELPHIA ACADEMY EXPEDITIONS

Species	Specimens
Cynomys near ludovicianus (Ord)	Left lower incisor, left p-4-M3
Parelephas cf. columbi (Falconer)	Front limb bones
Mammoth	Elements of 5 individuals
Bison sp.	Numerous skeletons
Equus cf. excelsus Leidy	Individual teeth
Platygonus sp.	Upper premolar, prob. p^3
Cervus sp.	Not indicated
Terrapene ornata agassiz	Not indicated
Rodent sp. indet.	Not indicated

these finds, at the time they were made, greatly augmented knowledge of Paleo-Indian cultures and the faunas associated with them.

Texas Memorial Museum Excavations, 1949-50

During the 1949-50 seasons, investigations were carried out around the entire perimeter of the North and South Pits. In addition, a series of test pits were dug outside the limits of the gravel pits in order to determine the extent of the pond deposits and to identify the presence of additional areas suitable for future excavation (Fig. 35). The field work included 584 man-days of excavation primarily at three major loci, Stations A, E, and G. In these major excavations broad exposures of all of the strata were examined with numerous artifacts and fossil bones being located in situ (Figs. 39, 44). A second major emphasis of the work was the geologic studies of Evans. The entire perimeter of the gravel pits was mapped in detail with measurements being taken to the top and bottom of all of the exposed strata (Fig. 36). This examination of the walls of the gravel pits revealed numerous bones and artifacts in situ as well as a number of hand dug wells. Fossils so revealed included elephant remains at two places on the south wall of the North Pit and an elephant molar in the northeast corner of the North Pit. Bison remains were located in quantity on the west side of the South Pit (Station E), in the trench in Station G, along the north wall of the North Pit, and in a test pit west of the North Pit. Also prepared at this time was a contour map of the site on which all the above mentioned features were plotted. The stratigraphic studies were keyed to the same vertical datum used in plotting the surface contours.

Extensive excavations were carried out at Stations A and E and finds at these features will be discussed in detail following a summary of the stratigraphy at the site.

STRATIGRAPHY

The generalized stratigraphic section is that described by Evans (1951, pp. 3, 4). A second description of the beds by Evans is recorded in the field notes on file at the Texas Memorial Museum (TMM accession record pp. 1-2).

A schematic profile of this section has been published by Sellards. This profile (Fig. 37) and the description of the beds (Table X) are reproduced below. Data are abstracted from both of the geologic descriptions of Evans to include all pertinent information.

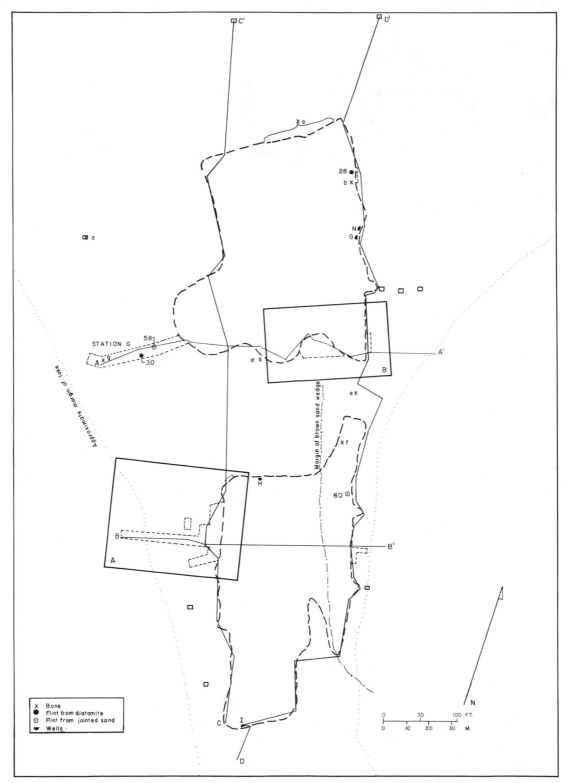

Fig. 35. Map showing 1949-50 Texas Memorial Museum excavations. Base map prepared by Glen Evans, courtesy of the Texas Memorial Museum. Detailed inset maps are shown in Figures 39 and 44. Profiles are illustrated in Figure 36.

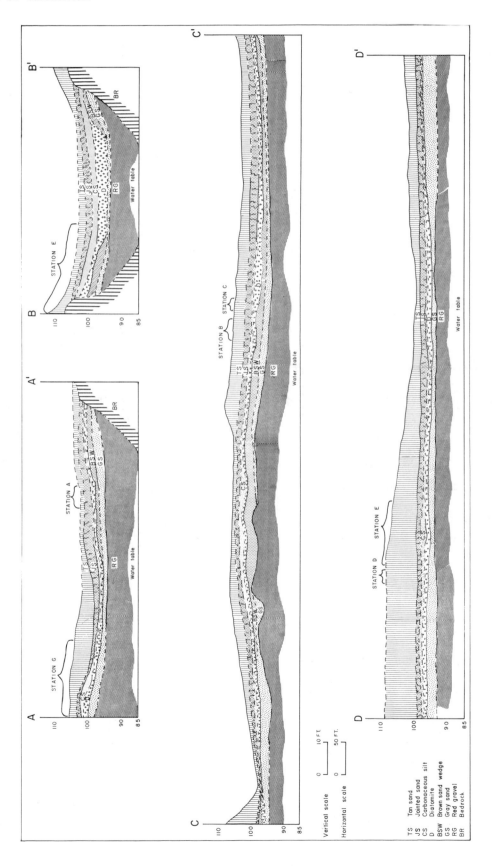

Fig. 36. Profiles of beds exposed in the North and South Pits, 1949–50. Profiles prepared from stadia measurements by Glen L. Evans. (Profiles keyed to map, Fig. 35.) Numbers in left-hand margin refer to arbitrary datum utilized by Evans (see Fig. 15).

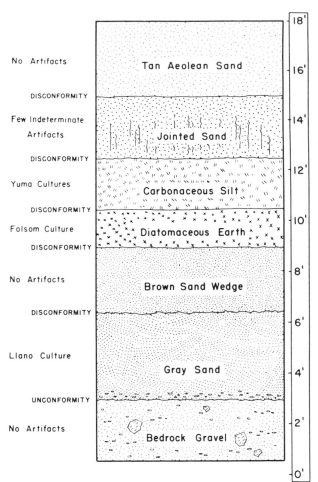

No Artifacts

DISCONFORMITY

Few Indeterminate
Artifacts

DISCONFORMITY

Yuma Cultures

DISCONFORMITY

Folsom Culture

DISCONFORMITY

No Artifacts

DISCONFORMITY

Llano Culture

UNCONFORMITY

No Artifacts

Tan Aeolean Sand

Jointed Sand

Carbonaceous Silt

Diatomaceous Earth

Brown Sand Wedge

Gray Sand

Bedrock Gravel

Fig. 37. Schematic profile of beds in the
gravel pit (after Sellards, 1952, p. 28).

TABLE X

STRATIGRAPHIC BED DESCRIPTIONS BY
GLEN L. EVANS, 1949-50

Bed 1   (Bedrock Gravel). Reddish gravel and sand with
some clean yellow sand, red clays, and caliche,
gravels contain large boulders of compacted,
weakly cemented sandstone and red clay apparently
derived from Ogallala bedrock. No fossils found in
this member. Deposit is of older Pleistocene or
Pliocene age. It is a member of the bedrock series
of strata in which the valley is entrenched and upon
which the much more localized lake deposits are
resting by disconformity. The gravel is a shallow
but permanent aquifer, the present water table being
an average of 8 to 10 feet below the upper contact as
exposed in the quarries. The full thickness of the
member is not exposed, although it is known to extend several feet below the water table level. [Core
drilling in 1961 revealed up to 90 feet of gravel.]

Bed 2   (Gray Sand or "Speckled Sand"). Bed 2 is the lowermost and oldest member of lake and pond deposits
at the Clovis site. In the middle part of the lake
area, Bed 2 consists of well-sorted, gray, <u>friable</u>

sands which were deposited on the valley floor by
gently flowing water derived from springs in the
immediate vicinity. The sands contain occasional
pellets of black and pink chert. There is a pavement or thin layer of pebbles or small gravel at the
basal contact with the older deposit. The pavement
suggests the possibility of wind erosion of the basal
surface, or of erosion by water of very gentle velocity which allowed lag of coarser pebbles. [This
gravel is described as a separate bed by Antevs].
The sand is clean in the middle part where water
washed away the finer clay particles, but it contains
angular lumps of reworked bedrock near the lake margins which forms a weakly cemented conglomerate.
The member ranges in thickness from less than a foot
in the middle area, where it was most eroded, to
about 5 feet near the margins. It is separated from
both underlying and overlying members by disconform-
ities.

Bed 3   (Brown Sand Wedge). A dark greenish-brown sand,
compact, partially cemented; a wedge extending into
the pond area from east side (may also appear on
west side which has not yet been exposed). "Worm
burrows" are common, bison bones are common, one
partial jaw of a large fossil wolf and fragments of a
medium-sized turtle are also present. The wedge
appears to be a sand-creep from springs seeping out
of sand (Bedrock) of the old valley wall. No artifacts
were found in this horizon. [More recent excavations
have revealed artifacts, see discussions later in
this volume.]

Bed 4   (Diatomite). A diatomaceous earth member, grading
to a carbonaceous sand toward the pond margins,
carbon flecks are common. Also characteristic is a
definite and persistent bone bed consisting mainly
of fossil <u>Bison</u> with artifacts. In many places this
member has a twisted or involuted structure presumably due to gently shifting movements by water cur-
rents during deposition or by frost action after the
diatomite was deposited and semicompacted. The
color of the relatively pure diatomaceous material
varies from white when dry to deep blue-gray when
wet. The stratum is saucer shaped in form, the central portion being about 5 feet lower than the marginal parts. The bed was deposited in a permanent,
spring-fed lake which probably had an outlet through
the connecting tributary valley to Blackwater Draw.
The deposit convincingly indicates a humid or pluvial
stage when the water table was at a high level and
provided a continuous flow of spring water into the
lake. The average preserved thickness of the member is between 1.0 and 1.5 feet, but the original
thickness was somewhat greater, as much of the surface was wind eroded prior to later deposition.

Bed 5   (Carbonaceous Silt or "Upper Diatomite"). The "upper
diatomaceous earth" or "carbonaceous silt" member,
is characterized by abundant flecks of carbonaceous
remains of plants in what appears to be a diatomaceous
clayey-silt, containing an abundant layer of fossil
<u>Bison</u> bones and associated artifacts in the upper half
of the bed. The unit is best developed on the west
side of the south pit. The member is massive and
homogenous in texture, dark blue-gray when damp,
lighter gray when dry. This unit is capped by an
erosional surface which in much of the lake has cut
down to the surface of Bed 4, thus removing Bed 5.
Where present, the bed attains a thickness of 0.5 to
1.5 feet.

Bed 6   (Jointed Sand). This is a compact gray, carbonaceous
sand, (locally deep brown), which exhibits prominent
vertical jointing on weathering. The darker lower

part locally contains numerous fragments of broken and reworked fragments of <u>Bison</u> bones and lumps of diatomite reworked by wind from underlying beds. The member rests disconformably on the lower beds. At times the unit may be difficult to separate from sandy marginal facies of Members 5 and 4. The bed grades upward and laterally to massive reddish-brown sands. These sands apparently were deposited mainly by the wind, but sheet wash from surrounding slopes may have contributed in concentrating the sand on the valley floor. No fossils or artifacts were found in primary position. There is no evidence of true lake facies in this member, but the relatively high percentage of carbonaceous material in the lower-lying parts of the bed indicates temporary ponding of surface waters. The degree of oxidation, leaching, jointing, and compaction of the marginal and upland facies of the member indicates a fairly stable surface with attendant soil development previous to deposition of the overlying surface sands of Bed 7. The member ranges in thickness from 1.5 feet to 3.5 feet.

Bed 7   (Tan Aeolean Sand). This is a light tan aeolean sand which is weakly compacted and massive to weak bedded. The surface of the deposit exhibits conspicuous dune-form topography with thin soil development and covering of tall bunch grass and shrub. The valley phase of this member is partially redeposited by slope wash. No archaeological materials or identifiable animal remains were found in exposures at the site, but at a number of places along Blackwater Draw campsites containing small arrow points and pottery characteristic of the later Plains Indians are weathering from the lower part of what appears to be the same member. The thickness varies from a few inches to more than 5.0 feet in the immediate area of the site.

During the 1949-50 seasons, a total of thirteen wells were located which have in common the following characteristics (Evans, 1951): (1) All were dug from the erosion surface which caps Bed 5. (2) All extend into the Bedrock Gravel. (3) The wells are deeper than they are wide. (4) Several of the wells have notches or steps from 3 to 12 inches wide cut into the sides. (5) All contain slump blocks of sediment from the various units through which they were cut. (6) They range from 5 to 6.5 feet in width at the top, and 1 to 2 feet in width at the bottom. Cross-sections of six of these wells are illustrated in Figure 38. The nature of the wells clearly indicates they were excavated at a time after the lake had dried up and the water table stood at a depth of 5 to 6 feet below the surface. Evans dates the excavation of these wells as occurring near the end of the arid interval which followed the deposition of Bed 5 (Carbonaceous Silt). From their stratigraphic position, the wells are later than the Parallel Flaked Cultures and earlier than the Recent Indian material. Most likely they were dug by peoples possessing an Archaic culture. Unfortunately, profiles of the other wells excavated by the Texas Memorial Museum are not available.

STATIONS A, B, AND C

Excavations at Station A consisted of the cutting down of a projecting remnant of the pond sediments on the south wall of the north pit (Fig. 39). Excavations revealed a fairly representative stratigraphic section although wind erosion subsequent to the deposition of the Carbonaceous Silt had removed much of that bed. Thus in some places there was direct contact between the Jointed Sand and the Diatomite. The Brown Sand Wedge unit was also missing. Three wells (J, E, and K) were located within Station A and three more (B, C, D) were present in the wall of the pit immediately to the west. Vertebrate fossils within Station A included disarticulated remains of a mammoth in the top 16 inches of the Gray Sand. Bones present included tusk, a humerus, part of a scapula, ribs, and several vertebrae. Bison bones were common in the Diatomite. The nature of these bones is not described in the field notes, but one photograph (Fig. 40) illustrates part of a semi-articulated skeleton, thus suggesting that a bison kill area was present.

Artifacts

Twelve artifacts were found <u>in situ</u> (3 in Station B, 9 in Station A) but were distributed in all of the beds between and including the Gray Sand and Jointed Sand (Fig. 39), thus indicating that no real concentration of artifacts was present. The vertical relationship of these artifacts has been plotted on a schematic diagram (Fig. 41) with data provided in the TMM accession record. Two additional artifacts (937-53 and 56) have no established vertical provenience. These artifacts were found within the Jointed Sand unit, but their exact location within that bed is unknown.

The artifacts found by bed are as follows: Jointed Sand--one flake and two scrapers; Diatomite--three Folsom points of which one was unfluted and two scrapers; and Gray Sand--one Clovis point, a curved bone foreshaft (?), and two split bone tools.

Data concerning the association of these artifacts are rare. However, it was recorded that Folsom point 937-57 was found four inches from a bison skull. The presence of points and

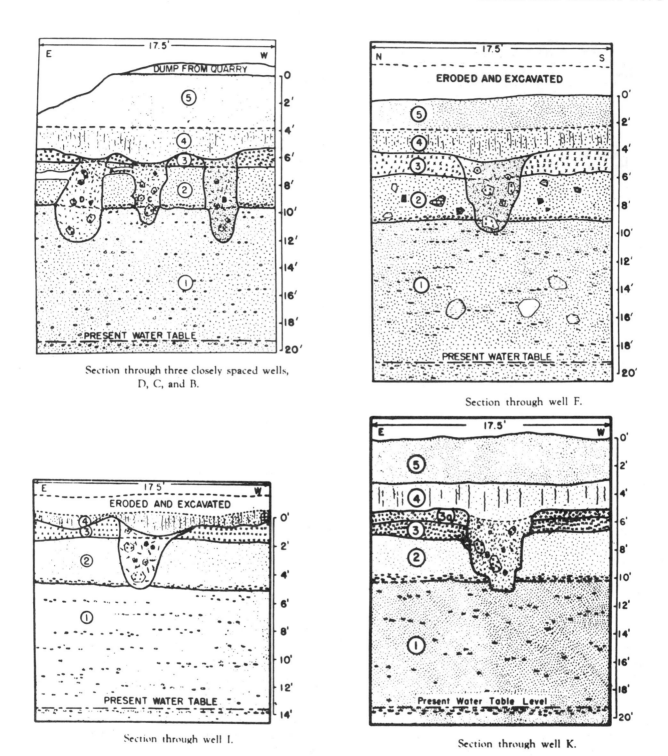

Section through three closely spaced wells,
D, C, and B.

Section through well F.

Section through well I.

Section through well K.

Fig. 38. Profile of some of the Archaic age wells excavated by the Texas Memorial Museum, 1949-50 (after Evans, 1951, Figs. 2,3,4,5). Wells B, C, and D were situated immediately west of Station A. Well K was within Station A; Well F was within Station C; Well I was situated in the south wall of the South Pit.

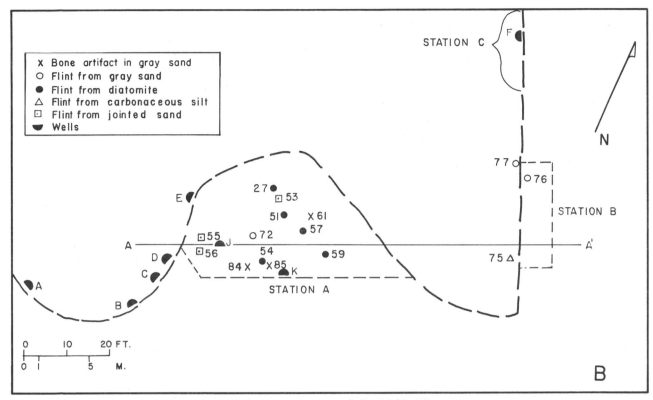

Fig. 39. Detailed map of finds at Stations A, B, and C, 1949-50.

Fig. 40. Bison bones _in situ_ in Diatomite, Station A, July 1950. Photo courtesy Texas Memorial Museum.

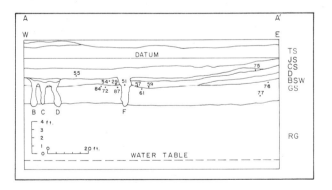

Fig. 41. Schematic profile of Stations A and B, 1949-50. Artifacts with known vertical and horizontal provenience are plotted. Cross-section is keyed to Figure 38. The datum is the arbitrary 100 ft. contour established by Evans.

Fig. 42. Bison bones <u>in situ</u>, section of
the pit wall at Station B, July 1950. Beds
present include; 2--Gray Sand, 4--Dia-
tomite, 5--Carbonaceous Silt, and 6--Join-
ted Sand. Photo courtesy Texas Memorial
Museum.

Fig. 43. View of east wall of North Pit
(Station C), showing geologic beds and ex-
posing Well F in profile. Hal Story is visible at left. Photo courtesy Texas Memorial
Museum.

scrapers in the Diatomite and Gray Sand all
suggest that the excavations were carried out
in killsite areas. The bone foreshaft (937-61)
and Clovis point (937-72) lie within the same
area as the scattered mammoth remains, and
while not in direct association they do suggest
that the Gray Sand contained a mammoth kill.

Excavations at the nearby Station B revealed few artifacts. These included a Plainview point in the Carbonaceous Silt, and a
scraper fragment and hammerstone in the Gray
Sand. The stratigraphic section was closer to
the pond margin than was Station A. Therefore,
the Brown Sand Wedge unit was present. Disarticulated bison bones were common in the
Carbonaceous Silt (Fig. 42), and this area in
subsequent excavations during 1954 revealed
evidence of a full scale bison kill.

Station C was relatively sterile with
the only cultural remains noted being Well F
(Fig. 43). During the 1954 excavations this
area was reinvestigated and an excellently
preserved bison skull was found in the Brown
Sand Wedge unit.

STATIONS D, E, F, AND H

Excavations in this area included a long
east-west trench from the west margin of the

South Pit west beyond the margin of the old
pond sediments (Station E) (Figs. 44, 46).
The remainder of this excavation consisted of
cutting back the sediments exposed along the
west wall of the pit in a type of broadside excavation. This cut extended 70 feet north-
south and 20 to 30 feet west of the gravel pit
wall (Fig. 47). Station E was the most important excavation in the south pit, and most of
this discussion will pertain to finds made there.
Station D was plotted on the Evans base map,
but to my knowledge no artifacts or other finds
are reported from there. A small test pit to the
north of the Station E trench has been labeled
Station F. Finds within Station F included a
bifacial blade fragment from the Carbonaceous
Silt and Well L for which no profile is available. Station H consisted of a small broadside 5 by 10 feet at the northwest margin of
the south pit. Finds included five split bone
tools, all from the Gray Sand (Fig. 44).

Finds within Station E included a bison
bone bed with several associated projectile
points in the Carbonaceous Silt and a second
bison bone bed within the Diatomite. Limited
data are available concerning these finds.
However, we can reconstruct the nature of the
upper bone bed in the Carbonaceous Silt to
some degree. Vertical provenience for most
of the artifacts is given in the TMM accession
record as simply "upper bone bed." However,

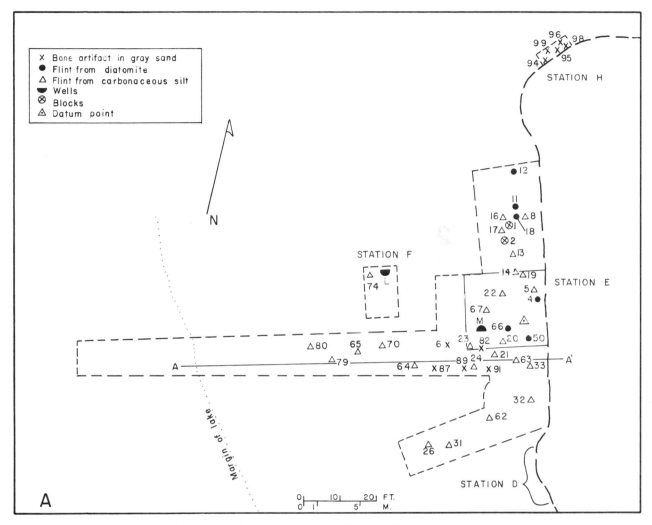

Fig. 44. Detailed map of finds at Stations D, E, and F, 1949-50.

one artifact (937-32) is recorded as having come from the upper bone bed with a depth of 6 inches below the top of the Carbonaceous Silt. The presence of three other artifacts with precise depth information in this same level (937-5, 13, 67), five to eight inches below the top of the Carbonaceous Silt, suggests that the artifact bearing level of the upper bone bed is at that elevation (Fig. 45).

If we may accept this reasoning then the remaining artifacts with provenience assigned to the upper bone bed may also be added to our sample from this specific bison kill. These artifacts are numbered 937-19, 20, 21, 23, 24, 26, 31, and 33. The total includes the follow-

ing artifactural types: one reworked Angostura point, two Milnesand points, an Eden point and a fragment of an Eden point, two Scotts-bluff points, fragments of three Parallel Flaked points, and two bifacial knife fragments. This assemblage forms the basis of Sellard's description of the Portales complex, a concept that will be discussed in detail in the artifact section. These artifacts are distributed over an area 52 feet north-south and 24 feet east-west.

This information suggests that this particular bison kill was one of the largest ever found at the site. The number of bison that were killed is not known, but a map of the

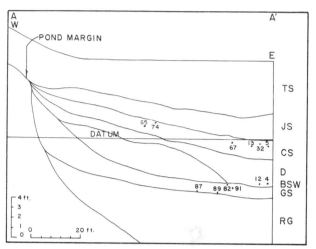

Fig. 45. Schematic profile of Station E, 1949-50, showing vertical location of artifacts. Profile is keyed to the map, Figure 44. The datum is the arbitrary 100 ft. established by Evans.

Fig. 47. View of area excavated at Station E. Photo courtesy Texas Memorial Museum.

Fig. 46. View to east showing 1949-50 excavations, trench in foreground is westernmost section of Station E. Photo by Glen L. Evans, courtesy Texas Memorial Museum.

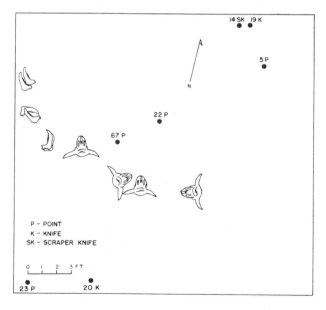

Fig. 48. Concentration of bison skulls after butchering. Location is within Station E (see Fig. 44), upper bone bed (Carbonaceous Silt), 1950. All skulls were lying with the palate up. Identification of locus by Adolph Witte.

distribution of a series of butchered bison skulls present at this location was prepared by the excavators and is illustrated in Figure 48. These skulls were all lying with the palette up. Their position with the mandibles removed suggests that a type of assembly line butchering was practised with the tongues being systematically removed. The location of Figure 48 within Station E is plotted on Figure 45. One Scottsbluff point (937-79) apparently not found within the main body of the upper bone bed was photographed *in situ* and is illustrated in Figure 49.

The bison bone bed in the Diatomite is not well recorded. However, two artifacts have an exact vertical location (937-4, 12), five inches from the base of the Diatomite. Two other artifacts have their vertical position listed as being near the base of the lower bone bed (937-18, 50). From these data we infer that the lower bone bed was probably in the bottom six to eight inches of the Diatomite at Station E. The artifacts included three Folsom points, a scraper, and a chip. Artifact 937-66, an end-scraper, was found high in the unit and was apparently not associated with the lower bone bed.

Artifacts in the Gray Sand were not common as only a large point or knife and two split bone tools were found. There was no concentration of fossil bones although scattered specimens were present (Fig. 50).

SUMMARY

Because of their excellent provenience data the 1949-50 artifact finds plus those of Howard and Cotter formed the basis of Sellard's descriptions of the various assemblages (Sellards, 1952, pp. 28-31, 54-58, 72-74, Figs. 13-18, 25-26, 37-38). While cursory, Sellards' account is the most definitive description to date of the culture complexes represented at the site.

The provenience of these artifacts is plotted on maps of the site (Figs. 35, 39, 44) and on schematic profiles (Fig. 41). Additional data recorded for the individual artifacts are summarized in Appendix I. A list of the artifacts by type is presented in Table XI.

Fig. 49. Scottsbluff point (937-79) *in situ* among Bison bones, Carbonaceous Silt horizon, west side of South Pit, Station E, July 1950. For exact location see Figure 44. Photo courtesy Texas Memorial Museum.

Fig. 50. Mammoth molar and horse tooth *in situ*, base of Gray Sand. The bed immediately underlying the teeth is the pink sand member of the gravel beds, west side of South Pit, Station E, May 1950, specimen numbers unknown. Photo courtesy Texas Memorial Museum.

TABLE XI

ARTIFACTS RECOVERED BY THE TEXAS MEMORIAL
MUSEUM, 1949-50, BY TYPE

Type	JS	CS	D	GS	RG	NIP	Total	Type	JS	CS	D	GS	RG	NIP	Total
Flakes		4	1			1	6	Unifacial knives						1	1
Scrapers	3		4	1		1	9	Flake scraper		1					1
Folsom points			5			3	8	Knife scraper		1					1
Scottsbluff points		5					5	End-scraper			1				1
Milnesand points		3					3	Core						1	1
Plainview points		1					1	Nodule			1				1
Eden points		3					3	Bone tools				2	3		5
Angostura points		1					1	Scraper graver		1					1
Clovis points				1			1	Hammerstones				1			1
Archaic points					1		1	Cut bone					1		1
Indeterminant points	1	4	1			2	8	Total	5	29	13	5	4	10	66
Knives		5					5								
Bifacial knives	1						1								

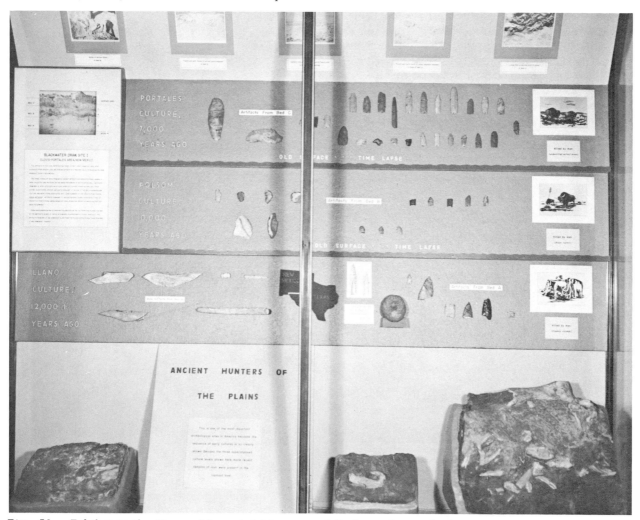

Fig. 51. Exhibit at the Texas Memorial Museum of finds made at Blackwater Locality No. 1, 1949-50. In the exhibit the beds are termed as follows: Bed A -- Gray Sand, Bed B -- Diatomite, Bed C -- Carbonaceous Silt. Photo courtesy Texas Memorial Museum.

A major concern during the 1949-50 seasons was the recovery of artifacts in situ in association with extinct fauna. Blocks of matrix with the bones and artifacts were removed to the museum (specimens 937-34, 79, and 80) and were incorporated into an exhibit (Fig. 51). One of these finds prior to removal is illustrated in Figure 49.

A total of 213 vertebrate fossils was obtained from the Gray Sand through the Carbonaceous Silt as a result of the 1949-50 excavations. These bones include those of horse, bison, elephant, peccary, cat, turtle, and birds. These specimens were not identified by a paleontologist during Sellards' lifetime. In his reports, Sellards referred to components of these faunas by their common names. The section by Lundelius in this volume describes the fauna of the Gray Sand in detail. Table XII below lists the specimens by bed, species, and bone.

Unfortunately, the documentation of vertebrates in situ is limited. The above figures (40, 42, 50) represent all the photographs available of bones in place. The individual vertebrate specimens were identified in the accession record to bed and locus station but were not plotted on the site maps.

The major contributions of the 1949-50 field seasons were the stratigraphic work and the documentation of finds in situ, especially in the Gray Sand, Diatomite, and Carbonaceous Silt units. While final publication of the findings was not achieved in Sellards' lifetime, the major results were made known through his summary in Early Man in America and Evans' (1951) report on the wells. In addition, finds from the pit were placed on exhibit at the Texas Memorial Museum.

TABLE XII

VERTEBRATE SPECIMENS FROM TMM
EXCAVATIONS 1949-50

Bones from White Sand (Pliocene? below Gray Sand)

Equus sp. - Scapula (1)
Elephant - Molar (1)

Species / Bones

Bones from Gray Sand

Species	Articulated feet	Calcaneus	Metapodials	Foot bone	Phalanges	Navicular	Astragali	Articulated ankles	Tibia	Limb bone	Radii	Humeri	Ulnae	Axis	Vertebrae	Scapula	Rib	Skull	Jaw	Teeth	Molar plate	Unidentified	Carapace	Plastron	Hoof	Sesamoids	Total
Terrapene caniculata															1								1	1			3
Smilodon californicus																				1							1
Ondatra zibethica																			1	1							2
Platygonus sp.																				1							1
Equus conversidens			2	1																4							7
Equus niobrarensis																				2							2
Equus scotti																				8							8
Equus sp.					1				1		1									26		1					30
Bison sp.	2																										2
Mammuthus sp.														1							3						4
Turtle										1													4	2			7
Carnivore																				1							1
Bird	1																										1
Unidentified					1					1							1					1	1				5
Total	2	1	2	1	1	1	1	1	2	1	1	1		2				1	1	44	3	2	5	3			74

Bones from Brown Sand Wedge

Species	Articulated feet	Calcaneus	Metapodials	Foot bone	Phalanges	Navicular	Astragali	Articulated ankles	Tibia	Limb bone	Radii	Humeri	Ulnae	Axis	Vertebrae	Scapula	Rib	Skull	Jaw	Teeth	Molar plate	Unidentified	Carapace	Plastron	Hoof	Sesamoids	Total
Bison sp.	4	2	1		3				1		1																12
Canis lupus																			1								1

Bones from Diatomite

Species	Articulated feet	Calcaneus	Metapodials	Foot bone	Phalanges	Navicular	Astragali	Articulated ankles	Tibia	Limb bone	Radii	Humeri	Ulnae	Axis	Vertebrae	Scapula	Rib	Skull	Jaw	Teeth	Molar plate	Unidentified	Carapace	Plastron	Hoof	Sesamoids	Total
Bison sp.	2*	3	22	8	34	1	8	3	3		1			1					3	2					1	2	94
Turtle																							1				1
Microtus pennsylvanicus																			1								1
Total specimens	2	3	22	8	34	1	8	3	3		1			1					4	2			1		1	2	96
Total individual bones	24	3	22	8	34	1	8	17	3		1			1					4	2			1		1	2	132

Bones from Carbonaceous Silt

Species	Articulated feet	Calcaneus	Metapodials	Foot bone	Phalanges	Navicular	Astragali	Articulated ankles	Tibia	Limb bone	Radii	Humeri	Ulnae	Axis	Vertebrae	Scapula	Rib	Skull	Jaw	Teeth	Molar plate	Unidentified	Carapace	Plastron	Hoof	Sesamoids	Total
Bison sp.		2	4						1		1															1	9

*One foot possessed 11 individual bones, the other 13. Articulated ankles included the following number of individual bones 4, 6, 7.

Note: In addition to the above talley by bed, several bones were found on the contacts between beds. These specimens are itemized below:
Gray Sand-Brown Sand Wedge--Equus tooth.
Brown Sand Wedge-Diatomite--elephant foot bone.
Gray Sand-Diatomite--turtle carapace.
Diatomite-Carbonaceous Silt--Bison sp. - metapodial, 5 phalanges, 1 hoof.
Within fill of Well M--turtle carapace, unidentified bone.

Texas Memorial Museum Field Seasons, 1953-57

Between 1953 and 1957 the Texas Memorial Museum investigations at the pit consisted of short excavations at irregular intervals, primarily in response to finds uncovered during the gravel mining. Two amateur archaeologists living in Portales served as part-time employees of the museum spending their weekends excavating at the site. Their work was described to Sellards by letter, and specimens recovered were shipped to the museum. Unusual finds were reported to Sellards by phone and he would then visit the site to record them. This method of research led to the receipt of many specimens at the museum with inadequate provenience data.

The correspondence between Sellards and these men records his efforts to resolve these problems, but frequently he was unable to do so. Another problem was that the facies changes in the beds made it difficult for the investigators always to be sure in which unit a specimen lay. Other serious discrepancies that raised questions about the reliability of some of the data also became evident.

The above considerations have presented a dilemma concerning how the finds resulting from this period of research should be reported. A decision was reached to report all finds for which there exists supporting data: maps, photos, or notes taken by Sellards. Those finds without such supporting data are here considered not scientifically valid and will not be utilized in the report.

Compilation of data on the Texas Memorial Museum excavations of 1954 to 1956 has been an extremely difficult task. Apparently no comprehensive record was kept of the many excavations that were carried out at the pit during this period. In addition, few maps or profiles were made documenting the finds. The maps and profiles extant are primarily sketch maps, frequently without scale or reference to a permanent datum. The most complete record kept was the accession record which contains a complete list of every specimen from the site. Unfortunately, in some cases, the specimens cannot be referred to a specific excavation, and, in other cases, the provenience could not be verified.

A series of field notebooks kept by Sellards is also on file at the Texas Memorial Museum. These notebooks yielded some information of value, but unfortunately they consist in large part of a running description of facies changes in the stratigraphic units rather than specific facts concerning the nature of the finds and their position. In addition, no photographic record was kept.

As a result of the difficulties, recourse was made to every kind of documentation available. A major resource was the file of over 200 photographs of activities at the gravel pit taken over the years by Gordon Greaves, editor of the Portales News Tribune. Photos were also provided by several amateurs. Also consulted was Sellards' correspondence file. Interviews were held with James M. Warnica and Don Krieble at which the correspondence file and photographs were reviewed. Their memories of these excavations, in which they participated, served to identify the specific locations of excavations and individual specimens.

The result of this research was the identification of the locations of almost all the excavations conducted during this period (Fig. 1) and a validation of the finds from these digs recorded in the accession record. It is obvious that much important data has been lost; but considering the factors contributing to the loss, the constant moving of datum points by the gravel mining, the limited funds at Sellards' disposal, Sellards' death, etc., it is remarkable that this much information has been preserved.

The excavations for which there are supporting data were conducted in April and May 1954, July 1954, June 1955, October and November 1955, May 1956, June 1956, and August 1956. These excavations were conducted by several different persons who worked at different locations and in different strata. In addition, the information from these various digs was not recorded in a standard format. As a result, each of these excavations and the material obtained will be described separately. The general style of excavation was the clearing of small areas which the gravel mining had revealed were rich in bones.

Unfortunately, the validation of specific finds made between 1953 and 1957 was a time consuming process continuing until the date of preparation of this manuscript. As a result these specimens were initially considered to be without valid provenience and were not utilized in the initial typological analysis of the artifacts (following section). As these artifacts are not itemized in Appendix I (the typological sample studied) they are listed in Appendix II. Specimens by accession number from the specific excavations are listed in Table XIII.

The list of accession numbers includes both artifacts and paleontological specimens. The artifacts number 215 of which 33 had unknown provenience, 27 were found in the Clovis level, 18 in the Folsom Level, 1 in the Portales

TABLE XIII

SPECIMENS WITH VALID PROVENIENCE,
TEXAS MEMORIAL MUSEUM EXCAVATIONS 1954-1956

TMM Accession Number	Excavation Party and Date
937-326 to 464	Warnica and Shay, 1954, Localities B and C
281-326, 465-473, 479, 516 to 555	Sellards April, 1954
585 to 620, 634 to 667, 669 to 695, 724 to 744, 762-764	Sellards May, 1955
745 to 761 and 855	Warnica and Brown July, 1955
776-828	Sellards October-November, 1955
857-860	Sellards May, 1956
862-864	Shay August, 1956

level, and 136 in the Archaic level. As a definitive analysis had already been performed on the much larger sample known to be valid (the more than 1000 specimens reported in the artifact section), it was decided to add to that sample only those specimens that would contribute to our knowledge. Therefore, all specimens with unknown provenience (except diagnostic point types), all Folsom specimens, all chips, spalls, natural stones, and questionable split bone tools were eliminated. The remaining 7 Clovis, 5 Portales, and 34 Archaic artifacts have been added to the definitive typological sample reported in the artifacts section. This control sample is utilized as the basis of all statements made concerning the nature of artifact types and assemblages known from the site.

All additional Texas Memorial Museum specimens are considered not to have sufficient provenience data to be accepted as valid. While this is a somewhat stringent view, it is believed that elimination of these dubious specimens has resulted in a more scientifically valid report.

In contrast to the study of the artifacts from these excavations, the vertebrate fossils from the Gray Sand found during the 1953-57 excavations have been studied in detail and are included in the section by Lundelius.

SELLARDS' EXCAVATIONS STATIONS B AND C
APRIL-MAY 1954

In the spring of 1954, the gravel mining extended the North Pit to the east. Excavations were undertaken by Sellards at an eastward extension of the Locality B excavated by Witte in 1949-50 (Fig. 15, location 4). There are no field notes extant describing this excavation, nor is there a map. However, considerable information is present in the accession record concerning the provenience and association of the specimens. Those excavating were E.H. Sellards, Oscar Shay, Otto Schoen, Don Krieble, Jim Warnica, and Adolph Witte. There is no record as to how long excavations continued.

A second area was also excavated slightly to the north of Locality B, termed Locality C (Fig. 15, location 5). This area yielded a number of artifacts and vertebrate fossils. Table XIV lists the artifacts from these locations by type. Vertebrate finds are itemized in Table XV.

The major importance of this excavation was the location of artifacts for the first time in the Brown Sand Wedge unit. Another find of interest was a bison skull in the same unit (Fig. 52). In addition, numerous samples for C-14 tests were collected. Several of these samples were later sent to Libby and Kulp, but none were dated. No evidence suggests that any butchering or campsite areas were located, and it is assumed that the finds pertained to materials that had been washed into the pond near its margin.

Fig. 52. Bison skull found *in situ*, Diatomite, Station B east side, North Pit, May 1954. Photo courtesy Don Kreible.

TABLE XIV

ARTIFACTS RECOVERED FROM STATIONS A, B, AND C,
BY SELLARDS APRIL–MAY 1954 BY TYPE

Type	JS	CS	D	BSW	Bed GS	NIP	UNK	Total
Station A								
Scraper			1	2or?				4
Station B								
Flakes	1		4					5
Flake scrapers				2				2
Folsom points						3		3
Eden point						1		1
Parallel Flaked point fragment	1							1
Chip			1					1
Graver						1		1
Core-burin	1							1
Flake scraper-graver		1	?		?			2
Worked bone?			1					1
Station C								
Angostura point frag.							1	1
Flake		1	1					2
Paralled Flaked point fragment	1							1
Flake scraper	1	1						2
Scraper	1							1
Hammerstone					?			1
Worked bone?			1	1				2
Totals all stations*	6	1	11	7	4	5	1	32

*A total of 32 artifacts were found but provenience to bed is questionable (?) for three artifacts. Also recovered on this excavation (but not tallied above) was a hammerstone (937-310) found in a well on the west side of the North Pit.

WARNICA AND SHAY EXCAVATIONS JULY–AUGUST 1954

As indicated in correspondence, Jim Warnica and Oscar Shay continued salvage operations in June and July 1954. The gravel mining continued extending the North Pit toward the east at Station B. At location 6, Figure 15, a bison bone bed with a concentration of artifacts was exposed.

Initially, this layer (located at the contact between the Carbonaceous Silt and Jointed Sand) was incorrectly thought to be of Plainview age, as one of the projectile points resembled a Plainview point. As a result, the specimens were listed in the accession record as coming from the "Plainview Stratum." Recent inspection of the entire collection from this locality indicates this level contained Archaic culture artifacts. The latter opinion is now also held by Warnica (personal communication). Margin notes in the accession record by Sellards also state: "may be Archaic." These artifacts (Table XVI) represent the largest collection of

TABLE XV

VERTEBRATE SPECIMENS FROM THE TMM EXCAVATIONS
APRIL 1954 STATIONS B & C

Bones from Pink and White Sand

Bison sp.--Tooth
Equus sp.--Tooth

Species	Astragali	Calcaneus	Vertebrae	Jaw	Carapace	Phalanges	Limb bones	Ribs	Skull	Femur	Scapulae	Metapodials	Metatarsals	Metacarpals	Unidentified	Humerus	Tooth	Total
Bones from Gray Sand																		
Bison sp.	1		1	1														3
Turtle					1													1
Unidentified	2	2																4
Elephant				1														1
Total	3	2	2	1	1													9
Bones from Brown Sand Wedge																		
Bison sp.			2															2
Unidentified	1						2	2	1									6
Canis lupus										1								1
Total	1		2				2	2	1	1								9
Bones from BSW-D Contact																		
Unidentified	1								1	1								3
Bison sp.											1							1
Total	1								1	1	1							4
Bones from Diatomite																		
Bison sp.		1								1								2
Unidentified	1					2	1			1								4
Total	1	1				2	1			1								6
Bones from Carbonaceous Silt																		
Bison sp.	1		2					2										5
Unidentified		1	1							1								3
Total	1	1	3					2	1									8
Bones from Jointed Sand																		
Bison sp.	1		3					5										9
Unidentified								1										1
Total	1		3					6										10
Bones with Unknown Provenience																		
Unidentified	6							1										7
Bison sp.	1		1							1								3
Equus sp.												1						1
Total	7		1					1		1		1						11

Archaic materials from the site. Unfortunately, no maps exist except Warnica's location sketch map, and no profiles were drawn or photos taken. Conversations with Warnica indicate the bone bed lay at the Carbonaceous Silt-Jointed Sand contact near the pond margin. Vertebrate specimens collected are itemized in Table XVII.

TABLE XVI

ARTIFACTS RECOVERED BY WARNICA AND
SHAY, STATIONS B AND C,
JULY-AUGUST 1954 BY TYPE

Type	Bed	
	JS	Hole In Bedrock
Archaic points	4	
Plainview point	1	
Ellis point	1	
Indeterminant points	7	
Scrapers	9	
Knives	1	
Scraper-graver	1	
Chips	19	
Chopper	1	
Bone tool	1	
Millstone	1	
Spalls and artifact fragments	36	
Indeterminant object	1	
Stones	36	
Carved stone		1
Beads	2	
Worked flints	3	
Hematite	3	
Marked hematite	1	
Used stone	1	
Total	129	1

TABLE XVII

VERTEBRATE SPECIMENS FROM WARNICA AND SHAY EXCAVATIONS
STATIONS B & C JULY-AUGUST 1954

Bones

Species	Astragali	Calcaneus	Foot bones	Scapula	Radius	Phalanges	Horn core	Ribs	Jaw	Vertebrae	Limb bone	Skull frag.	Teeth	Unidentified	Total
Bones from Diatomite or Carbonaceous Silt															
Bison sp.					1	1					3				5
Unidentified											1				1
Bones from Jointed Sand															
Bison sp.				1											1
Unidentified	36	12	2	1		2	1	1			2	1		14	72
Bones from Carbonaceous Silt															
Unidentified	4														4
Total all Levels	41	12	2	1	1	2	1	2	1	1	6	1	3	14	88

Bones from Jointed Sand-Carbonaceous
Silt contact - one Bison astragalus.
Bones from Gray Sand--one elephant
tooth, one small rib, a bison tooth,
and a horse tooth, with unknown provenience.

The bone bed was also extensively sampled for radiocarbon tests. A total of eleven packages of charred bones each weighing two to three pounds was collected from the Carbonaceous Silt and given the accession number 937-454. Three of these packages (Nos. 5, 9, 11) were sent to Lamont Laboratory July 29, 1955, but were not dated.

The bones in the next overlying unit termed by the excavators, the "dark brown sand" (Jointed Sand), were also extensively sampled with twenty packages of charred bones (937-464) being collected.

On August 1, 1955, Sellards sent two packages of charred bones from the bone bed in the Jointed Sand (937-464, package numbers not specified) to the Humble Oil Company radiocarbon laboratory. One of these samples yielded a date of 4,950 B.P. ± 130 years, Humble sample number 0-157 (Brannon et. al., 1957, p. 149).

The artifact total from the excavation is sizable (130 specimens) and it is interesting to note that they include several categories indicative of occupational debris. The chips (19), spalls and artifact fragments (36), and imported stones (36) all suggest that the area along the margin of the pond was utilized as an occupation area. Unfortunately, there is no indication in any of their correspondence to Sellards that the excavators realized that they were digging in a campsite. It is also probable that the bone bed found is part of the same one later excavated by Dittert and Wendorf. These two excavations provided most of the Archaic material found at the site.

In addition to the bison bone bed certain stratigraphic information was recorded. Warnica and Shay report in correspondence that they were able to trace an indurated sand unit from this eastward extension of Station B (Fig. 15, location 6) to Station A, where it could be correlated with the Brown Sand Wedge. The unit in this transect had a dip of 9 feet, 10 inches over a distance of 183 feet. This information suggests that this exposure represented a cross-section of the pond margin similar to that excavated by Dittert and Wendorf at a later date. Of great additional interest is the fact that Warnica and Shay report that numerous man-made pits had been excavated into this unit (a calichified facies of the Brown Sand Wedge). These may have been used as fire-pits. The pits were about 36 inches in diameter, 8 inches in depth, and were filled with oxidized sand. Upon excavation of these pits they report that the marks of the original tools used to dig them were preserved as impressions

in the pit walls. It is unfortunate that no photographs of these pits were taken. The age of
these firepits is uncertain, but they are probably Post-Folsom as they were found excavated
into the unit which elsewhere in the pit contained Folsom artifacts.

SELLARDS' CLOVIS BISON KILL, MAY 1955

A major discovery was made in May
1955 at the south end of the North Pit (Fig.
15, location 7). A total of seven bison skulls
were located in the Gray Sand unit in association with Clovis artifacts. Unfortunately, no
photographs of the remains in situ appear to
have been taken. A sketch map (Fig. 53) is
reproduced from Sellards' notebook. A saving
feature was the removal of artifacts in blocks
of matrix one of which was a bison scapula
with a Clovis point in association. This specimen serves to validate the association of the
bison skeletons with Clovis artifacts. Also
associated with the scapula and point was the
patella of an elephant.

Only five of the skulls were excavated by
the party under Sellards' direction, and the location of four of those was recorded on the
sketch map (Fig. 53). In a letter to Sellards,
June 19, 1955, Oscar Shay reports the finding
of two additional bison skulls at this locality.
One of these skulls was located 9 feet southeast
of the plat in Figure 53 and the second was 3
feet farther to the east and was associated with
an entire skeleton.

In correspondence to Kathryn Clisby,
dated July 6, 1955, Sellards mentions the fact
that "At one place in Blackwater No. 1 locality
a pond-like deposit containing numerous bison
skulls lies between the recognized basal artifact-bearing deposit of the region [the Gray
Sand] and the Diatomite horizon." This information suggests that the bison were killed at
a pond, perhaps temporary, which lay near the
contact between the Gray Sand and the Diatomite.
The sediments which filled this pond and sur-
round the bones were probably contemporaneous
with the lower portion of the Brown Sand Wedge
deposits elsewhere at the site.

Five projectile points (Table XVIII) in
blocks of matrix were collected as were two

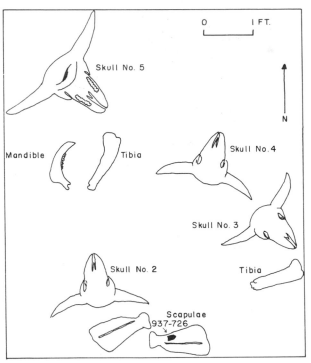

Fig. 53. Reconstruction drawing of Sellards'
1955 Clovis Bison Dig. Clovis point (937-
726) is in situ on a right scapula. Only 4
of the 7 skulls found were located on Sellards'
original sketch map.

TABLE XVIII

ARTIFACTS RECOVERED FROM SELLARDS
CLOVIS BISON DIG MAY 1955 BY TYPE

| Type | | Bed | | |
| | | | Gravel | |
	Surface	GS	Pit Dump	UNK
Flake knives		2		1
Clovis points		1		
Indeterminant points		3	3	
Archaic points			3	
Atlatl weights		2		
Pebble	1			
Flakes		1		
Ornaments		1		
Bone tools		2		
End-scrapers			4	
Scrapers			2	
Neo-Indian point			1	
Plainview point			1	
Parallel flaked points			2	
Folsom point			1	
Drill			1	
Knife			1	
Potsherd			1	
Total	1	12	20	1

flake knives. Three of the skulls were collected, one of which (937-764) is described
in detail by Lundelius (this volume) and is
assigned to <u>Bison antiquus</u>. We know, from
the notes, that one of the three skulls collected
was Skull No. 5 (Fig. 53). It is also recorded
in the notes that skull No. 7 (not collected)
was right side up pointing toward the south.
Presumably, this specimen lay outside the area
mapped.

It is assumed that the artifacts removed
in blocks of matrix (except 937-729) are in
storage somewhere in the Texas Memorial
Museum and that these blocks probably have
never been opened. In our study of the artifacts from the site in the Museum these specimens were not located. It is interesting to
note that the one artifact from this excavation
studied was a diagnostic Clovis point with an
impact flute at the tip on one side. The opposite side of the point appeared to have been
reworked at the tip, suggesting that the point
had been resharpened before it was last used.
Vertebrate fossils collected from this excavation are itemized in Table XIX.

WARNICA AND BROWN PECCARY DIG

In July 1955, Jim Warnica and Gordon
Brown excavated at two localities on the south
edge of the North Pit. Labeled sites 1 and 2
(Fig. 15, location 8), these sites produced
several interesting fossils and a few possible
bone artifacts from the Gray Sand (Table XX).

The most important find was the mandible
of an extinct peccary (<u>Platygonus</u> sp.). Unfortunately, the peccary jaw was smashed in
shipment and photos taken are not of publication quality. However, the jaw was clearly
in place in the Gray Sand and has been adequately identified. In·addition, nine split bones
were found which Warnica believes to be artifacts. In Hester's opinion, based on examination of the specimens in the Texas Memorial
Museum, they are probably not artifacts. One
stone artifact, a scraper-knife, was also recovered.

SELLARDS' OCTOBER 30-NOVEMBER 7, 1955 DIG

Late in October 1955 Sellards and Otto

TABLE XIX

VERTEBRATE SPECIMENS FROM SELLARDS'
CLOVIS BISON DIG MAY 1955

Species	Metapodial	Astragali	Calcaneus	Phalanges	Tibiae	Limb bones	Foot bone	Ulna	Patella	Scapulae	Rib	Vertebrae	Teeth	Jaws	Skull	Antler	Horn core	Unidentified	Carapace	Total
Bones from Gray Sand
<u>Bison antiquus</u>													1							1
<u>Bison</u> sp.	1	3	2	4	1	2				3		4	2	5	3		1	2		32
<u>Bison</u> or horse							1													1
<u>Equus niobrarensis</u>										2										2
<u>Equus scotti</u>										2										2
<u>Equus</u> sp.												4					1			5
<u>Camelops</u> sp.												4								4
Camel												3								3
Deer														1						1
Wolf											1									1
<u>Mammuthus</u>							1										1			1
Turtle																			1	1
Unidentified	1	1	1	2	1		1	1			1	3	6		1			18		37
Total	2	4	3	6	2	2	1	1	1	3	2	7	23	6	5	1	1	21	1	91

Fossils with other provenience:

Diatomite--<u>Mammuthus</u> femur head, 2 <u>Bison</u>
astragali, and one unidentified
astragalus.

Fossils without provenience:

Antelope or deer teeth, 1 cut bone,
2 camel teeth, 1 horse tooth, 1 unidentified skull bone, 1 <u>Bison</u> radius,
1 <u>Bison</u> tibia, 6 packages of <u>Bison</u>
tibia, 1 phalanx, 1 foot bone, and
unidentified small teeth.

TABLE XX

VERTEBRATE SPECIMENS FROM WARNICA
AND BROWN PECCARY DIG AUGUST 1955

Species	Astragalus	Foot bone	Teeth	Jaw	Unidentified	Total
Bones (All from Gray Sand)
<u>Equus scotti</u>		1	4			5
Elephant or sloth	1					1
Peccary				1		1
Unidentified					3	3
Worked? bones					9	9
Total	1	1	4	1	12	19

Schoen returned to the site. Three pits were
opened by the gravel pit operator testing for
gravel, and stratigraphic information was recorded (Fig. 15, locations 7b-7d). An additional excavation was undertaken along the
side of the easternmost of two ditches for
drainpipes cut between the South and North
Pits. Unfortunately, the exact location of
this dig is uncertain, although its general

position can be plotted (Fig. 15, location 7f).
Another locality (Fig. 15, location 7e) yielded
elephant remains, but details on this find are
lacking.

The stratigraphy in Pits 2 and 3 revealed
a section of the Jointed Sand 52 inches thick
overlying a thin (8 inches) unit of light colored
sand. Beneath this unit was a 18-inch thick
unit of blue clay, presumably the Carbonaceous
Silt. Beneath this was a 52-inch thick unit of
calichified yellow sand which appears to cor-
relate with the Brown Sand Wedge unit. Bedrock caliche was then encountered. These
sections undoubtedly record the beds in the
arroyo draining into the pond from the northwest (Fig. 15).

Another major concern of Sellards at this
time was the recording of the stratigraphy exposed in the gravel pit wall. As a result, a
map was made with 20 stations, each recording
the elevations of the strata. These 20 stations
were around the perimeter of the pit at that time
(shown in Fig. 15). Artifacts and fossils and
radiocarbon samples were also collected from
the pits described above (Tables XXI, XXII,
LIV).

The major vertebrate finds were part of
an elephant skull and tusk (937-780) and a
mammoth tooth (937-818) in Pit 2 (Fig. 15,
location 7c). There is no evidence of any
associated artifacts. Presumably these remains pertain to naturally deposited bones.
Several pieces of elephant bone were recovered
from Pit 3 (Fig. 15, location 7d), including a
foot bone and a long bone.

TABLE XXII

VERTEBRATE SPECIMENS FROM
SELLARDS EXCAVATIONS
OCTOBER - NOVEMBER 1955

Species	Astragalus	Foot bone	Teeth	Tusk	Patella	Metacarpal	Unidentified	Total
Bones from Gray Sand								
Equus conversidens			1					1
Equus sp.			4					4
Bison sp.		1	1		1	1		4
Camel			2					2
Elephant		1	1	1			2	5
Unidentified			1			1	1	3
Total	1	1	10	1	1	1	4	19

Bones from Jointed Sand--1 unidentified foot
bone, 2 astragali, and 1 unidentified bone.
One unidentified Bison bone was assigned to
the Folsom level, bed not stated.

Radiocarbon samples were collected of
both charred and uncharred bison bone, from a
bone bed in the top of the Carbonaceous Silt
exposed in the wall of the east ditch (Fig. 15,
location 7f). Three samples were collected
(937-779 A,B,C) of which two (A and B) were
sent to the Lamont Laboratory December 8, 1955.
Samples were also sent to the Humble laboratory
and two dates were reported as follows (Brannon
et. al., 1957, p. 149): 0-169--6,300 B.P. $\pm$
150 years (uncharred bones, 937-779B); 0-170--
6,230 B.P. $\pm$ 150 years (charred bones, 937-
779A). The samples sent to Lamont were not
dated.

TABLE XXI

ARTIFACTS RECOVERED FROM SELLARDS
EXCAVATIONS OCTOBER-NOVEMBER
1955 BY TYPE

Type	Bed			
	JS-CS Contact	GS	Gravel Pit Dump	Unk
Unfluted Folsom point			1	
Atlatl weight		1		
Scraper				1
Worked bones		5		
Bone tool				1
Hammerstones		1		1
Polishing stone	1			
Total	1	7	1	3

TABLE XXIII

VERTEBRATE SPECIMENS FROM
SELLARDS EXCAVATIONS
MAY 1956

Species	Tooth	Bone
Bones from Gray Sand		
Equus scotti	1	
Equus sp.	1	
Unidentified		2
Total	2	2

Two unidentified bones were found in the Jointed
Sand.

Fig. 54. Mammoth remains associated with an obsidian point of Clovis type found by Oscar Shay, August 16, 1956. Photo courtesy Gordon Greaves.

TABLE XXIV

ARTIFACTS ASSOCIATED WITH
SHAY MAMMOTH AUGUST 1956

Type	Bed (probably BSW)
Clovis point	1
Flakes	2
Total	3

SELLARDS' MAY 1956 DIG

In May 1956, Sellards, Otto Schoen, and Jim Warnica revisited Pit No. 2 (Fig. 15, location 7c) and collected a few specimens (Table XXIII). Presumably, only one day was spent at the site and little of importance was found.

SHAY MAMMOTH KILL

In August 1956 Oscar Shay, working alone, excavated a mammoth kill in the peninsula between the two ditches at the south end of the North Pit (Fig. 15, location 9). While little written documentation exists on this mammoth find, good photo coverage was obtained by Gordon Greaves of the Portales News Tribune. The exact unit in which the bones were found is unknown. The notes state the mammoth lay in the next stratum above the Gray Sand. The bed may have been the "Brown Sand Wedge." A shattered obsidian projectile point of undoubted Clovis type was present two inches from the neck vertebrae; also in association were two flakes perhaps used in butchering. Bones present included the mandible with teeth and some vertebrae (Fig. 54).

It is possible, from the close proximity of the finds and the limited number of bones present, that this find represents portions of the same mammoth reported from Station A. Artifact data are presented in Table XXIV.

Museum of New Mexico Excavations, May 1956

As discussed earlier, after failure of the negotiations to set aside a portion of the pit as a scientific preserve, Fred Wendorf and A.E. Dittert Jr. spent a week during May 1956 in salvage excavations at the site. Excavation units consisted of a long trench which cross-sectioned the beds at the pond margin and a second test on the south bank of the North Pit which exposed the lower pond beds (Fig. 15, location 10; Figs. 55 and 56). The excavation is well reported by Dittert (1957) and hence will be briefly summarized here. The major beds exposed were the Jointed Sand and Carbonaceous Silt. While artifacts were not common, bones were numerous and large samples were collected for species identification,

radiocarbon analysis, radioactivity tests, etc. (Appendix 3). Some radiometric analyses carried out on these bone samples are reported by Fitting (1965).

Stratigraphic findings indicate that Trench A did cross-section the former pond margin. According to Dittert (1957, p. 8), "Both the Jointed Sand and the Carbonaceous Silt show rapid changes in Section 2. Westward preserved bison bones become plentiful and indicate water deposition with rapid burial. The extent of bone deterioration in Sections 2 and 3 implies inadequate preservation factors as would occur on the beach. From these conditions, it appears that the water edge was almost constant during the

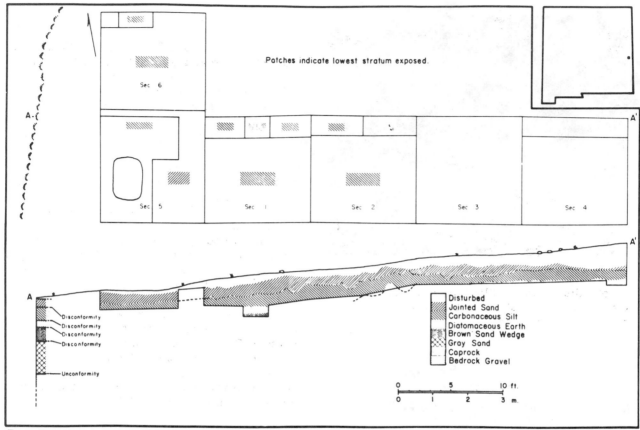

Fig. 55. Plan and profile of Trench A, Dittert and Wendorf Dig (Fig. 15, location 10), May 1956 (after Dittert 1957, Fig. 1). Dotted lines connecting beds have been added in an attempt to reconstruct the former pond margin.

Fig. 56. View of Bison bones in situ, on the contact between the Jointed Sand and Carbonaceous Silt, Section 5, Trench A.

times when the upper strata were deposited. Recession of the water is indicated in the erosion surfaces between, above, and below the two deposits.

"Even though the strata below the Carbonaceous Silt had been removed from the caprock, the occurrence of artifacts in Trench B in offshore deposits suggests that the water was never very deep. Therefore the edge of the caprock could mark average water edge during the earlier periods as well as in the later ones."

Ditterts' point about the average water edge seems well taken. He goes on to postulate that counterparts of the Diatomite and earlier strata once existed on the caprock but had subsequently been eroded away (Dittert, 1957, p. 9). In my opinion, there is some doubt that strata earlier than the Carbonaceous

Silt were _ever_ deposited on the caprock. It is possible that the pond did not overflow the caprock margin until the pond sediments had filled the original basin. This latter point of view is substantiated to some degree by data from the western margin of the pond (see Fig. 70).

The condition of the bison bones found is well described by Dittert (1957, p. 8). "Bones recovered from Trench A were predominantly articulated lower legs, lower jaws, and a few scapulae and ribs. Tails were absent. Upper leg portions and pelvic bones were rare. This distribution of bones together with the variety of artifacts indicates that animals were killed and partially prepared on the beach with subsequent removal of desired portions to a camp elsewhere. At least some of the tools used for this pursuit were manufactured on the beach."

The geographic separation (about 50 feet) between this bone bed (Fig. 56) and that located by Warnica and Shay in 1954 is slight. It is possible that these two excavations represent studies of the same prehistoric bison kill. If so then the Humble Oil Company radiocarbon dates of 6,230 B.P. ± 150 years and 6,300 B.P. ± 150 years obtained on bones from the nearby east ditch dig also date the bone bed in Trench A.

Artifacts from the smaller test excavation (Trench B) included four Clovis bone implements from the Gray Sand. These artifacts have been drawn for this report (Figs. 102, 103) to illustrate details of manufacture. Artifacts from the main excavation (Trench A) were limited to non-diagnostic implements of the Portales and Archaic horizons. A hammerstone, 2 gravers, and 31 flakes were found in the Jointed Sand (Archaic Horizon). The grinding stone was the only artifact located in the Carbonaceous Silt. According to Dittert (1957, p. 8), the grinding stone "was of too friable a material to retain characteristics which could indicate use on skins or preparation of gathered plants." A list of artifacts recovered by type is presented in Table XXV.

TABLE XXV

ARTIFACTS RECOVERED BY DITTERT
AND WENDORF, MAY 1956, BY TYPE

Type	Bed			
	GS	CS	JS	Total
Bone artifacts	4			4
Flakes			31	31
Hammerstone			1	1
Side-scraper, fragment			1	1
Gravers			2	2
Grinding stone, fragment		1		1
Total	4	1	35	40

Excavations by Arthur J. Jelinek, 1956-57

Limited excavations at the pit were conducted during the summers of 1956-57 by Arthur J. Jelinek, at that time with the University of Chicago. These studies formed a portion of a broad scale paleoecological study of the middle Pecos River valley reported by Jelinek in his dissertation (Jelinek, 1960). However details of the Blackwater Draw excavations were not included in that volume.

His excavations at Blackwater Locality No. 1 were in direct response to exposures made during the gravel mining. At this time the North and South Pits were connected by two trenches cut to receive pipes used to transfer water from the South to the North Pit as part of

the mining operation. These trenches presented good exposures of the original stratigraphy, and it was along these trenches that most of the excavations of all parties between 1955 and 1957 were conducted.

The find investigated by Jelinek consisted of the partially articulated remains of a single adult mammoth lying within the Brown Sand Wedge. It is obvious from the plan (Fig. 57) that many of the long bones had been scattered by man or carnivores after the animal died. It is Jelinek's view (personal communication) that the mammoth was an _in situ_ specimen in primary association with the geologic bed (the Brown Sand Wedge). This evidence would make this mam-

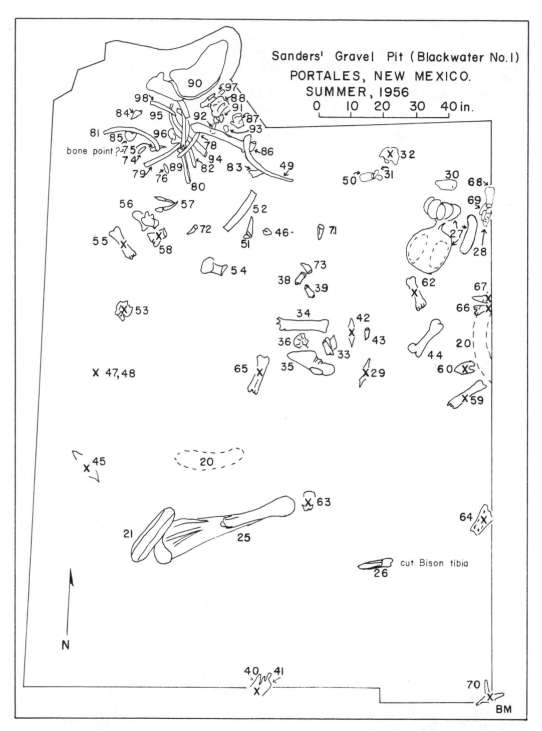

Fig. 57. Plan of bones found in the Brown Sand Wedge by Arthur Jelinek, 1956-57 (Fig. 15, location 11). Numbered bones include a mammoth maxilla, occipital, and zygomatic fragment, 27; a mammoth ramus, 90; mammoth vertebrae, 10; tusk fragments, 20; mammoth humerus, 25; and a mammoth longbone, 21. The other bones are mostly Bison sp. Plan courtesy of Arthur J. Jelinek.

moth the most recent specimen at the gravel pit and possibly the most recent recorded from the Great Plains (if we accept Jelinek's viewpoint). Based on radiocarbon dates from other finds at the gravel pit the age of this mammoth would be between 11,500 and 10,490 years B. P. Other mammoth remains from the pit found in this same geologic unit are all scattered bones and obviously record secondary deposition. No artifacts were associated with

Jelinek's mammoth. Additional finds included bones of the antelope jack rabbit (<u>Lepus alleni</u>) and the meadow vole (<u>Microtus pennsylvanicus</u>). Neither species inhabits the area today. Vertebrate specimens including both mammoth and bison were sent to Sellards where they were accessioned as part of the Texas Memorial Museum collections under the number 937-873.

Wendorf and Green Salvage, November 1958

On November 6, 1958, F. Wendorf and F.E. Green were engaged in research on the first portion of the High Plains Ecology Project, at that time sponsored by Texas Technological College. On a routine visit to the gravel pit to determine what new materials had been exposed by the gravel mining, they recovered portions of an in situ bison kill in the Diatomite (Fig. 15, location 11A). The bison remains had been partially disarticulated with the skull and portions of the vertebrae having been removed. The vertebrae, left limb elements, and part of the right limb were articulated. A small Folsom point was found between the humeri and the mandible but lying in the next lower bed. It is probable that the kill occurred on the eroded surface of Bed 3 (probably to be correlated with the Brown Sand Wedge) and the point was intruded into Bed 3 through natural causes. An alternative explanation that the association is fortuitous seems less probable. A second find of importance in the Diatomite was a carnassial tooth and part of a jaw assigned to the species <u>Canis diris</u> by Green. Similar specimens found elsewhere in the Gray Sand by the Texas Memorial Museum are assigned by

Lundelius (this volume) to the species <u>Aenocyon dirus</u>. Beds identified at the site are listed in Table XXVI. A plan and section of the find is presented in Figure 58. Subsequent to the excavations of Wendorf and Green at this locality James Warnica examined the beds and located an artifact in situ. The artifact was a flake scraper (W-5) found in the Diatomite.

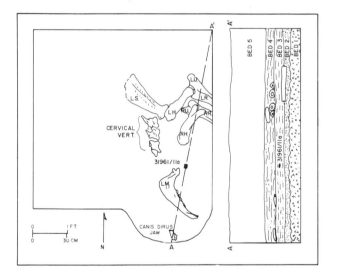

Fig. 58. Portion of butchered bison kill in the Diatomite with Folsom point, excavated by D.F. Wendorf and F.E. Green in 1958 (Fig. 15, location 11A). Bison bones present are: LM, left mandible; RH, right humerus; RR, right radius; RU, right ulna; LR, left radius; LU, left ulna; LH, left humurus; LS, left scapula; and three cervical vertebrae. Note vertical separation between point and bison bones. Map prepared from sketch map and photo by F.E. Green now in files of Museum of New Mexico.

TABLE XXVI

STRATIGRAPHY AT WENDORF AND GREEN SALVAGE EXCAVATION, 1958

Bed 1   Red Gravel

Bed 2   Light gray, unconsolidated, fine to very coarse-grained sand, with a horse (<u>Equus</u> sp.) cannon bone. This is the "Gray Sand."

Bed 3   Dark gray, hard friable silty clay with Folsom point. This bed seemingly may be correlated with the Brown Sand Wedge.

Bed 4   Dark gray laminated diatomaceous earth with <u>Bison</u> remains, the Diatomite.

Bed 5   Gray, hard friable silty clay with scattered <u>Bison</u> bones, the Carbonaceous Silt.

High Plains Project Excavations, 1961

During August and September 1961, James J. Hester and Jerry Harbour were engaged in paleoecological research at the gravel pit as part of the High Plains Ecology Project. Sam Sanders, the gravel pit operator, directed a bulldozer operator to clear an area down to a bone bed. A suitable bison bone bed was discovered and, therefore, Hester undertook excavation. In all, three areas, designated Localities 1, 2, and 3, were studied (Fig. 15, locations 12a, b, and c). These areas were located to the northwest of the North Pit.

LOCALITY 1

Locality 1 consisted of a vertical exposure of an old wall of the former North Pit. At the time of study (August 1961), this was the only portion of the original stratigraphy of the site exposed. This section was of interest because of the molluscan fauna present in one of the beds, presumed to be the Diatomite. Two days

were spent in washing and screening snails from this deposit preparatory to submitting them for species identification. As this fauna was studied as part of the High Plains Ecology Project it is described in the report on that project (Wendorf and Hester, n.d.).

LOCALITY 2

This locality was exposed by the bulldozing operation described above. The remains uncovered consisted of scattered bison bones in the Carbonaceous Silt unit. A small area was excavated in detail, but produced little information due to the scattered nature of the bones and the absence of artifacts. One small flake was the only artifact located. It is presumed this site represents a bison kill and butchering site at the pond margin about 8,000 years ago. No additional information about the culture of

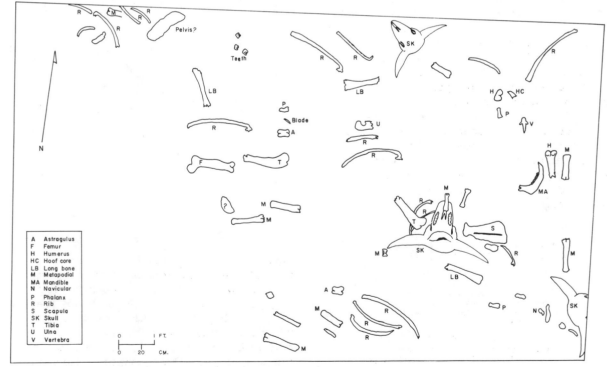

A	Astragalus
F	Femur
H	Humerus
HC	Hoof core
LB	Long bone
M	Metapodial
MA	Mandible
N	Navicular
P	Phalanx
R	Rib
S	Scapula
SK	Skull
T	Tibia
U	Ulna
V	Vertebra

Fig. 59. Plan of Folsom age bison bone bed (upper level) in the Brown Sand facies of the Diatomite, Locality 3. Note location of blade found in situ. The lower bone bed (not shown) consisted of two skulls and numerous associated bones at the southeast corner of the excavation.

Early Man was recovered and the site was abandoned.

LOCALITY 3

This locality included the primary bone bed exposed by Sanders' bulldozing. As the bone bed was located some eight feet below the modern surface, excavations were limited to the exposure of bones within the bulldozer cut. No stratigraphic details were obtainable from the walls of the cut as the overburden consisted of backfill from previous gravel mining.

The area cleared (Fig. 59) contained bones of at least five bison situated in a laminated brown sand and diatomaceous silt. At the time of excavation this member was termed "Diatomite." At the present writing, the bed is believed to be a sandy shoreward facies of the Diatomite, the same bed that is termed Brown Sand Wedge at Localities 4 and 5 and El Llano Dig 1. A more complete description of this unit is presented in the stratigraphic section in the report on the El Llano excavation later in this volume. Unfortunately, Locality 3 has subsequently been removed by gravel mining, and the stratigraphy cannot be reexamined.

The Bone Bed

The five bison were separated vertically into two distinct layers. The upper layer contained bones of three individuals associated with several artifacts of Folsom type. The lower bone bed, containing bones of at least two individuals, continued underneath the overburden and could not be excavated in entirety. Sufficient bones were cleared to determine at least two and probably more bison had been killed and butchered on that spot. No artifacts were located, and the bones were in no apparent pattern. As 5 to 6 inches of fill separated the bone beds, it is presumed that a number of years intervened between the two kills, although it is assumed that the lower bone bed was also of Folsom age.

There appears to be a normal representation of bones at the site indicating that no parts were carried away (with the possible exception of the hide and tail). The animals were heavily butchered as bones are scattered in apparent confusion. It is also probable that they were scattered by carnivores after being butchered. Significant characteristics of the bone bed are:

1. All the bones are disarticulated.

2. One skull (palate up) had a metapodial lying on the palate suggesting the metapodial was used as a lever to break the mandible loose in order to remove the tongue.

3. The other two skulls were lying palate downward.

4. The size of the skulls suggests that two of the animals were probably young adults. A confirming fact is the absence of articular ends of the long bones which indicates the epiphyseal unions were not sealed at the time of death.

5. The size of the large skull, 36 inches between the horn core tips, suggests the bison might be assigned to Bison antiquus.

Due to poor preservation of the bones it was extremely difficult to excavate them without brushing away pieces. As a result, some bones could not be identified as to type, limiting our knowledge of the butchering pattern. A list of bones identified is presented in Table XXVII.

TABLE XXVII

VERTEBRATE SPECIMENS RECOVERED FROM
LOCALITY 3 (UPPER BONE BED)
EXCAVATED BY HESTER
AUGUST-SEPTEMBER 1961

Bones

Species	Astragali	Femur	Humeri	Hoof core	Long bone	Metapodials	Mandible	Navicular	Phalanges	Ribs	Scapula	Skull	Tibiae	Ulna	Vertebrae	Teeth	Pelvis?	Unidentified	Total

Bones from Brown Sand Wedge

| Bison Sp. | 2 | 1 | 2 | 1 | 2 | 9 | 1 | 1 | 3 | 16 | 1 | 3 | 2 | 1 | 1 | 3 | 1 | 14 | 64 |

Artifacts

Three artifacts were located (Appendix I); two broken Folsom points and an unifacial knife made on a blade. Both projectile points were found screening the earth disturbed by the bulldozer. The blade was found <u>in situ</u> (Fig. 59). Its location, between a phalanx and an astragalus, does not permit inferences as to function. The animals were probably killed in shallow water, and the artifact was lost during butchering.

Eastern New Mexico University Mammoth

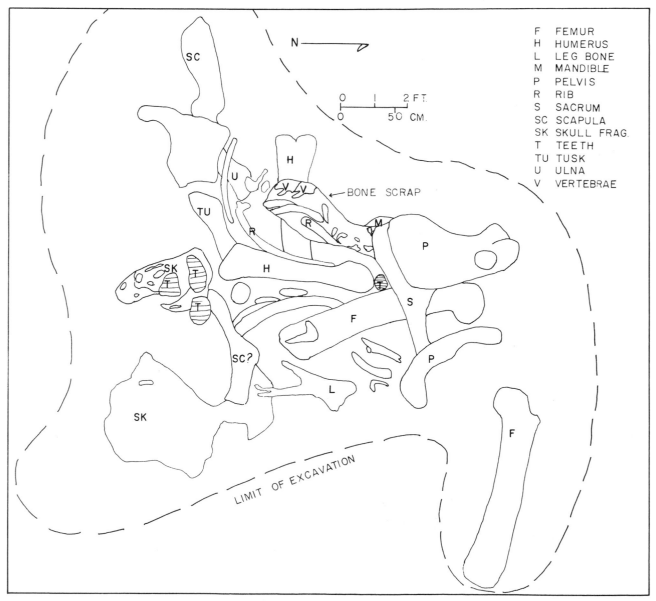

Fig. 60. Plan of mammoth excavated by Eastern New Mexico University, November 1961. No artifacts were found in direct association with the skeleton.

In November of 1961, Hester received a telephone call from Sam Sanders to the effect that a mammoth had been located which he wanted salvaged. Arrangements were made for Hester to come as soon as possible. Upon his arrival in Portales, it was learned that Sanders had also contacted Eastern New Mexico University and that students from that institution, under direction of Dr. William King of the Geology department, were excavating the mammoth. Later, the bones were encased in plaster and removed to the Roosevelt County Museum in Portales for eventual display.

The remains consisted of the slightly disarticulated bones of a single large adult mammoth. While the skull was in pieces, the apparent absence of artifacts suggests the animal died a natural death at the edge of the pond. The skull could have suffered erosion through exposure above the water level for some time after death. There is no evidence of butchering or any other activity by man. One small non-diagnostic projectile point was claimed to have been found with the bones by an amateur. No confirmation of this association is possible.

The bones were lying in the Gray Sand unit with some higher portions projecting into the overlying Diatomite. A plan of the position of the bones is presented in Figure 60. The location of the bones (Fig. 15, location 13) is within the area stripped and backfilled between 1955 and 1957. The stripping of overburden at that time came within six inches of the top of the bones as indicated by the presence of red clay backfill immediately above the bulldozer cut surface on the original pond sediments. The area was reexposed in 1961 in order to mine the underlying gravel.

High Plains Project Research, 1962

During 1962, Hester maintained close communications with amateur archaeologists in Portales and the gravel pit personnel. As a consequence, whenever finds were made, a trip was made to the pit as soon as possible to record the material before it was destroyed.

MAMMOTH EXCAVATION, JANUARY 31, 1962

In late January, Sam Sanders notified Hester that another mammoth had been exposed and excavation began the following day. The bones were fragmentary and scattered. Portions remaining included two teeth, one tusk, fragments of skull, and a few unidentified bone scraps (Fig. 61).

The bones were lying in the Gray Sand unit (Fig. 15, location 15A) overlain by a mixed zone of black soil and red clay. The red clay was clearly derived from the sterile clay lenses in the underlying gravel beds indicating that the mammoth had been exposed by the gravel mining at an earlier date, presumably between 1955 and 1957, and then recovered with backfill. No artifacts were located, and the condition of the bones did not indicate whether the animal died a natural death or not.

RADIOCARBON AND POLLEN SAMPLING

During 1962, Vance Haynes and the author made several trips to the pit collecting samples for environmental studies as part of the High Plains project. Early in the year, on a field trip accompanied by Jerry Harbour, an exposure which contained a truncated section of the original stratigraphy (Fig. 15, location 15c) was noted. A summary of the beds exposed with location of samples collected is presented below.

TABLE XXVIII

STRATIGRAPHY AT SITE DATED BY
ARIZONA C-14 LABORATORY

		Modern Surface
8	ft.	Laminated clays deposited in gravel pit slush pool
		Truncated Surface
		A 386, A 379, A 380
2	ft.	Diatomite
3.5	ft.	Gray Sand
1	ft.	Gravel

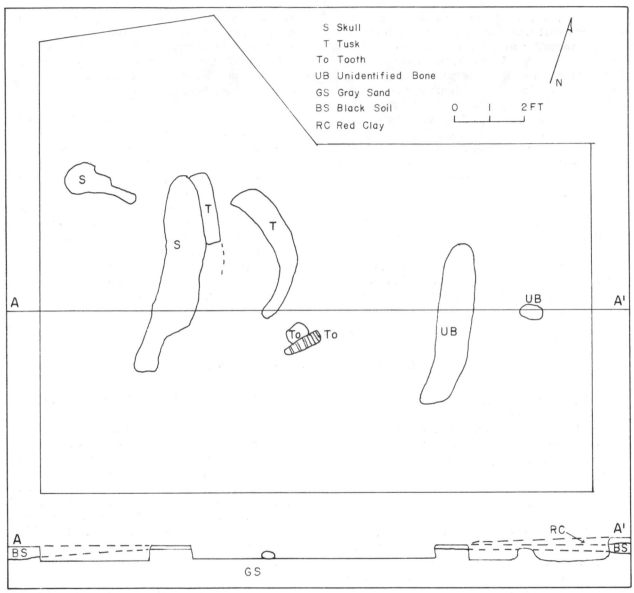

Fig. 61. Plan of mammoth remains excavated by James J. Hester January 31, 1962 (Fig. 15, location 15A).

Several hundred pounds of the Diatomite were collected for radiocarbon analysis as it was noted that small flecks of carbonized plant remains were scattered throughout the bed. The samples were processed by Vance Haynes at the University of Arizona Radiocarbon Lab whose report is presented below.

Blackwater No. 1 series,
Clovis, New Mexico

The Blackwater No. 1 locality (34° 17' N Lat, 103° 19" W Long), Roosevelt Co., New Mexico, is described by Sellards

(1952, p. 29-31) and by Wendorf (1961, p. 115-117). Other radiocarbon dates are 6230 ± 150 (0-170) and 6300 ± 150 (0-169) on burned and unburned bone from the "Carbonaceous Silt" unit; and 4950 ± 150 (0-157) on burned bone from the "Jointed Sand" unit (Brannon, et al., 1957, p. 149). Coll. 1962 by Vance Haynes, Jerry Harbour, and James Hester: submitted by Fred Wendorf and James J. Hester, Museum of New Mexico, Santa Fe.

A-386.   Diatomite unit,   10,490 ± 900
              Folsom occupation

Humic acids extracted from fossil plant remains in Diatomite between Carbonaceous Silt above and Gray Sand below. Comment: date is comparable to Folsom dates at other sites.

A-379.	Fine-grained carbo- naceous matter in silt	9,900 ± 320
A-380.	Humic acids fraction	10,600 ± 320
	Average	10,250 ± 320

A transitional zone of interbedded silt and diatomite layers between Silt above and Diatomite below was sampled to provide a maximum age of Carbonaceous Silt deposition and a minimum age of Diatomite deposition. Comment: dates are comparable to A-386 and suggest that the transitional zone is part of the Diatomite unit.

Bone specimens collected from the same locality were submitted to Authur J. Jelinek of the University of Michigan for radioactivity studies. Results of this research are reported by Fitting (1965).

A series of pollen profiles were collected from an exposure on the south side of the pit near the area excavated by Cotter in 1936 and 1937. Results of pollen analysis of these samples are presented in Wendorf and Hester (n.d.). Stratigraphy exposed in this section of the pit is illustrated in Figure 10. The Brown Sand Wedge unit in this section is that washed by Bob Slaughter for microvertebrates. This work resulted in the recovery of a sizable microfauna (also reported in Wendorf and Hester, n.d.).

EXCAVATIONS AT LOCALITIES 4 AND 5

In September of 1962, James M. Warnica of Portales notified Hester that a number of artifacts had been located by amateurs digging in the recently stripped area on the west side of the pit. Hester joined Warnica the next day, the site was examined, and it was apparent that extensive deposits containing artifacts were exposed. These deposits consisted of two areas, a cutbank eight feet in height adjoining a flat area approximately 200 feet in width which had been stripped down to the artifact bearing level (Fig. 62). Two excavations were laid out, one along the cutbank termed locality 4 (Fig. 15, location 15e) and a second at a concentration of bones in the stripped area termed Locality 5 (Fig. 15, location 15f). The amateurs continued excavations in the vicinity, and their finds were plotted on the area base map (Fig. 62). These finds include the Agate Basin Locality mentioned by Green (1963, p.

160). While the Agate Basin point overlay the Folsom level, its relationship to the Portales Complex is not clearly demonstrated. The Agate Basin point was within the Carbonaceous Silt unit as is the so-called Portales Complex (see discussion in the artifact section). The point raised here is that the Carbonaceous Silt unit at this point was truncated by bulldozer activity, and the relationship of the Agate Basin point to other artifacts of the "Portales Complex" is not stratigraphically clear. A total of nine artifacts were recovered by the amateurs from this "Agate Basin locality" (Fig. 15, location 16).

Stratigraphy

The beds exposed in the cutbank from top to bottom (Figs. 65 and 66) are a massive diatomaceous gray silt, a laminated brown silt and sand, a massive brown sand with caliche nodules, artifacts, and bones termed "Brown Sand Wedge;" and a unit of fine whitish-tan sand with caliche nodules and artifacts, the Gray Sand. A stratigraphic problem concerns us with respect to the "Brown Sand Wedge" unit containing Folsom culture (Fig. 66, **bed 3**). Is this unit a shoreward facies of the "Diatomite" exposed in the center of the pond, or is the next overlying unit the "laminated brown silt and sand" the Diatomite equivalent? The former seems more likely to be true due to the inclusion of the Folsom artifacts. See Haynes and Agogino (1966) for a more complete discussion of this problem.

The presence of Folsom artifacts at Locality 4 in this unit are the result of its proximity to a former campsite on the bank nearby. Obviously these implements were swept into the pond by flash floods. The position of the artifacts at Locality 4 may mean that only a short interval of time separated the Clovis and Folsom occupations of the site. The artifacts are separated by as little as three inches vertically and a minor unconformity. Details on the artifacts located are presented in Appendix I.

LOCALITY 5

A concentration of bison bones in the laminated diatomaceous pondward facies of the "Brown Sand Wedge" unit was exposed by the bulldozer. This concentration attracted

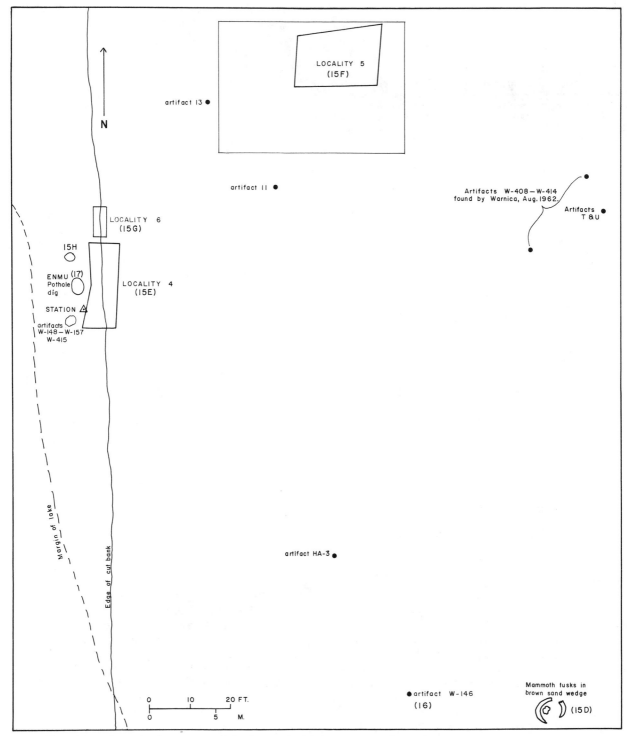

Fig. 62. Map showing location of finds made by amateur archaeologists and Localities 4, 5, and 6 excavated by James J. Hester in August and September 1962. The Agate Basin finds of Warnica include artifacts W-408 to W-414 in the northeastern section of the above map (Fig. 15, location 16).

the attention of Jesse Collins and Gordon Brown, Portales amateurs. Artifacts secured by them clearly indicate this bone bed represents a Folsom age bison kill.

After the amateurs had cleared a small section they abandoned the area. At this time, Hester initiated excavation of the bone bed. An area 10 by 20 feet was cleared and the bones exposed in detail. Only one additional artifact, a scraper, was obtained, but the nature of the bone bed is of interest.

The Bone Bed

The number and position of the metapodials suggests that two or possibly three bison were killed and butchered on the spot. The metapodials were found in a near vertical position (Fig. 63) suggesting that the animals were mired

in mud at the time they were killed. The scattered nature of the bones implies that carnivores had mauled the carcasses, and some substantiation of this inference is provided by a carnivore tooth found lying within the bone bed (Table XXIX).

Certain bones were conspicuously absent, especially as the carcasses were left lying where the animals fell. No skulls are present, there is only one scapula and one pelvis, and ribs are rare. It is possible that portions containing these bones were carried elsewhere by the hunters. Again poor preservation of the bones limits our knowledge of the butchering pattern.

Also located within the same straigraphic unit, lying within ten feet of the bison bone bed, were two isolated mammoth teeth and a

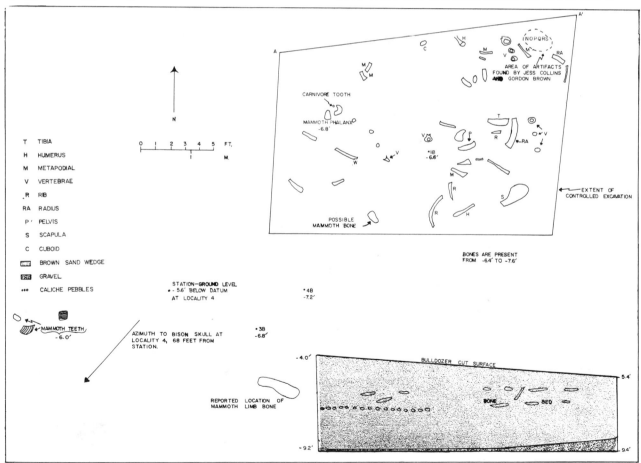

Fig. 63. Plan and section of bison bone bed in the Brown Sand Wedge, Locality 5 (Fig. 15, location 15f).

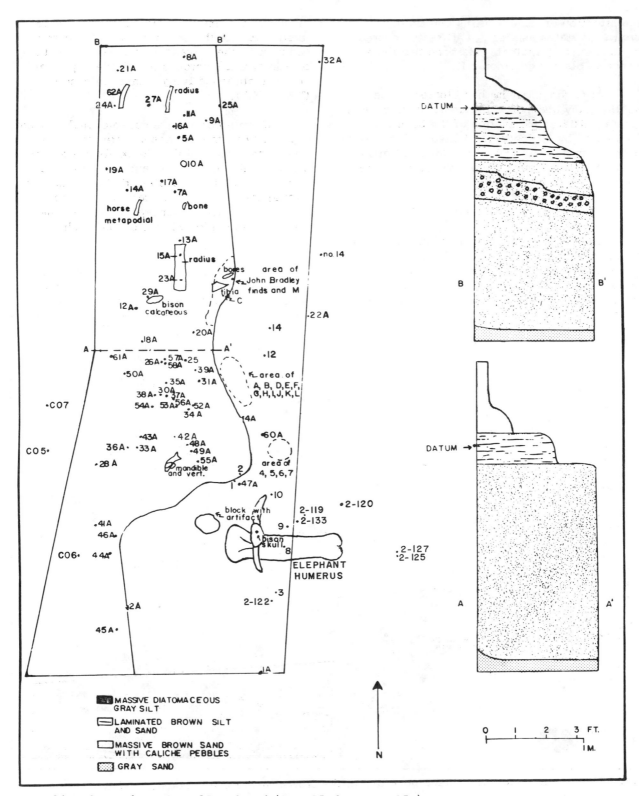

Fig. 64. Plan and section of Locality 4 (Fig. 15, location 15e).

Fig. 65. View of Locality 4 during excavation. The two men with hand picks are excavating in the top of the Folsom level. The men with shovels are standing on the contact between the Brown Sand Wedge, Bed 3, and the Gray Sand, Bed 2.

mammoth limb bone. The position of the latter is based on reports from the amateurs who removed the limb bone before Hester began excavations.

TABLE XXIX

VERTEBRATE SPECIMENS RECOVERED
FROM LOCALITY 5, SEPTEMBER 1962

Bones

Species	Tibia	Humeri	Metapodials	Vertebrae	Ribs	Radii	Pelves	Scapula	Cuboid	Teeth	Phalanx	Limb bone	Unidentified	Total
Brown Sand Wedge														
Bison sp.	1	2	5	8	3	2	2	1	1				16	41
Mammuthus sp.										2	1	1	1	5
Carnivore											1			1
Total	1	2	5	8	3	2	2	1	1	3	1	1	17	47

One mammoth tooth was recovered
from the upper portion of the underlying
Red Gravel bed.

These mammoth remains were scattered and are presumed to be redeposited. However, they are present at the same vertical elevation and within the same bed as the Folsom age bison kill. This is again evidence (also present in Jelinek's excavation) of close age relationship between the extinction of the mammoth in the plains and the appearance of Folsom culture. It is even possible that there is a slight temporal overlap between the two at this particular site.

Artifacts

While most of the specimens were recovered by the amateurs (Appendix I), four additional implements were located in situ at Locality 5. The artifacts are of Folsom type. They were not appreciably different from those recovered from Locality 4 and will not be discussed in detail at this point. A list of all

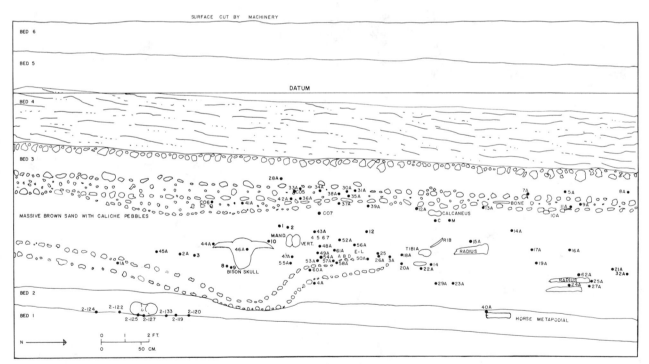

Fig. 66. Schematic north-south profile of Locality 4 showing locations of bones and artifacts in situ. Bed 3 contained Folsom artifacts throughout. Bed 2 artifacts were of Clovis type. All bones and artifacts were secondarily deposited. It is possible the mammoth bone and artifacts in Bed 2 were deposited in an old arroyo channel. Irregular lumps in Bed 3 are caliche nodules. Bed 1 -- Red Gravel, Bed 2 -- Gray Sand, Bed 3 -- Massive Brown Sand (BSW), Bed 4 -- Laminated Tan Silt and Gray Sand, Bed 5 -- Massive Diatomaceous Gray Silt (probably the carbonaceous silt), Bed 6 -- Jointed Sand.

However, the earth was thoroughly screened for artifacts. Surprisingly, the material in one container is of Folsom type and the other of Clovis type. Determination of the cultural assignment is based on both the presence of diagnostic projectile points and the stone types utilized. Artifacts from this excavation are listed in Appendix I.

The photos from the excavation reveal the following geologic units: a laminated bed (at the level of the man's head in Figure 67) overlying a massive unit with caliche pebbles. Comparison of these photos with those showing beds at Locality 4, 10 feet away (Fig. 65) suggests that similar stratigraphy is present at both sites. Evidence in favor of the "spring conduit" hypothesis is the glossy polish on the Folsom artifacts suggesting extensive water action. Articles published by the Portales News Tribune mention that the site was located because it was a "soft spot" in the hard clay. In addition, it was mentioned that the tunnel possessed two small branches leading off to the side. Both of these reports substantiate the point of view that the spring conduit was in fact similar to those reported by Haynes and Agogino (1966) from the northwest corner of the pit.

The initial sample of artifacts from this site was obtained by two employees at the gravel pit, J.D. Murray and Joe Charbonaugh. Their excavation consisted of the digging and screening of the top portion of the "spring conduit." They recovered about 50 artifacts in two hours (Appendix I). The following day, Rowan learned of their finds and initiated the excavation described above. The finds of Murray and Charbonaugh were also borrowed for study and are described in the artifact section. A list of artifacts recovered from the spring conduit by type follows (Table XXXIII).

TABLE XXXIII

ARTIFACTS RECOVERED FROM THE EASTERN NEW MEXICO UNIVERSITY SPRING CONDUIT BY TYPE

Type	Bed	
	BSW	GS
Flakes	92	23
Flake scrapers	34	2
Folsom points	23	
Clovis points, Type I		2
Indeterminant projectile points	2	
Side-scrapers	20	7
End-scrapers	17	1
Unifacial knives	7	4
Bifacial knives	5	4
Gravers	3	
Flake knives	21	
Channel flakes	7	1
Abrader	1	
Pebbles	4	
Indeterminant scrapers	1	
Hammerstones	2	
Chopper	1	
Cores	1	1
Knife fragments	3	
Total	244*	45

* Artifacts within the above total include eighteen obtained from the base of the Brown Sand Wedge by J.D. Murray. These artifacts have been assigned to the Clovis complex on the basis of their form and material. By type these artifacts include the following: 7 flakes, 3 flake scrapers, 3 pebbles, 2 side-scrapers, 2 flake knives, and 1 knife fragment.

Fig. 68. View to south showing the Eastern New Mexico University Spring Conduit excavation at far right and the Locality 4 excavation in the left foreground. Photo courtesy William E. King.

Excavations at Locality 6

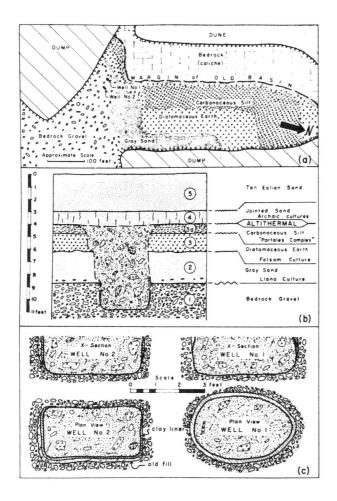

Fig. 69. Plans and profiles of two wells located near the southwest corner of the pit (after Green, 1962, Fig. 1) (Fig. 15, location 14). Note that c documents the plans and profiles of the wells as actually found. The illustration b is a reconstruction.

On September 29 and 30, 1962, excavations were continued in the vicinity of the Eastern New Mexico University spring conduit and Locality 4. This excavation was a joint project sponsored by the Museum of New Mexico and Eastern New Mexico University. Excavators included James J. Hester, William E. King, Jack Cunningham, and six geology students. This excavation, termed Locality 6, was located just north of Locality 4 (Fig. 15, location 15g). The dig was relatively unproductive with 15 flakes and one Folsom point base being recovered. In the interim between the Locality 4 dig and this one, a substantial portion of the vertical cutbank had been removed by the bulldozers. This includes the ridge visible in the center of Figure 68. The loose earth from this grading was pushed over the Locality 4 cut. As a result, it was difficult to reestablish datum points utilized during the Locality 4 dig. After this was accomplished, and much of the loose overburden removed by hand, it was determined that the excavation was being conducted in reworked backfill which had been packed by the bulldozers and carryalls. As a result, it was determined that the site was not worthy of continued excavation, and it was abandoned.

Also in the interim between the Locality 4 and Locality 6 excavations a number of artifacts were recovered by one of the amateurs, Jesse Collins. These artifacts were referred by Collins to two localities, Locality 6 (location 15G, Fig. 15) and an area approximately 15 feet north of the ENMU spring conduit, termed here Location 15H (Fig. 15). Whereas all the artifacts from these two areas have been assigned provenience to stratigraphic unit, those from Locality 6 must be viewed with suspicion as this was the area that had been reworked by the bulldozers.

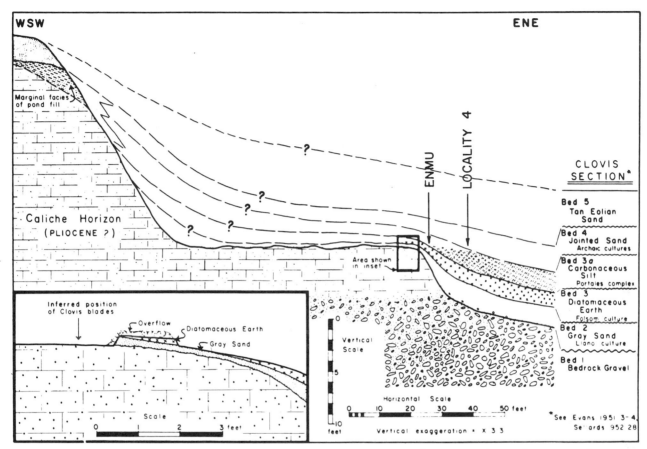

Fig. 70. Schematic profile of caliche shelf and pond sediments showing inferred location of Clovis blades (after Green, 1963, Fig. 2). The position of the ENMU Spring Conduit and Locality 4 have been added to show their spatial relationship to this section.

Texas Technological College Excavations, 1962

Limited salvage of exposed bones and artifacts was carried out at irregular intervals during 1962 by F.E. Green of Texas Technological College (Green, 1962, 1963). Two Archaic age wells were located and described (Fig. 69), and a number of presumed Clovis age blades were obtained from tailings in an area exposed by the bulldozers. The location of the wells is not given precisely by Green, but they were probably near the position shown on Figure 15, location 14. The "Clovis" artifacts were collected near the Eastern New Mexico University Spring Conduit excavation (Fig. 15, location 17). While Green's provenience data of these "Clovis" blades are not conclusive, his assignment of these specimens to the Clovis culture is accepted as they are duplicated by specimens with undoubted association in the Clovis age mammoth kill from El Llano Dig 1.

The stratigraphic diagram of this locality published by Green and reproduced below (Fig. 70) is schematic and differs in some details from that prepared by Hester from Locality 4 only 10 feet to the east (Fig. 66).

Salvage by Green was also carried out at remnants of a mammoth skeleton exposed August 8, 1962 (Fig. 15, location 15d). Green's activities consisted of limited excavations around the bones and removal of a portion of them in plaster (Fig. 71). No artifacts were reported found.

The following week, Hester visited the site and, unaware that Green had been excavating there, proceeded to record the same mammoth. The exposed nature of the bones and the lack of stratigraphic control was assumed to be the result of digging by amateur archaeologists (Fig. 71). Although little remained of the mammoth, owing perhaps to its having been previously exposed in the bank of the pit in 1957, a sketch map and profile were made (Fig. 72). Radiocarbon samples of tusk were collected, and the sediments were sampled for pollen. The stratigraphy was simple, consisting of two units, the Gray Sand overlain

Fig. 71. View of salvage excavations of a mammoth conducted by F.E. Green of the Texas Technological College Museum, Lubbock, Texas, August 8, 1962 (Fig. 15, location 15d). Photo courtesy Gordon Greaves.

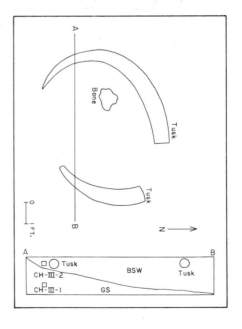

Fig. 72. Plan and profile of mammoth recorded August 1962.

by a section of the Brown Sand Wedge (an eastern extention of the bed identified at the Locality 4 dig) containing the bones. The section had been truncated above this unit by the bulldozer. The association of mammoth in the Brown Sand Wedge is thus established as it is also reported from Jelinek's excavation.

The tusk samples collected were processed by Vance Haynes of the University of Arizona Radiocarbon Lab who reported insufficient carbon remaining to obtain a date. The pollen samples have yet to be analyzed.

El Llano Dig. No. 1

INTRODUCTION

On Sunday morning, November 25, 1962, F.E. Green of Texas Technological College partially uncovered a femur and pelvis of a large adult mammoth in a recently stripped area at the northwest margin of the pit. Upon making this discovery, he notified Sam Sanders of the find. Mr. Sanders asked Green to notify James M. Warnica, President of the El Llano Archaeological Society of Portales, of the find and to ask Warnica to hire two laborers at Sanders' expense to begin excavation of the mammoth bones.

On the next day, Warnica and Jess Collins, a Society member, and the laborers began excavations. After uncovering the mammoth pelvis located by Green, Collins and Warnica noticed another bone exposed a short distance to the northwest. Upon removing a small amount of sand from around this second bone it became apparent that this specimen was the mandible of a second mammoth. This mandible was part of the first mammoth fully excavated by the members of the Society designated "Mammoth No. 1." The mammoth located by Green is referred to as "Mammoth No. 2."

At the time the excavation was being conducted, negotiations were underway to try to preserve the bones in place as a permanent exhibit. This situation necessitated leaving all bones in place and excavating around them.

The first artifact was recovered from the Gray Sand Wednesday, November 28, by Rudy Burdine, an employee of Mr. Sanders. The following day five artifacts were recovered in association with Mammoth No. 1. Realizing the importance of the finds, Warnica consulted with Sanders, and the latter agreed to continue

funds for the two laborers. Labor was also provided by the El Llano Society members and members of the South Plains Archaeological Society of Lubbock, Texas.

After one week, James Hester of the Museum of New Mexico, joined the excavation and served as director during the times Warnica was absent from the site.

Following a visit to the site by Tom Bolack, then Governor of New Mexico, the State of New Mexico appropriated $1,000 to expedite and expand the excavations. As a result of this action, not only was the Society working at the site, but a crew hired by state funds directed by Hester was also conducting excavations under the auspices of the Museum of New Mexico. This crew squared up the margins of the excavated area and dug three exploratory trenches extending east, west, and south in order to define the limits of the mammoth bone bed. A section of the vertical, south-facing earthen bank which lay at the north edge of the bone bed was also cleared off. This bank contained all of the late Quaternary pond sediments represented at the Clovis site and is here termed the "North Bank."

The Museum of New Mexico crew excavated at the site until January 5, 1963, at which time the state funds were exhausted, and Hester returned to Santa Fe. The Museum of New Mexico explorations revealed the bones of two additional mammoths designated Mammoths 3 and 4, and a few isolated bones of a fifth mammoth (Fig. 73). Close-up photos (Figs. 74, 75) show the distribution of the best preserved of these specimens, Mammoths 1 and 2.

Artifacts recovered from the North Bank

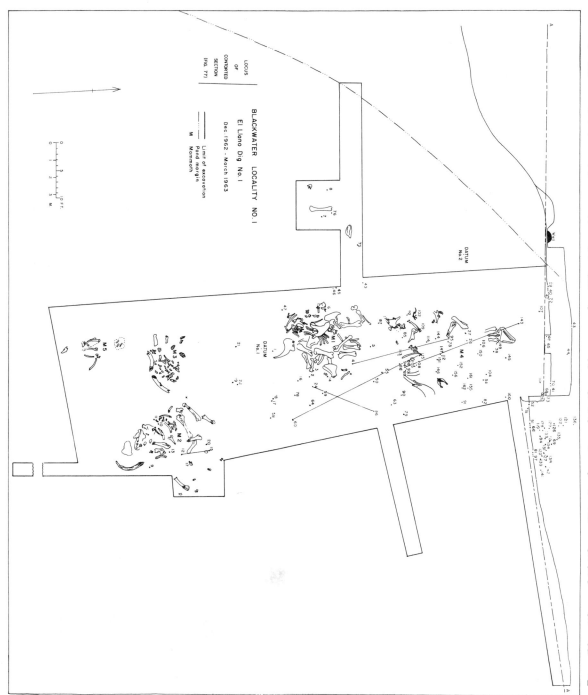

Fig. 73. Plan of El Llano Dig 1 showing details of bone and artifact locations. Lines joining artifact numbers indicate direction of transport of fragments of the same artifacts. This figure is almost identical to that published by Warnica (1966, Fig. 1). Map prepared by Darwin Simnacher and Phyllis Hughes.

included materials from the Jointed Sand, Carbonaceous Silt, Diatomite, and Gray Sand. All of the artifacts, with the exception of the Clovis materials associated with the mammoth bone bed (Fig. 76) were recovered from the North Bank. At this point we are mainly concerned with the Clovis artifacts associated with the bone bed. Artifacts found in the other strata will be treated in the artifact section.

A total of 166 artifacts were recovered from the Gray Sand associated with the remains of the mammoths (Appendix I). The artifacts may be grouped into two categories: campsite debris and hunting debris. The campsite material consisted of bone artifacts, scrapers, gravers, hammerstones, cores, knives, flakes, and two possible grinding stones. The hunting material included four Clovis projectile points and the basal tang of a fifth, and knives and scrapers directly associated with the skeletal remains of the four mammoths.

It is apparent that these early peoples

Fig. 74. Close-up of Mammoth No. 1, a large juvenile, showing orientation of remains. The skeleton is resting on its right side with the skull to the left. Note slight disarticulation, especially the scapula in the foreground. One tibia has been reversed end for end, and the ankle and foot bones are missing.

camped and cooked nearby. Flecks of charcoal were found near Mammoths 1 and 2, and
a slightly charred horse metapodial was found
near the tusks of Mammoth No. 4.

The newly discovered information regarding the Clovis Complex included approximately
five times as many artifacts as those known
from the next largest Clovis assemblage in
the western United States, that from the Lehner
site (Haury, Sayles, and Wasley, 1959). In
addition, new artifact types are present including bone implements, gravers, a grinding stone,
and end-scrapers made on prismatic blades.

An article describing the excavations and
the various finds has been published by Warnica
(1966). In the subsequent descriptive sections

on the El Llano excavations this article will be
extensively quoted in order to avoid possible
confusion. It should be pointed out here that
Warnica's article describes finds made throughout 1963 during the entire salvage of the bone
bed. As a result, his article includes some
artifacts discovered after the termination of
Hester's participation in the project. Of the
166 Clovis age artifacts reported by Warnica,
117 (through catalogue number EL-167) are
described in detail in this report (Appendix I
and the artifact section.)

DESCRIPTION OF EXCAVATIONS

"The principal excavated area, which
included the bone bed, covered approximately
2475 sq. ft. (Fig. 1) [reproduced as Fig. 73

Fig. 75. Close-up of Mammoth No. 2, a large adult, in same orientation as Mammoth No. 1.
The skull and pelvis are badly smashed and in general the bones are more disarticulated than
Mammoth No. 1.

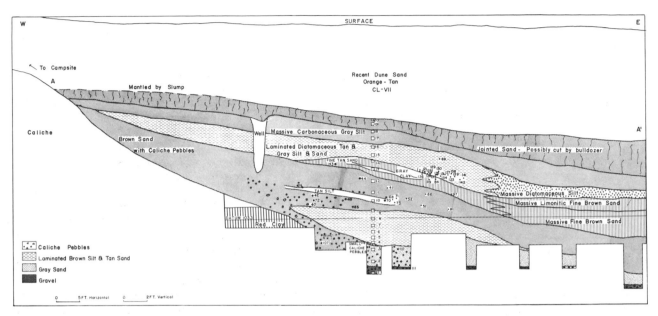

Fig. 76. Profile of the North Bank, El Llano Dig 1, showing geologic strata, artifacts located *in situ*, an Archaic well, and pollen section CL-VII. Figure 2 published by Warnica (1966) includes a 25-foot-long portion of the above section extending from just left of the well to the pollen profile.

in this report], extending north-south for 82.5 ft. This bone bed occurred in the Gray Sand or Clovis horizon and lay near the northwestern margin of the Pleistocene pond. The pond margin consists of relatively low, gently sloping caliche banks that reached to within 16 ft. of the bone bed at the closest point.

"An important stratigraphic feature on the northern edge of the mammoth-bone bed was a vertical, southward-facing earth bank (Fig. 2) [see Fig. 76] which had been exposed by the gravel-mining operations. This bank contained all of the major artifact-bearing strata at the Clovis site (Sellards 1952) and is here referred to as the "North Bank". In the face of the North Bank a hand-dug well was exposed (Fig. 2; see Evans 1951, Green 1962). This well was originally dug from the top of the Carbonaceous Silt and extended downward into the Folsom horizon.

"The gravel-mining operations had removed all of the overburden from the bone bed, and the remainder of the excavation was completed with hand tools. The first mammoth skeleton completely exposed by the excavations was referred to as "Mammoth No. 1", and the

remaining mammoth skeletons were numerically designated in order of excavation (Fig. 1). Because of uncertainty regarding preservation of the site, all bones were left in place; the Gray Sand over and around them was removed, leaving the bones resting on pedestals of earth. The following paragraphs described the individual mammoth skeletons and the one articulated bison skeleton that were excavated at El Llano No. 1.

"Mammoth No. 1 was the semiarticulated skeleton of a young adult that lay on its right side with the head pointing south. The remains of this mammoth were the best preserved and the most nearly articulated among those found. The first artifacts were found near this mammoth in the Gray Sand stratum.

"Mammoth No. 2 was nearly mature, and this is indicated by the size of the limb bones and tusks and by the fact that the epiphyses are partially fused. The orientation of this skeleton was similar to that of Mammoth No. 1; it lay on its right side with the head pointing in a southerly direction. Of the four mammoth skeletons, this is the only one that was associated with artifacts used in killing and butchering the animal.

"Mammoth No. 3, a mature individual, was poorly preserved. It seems likely that the bones were deposited in the shallow water of the pond margin and were trampled and broken when other animals came to drink. The two tusks, which protruded up into the overlying Diatomaceous Earth, were incomplete; both ends were sheared off relatively straight, as though erosion had removed the top of the Gray Sand and eroded the ends of the tusks at the same time.

"Mammoth No. 4, another large adult, with the head pointing southward, was also poorly preserved and poorly articulated. The bones may have been broken and scattered by the movement of water or by human action and were strewn over a larger area than the bones of the other mammoths. The two tusks of Mammoth No. 4 were lying in such a position as to suggest that the animal fell forward with the head in an upright position, the head remaining in this upright position as sediment covered the bone bed. The two tusks of Mammoth No. 4 were the largest and best preserved of the mammoths found. [A more complete description of these mammoths is given in the section by Lundelius in this volume.]

"The articulated skeleton of a bison was uncovered west of Mammoths 1 and 3 (Fig. 1) [see Fig. 73]. The bones covered an area of approximately 45 sq. ft. The animal lay on its right side with the head pointing southward. All the postcranial bones were present, but the skull was missing. This bison apparently became mired in the muck of the pond because, when the upper bones of the bison were removed in blocks, the foot bones of one front foot and one back foot were found underneath in a vertical articulated position.

"One mammoth long bone (Fig. 1) [see Fig. 73] was found 18.5 ft. west of Mammoth No. 1 and was associated with two scrapers and one core. This bone may have been severed from the carcass of one of the mammoths and dragged aside to be butchered at leisure. It is uncertain to which animal this bone was originally attached. However, it definitely does not belong to Mammoths No. 1 or 2 because all

long bones of these two specimens are accounted for.

"It is believed that these four mammoths were not mired, because all of the limb bones were lying in a horizontal position on the gravel of an old channel fill (Fig. 2) [see Fig. 76]. The major portion of the bone bed was laid down on this channel fill, which roughly paralleled the bone bed in a south-southeasterly direction. The channel fill, which consists of sand, white, water-worn caliche pebbles, red clay balls, and quartzite pebbles that had been reworked from the bedrock gravels, is the fill of an older stream channel that was cut and refilled before the bone bed was laid down and subsequently covered by the Gray Sand. Later this channel swung toward the west margin of the pond and cut a new channel on the west side of the bone bed. The westernmost portion of the bone bed was deposited in this more recent stream channel and lay at a lower elevation than the portion of the bone bed that was deposited on the channel fill on the east side.

"Coarse white sand lay over and around the bone bed, and in some places this sand was more tightly packed than elsewhere. Immediately west of the bone bed the sand contained more clay and was greenish-gray in color, but on the east side of the bone bed the sand was light gray in color, was not so tightly packed as on the west side, and contained small caliche pebbles.

"At bedrock level on each side of the channel fill, small caliche boulders were present, some up to 10 or 12 in. in diameter. Many of these small caliche boulders were present under the northern and eastern edges of Mammoth No. 4.

"The contact surface of the Diatomaceous Earth with the Gray Sand was irregular and undulatory, and in some places the bone bed was more deeply covered by this Diatomaceous Earth than elsewhere (Fig. 9) [see Fig. 77]. It is probable that the Gray Sand which covered the upper portion of the bone bed was eroded away during an arid climatic interval represented by the disconformity between the Gray Sand and the overlying Diatomaceous Earth. After the mammoth bones were exposed, a return to pluvial conditions probably favored the

Fig. 77. Contorted section of sediments exposed on west side of excavations, El Llano Dig 1.

deposition of Diatomaceous Earth, and this material accumulated over the bones that had been exposed by erosion.

"The mandible of Mammoth No. 1, which extended upward into the overlying Diatomaceous Earth for a distance of 5.5 in., was in one of the highest points of the bone bed. A mammoth tooth removed by Green was 18 in. below the skeleton of Mammoth No. 2. In all cases, the bones that extended upward into the overlying Diatomaceous Earth were more poorly preserved than those which lay entirely within the Gray Sand stratum.

"After work was finished on the bone bed, it was noted that all the mammoths and the bison in the Clovis horizon faced downstream and were lying on their right sides with backs to the shore. It seems likely, considering the state of preservation, that all of the mammoths were not deposited in the Gray Sand at the same time.

"Green has identified some of the broken limb bones (Fig. 7) associated with the mammoth-bone bed and comments (letters, 1964) as follows:

'The broken bone (Fig. 7a) is the distal end of a camel tibia. The maximum width of this specimen is slightly less than that given by Mcade for the giant camel _Gigantocamelus_ from the Blancan deposits (Early Pleistocene) of Crosby County [Texas]; but it is also somewhat larger than a _Gigantocamelus_ tibia in our collection from Blancan deposits in Hartly County. Insofar as I know, remains of the giant camels, _Gigantocamelus_ and _Titanotylopus_, are restricted to early Pleistocene deposits, and the presence of a specimen referable to _Gigantocamelus_ from the Gray Sand complicates the faunal picture. As you have noted, the lowermost part of the Gray Sand occasionally produced broken, slightly water-worn bone fragments of a more highly mineralized nature than most of the bones from this stratum, and it is highly probable that these fragments, as well as the fragmentary camel tibia, have been reworked from older deposits. The paucity of bones in the Bedrock Gravels, and the completely mineralized nature of the few bones that have been found, definitely preclude these deposits as a source, and the only other plausible origin would be from older basin deposits which had been almost completely removed prior to deposition of the Gray Sand stratum. There is, in fact, good evidence pointing toward the presence of an older localized basin predating the depression in which the Gray Sand accumulated. I had not suspected that these older basin sediments might go back as far as early Pleistocene time, but this must now be considered as a possibility, and it may or may not be confirmed by the eventual analysis of paleontological specimens from the Gray Sand'"(Warnica, 1966, pp. 345-9).

In summary, it is difficult to be sure how many of these mammoths were killed and butchered. Mammoth 2 certainly was due to human activity. The end for end turning of some of the long bones of Mammoth 1 suggests butchering. The scattered and broken bones of Mammoths 3 and 4 give less conclusive information. However the isolated long bone west of Mammoth 1 probably represents part of either 3 or 4 selected for further butchering. This suggests to me (Hester) that at least three of the mammoths were butchered. As all four mammoths fell in approximately the same manner I am willing to believe all four represent kills by men, but of course positive proof is lacking.

In addition to the mammoth remains a number of individual bone specimens were collected from the El Llano excavations (Table XXXIV).

TABLE XXXIV

INDIVIDUAL VERTEBRATE SPECIMENS
COLLECTED FROM EL ELANO DIG 1

.1.   *Tanupolama* cf, *macrocephala* jaw from the Gray Sand, 17 feet 1 inch from datum stake, 12° east of north. The badly worn P$\overline{4}$ with a small enamel lake in the center anterior end is apparently simple; P$\overline{3}$ present but small; diastema is apparently short.

2.   Bison calcaneum from the Gray Sand.

3.   Bird bones from Gray Sand-Diatomite contact.

4.   Turtle frag, bison (?) tooth frag, bird coracoid.

5.   Bison phalanx from the Diatomite.

6.   Bird ulna from Diatomite.

7.   Bird wing bone, Diatomite-Gray Sand contact.

8.   Small bone, ? rodent? from a burrow in the Diatomite.

9.   Horse-distal end of metapodial and phalanx #1 from Gray Sand, 58° East of South, 14 inches from datum stake.

10.   Femur (?) from the Gray Sand, 23 feet 2 inches from datum, 20° East of North, 6 inches below Diatomite.

11.   Antilocaprid M$\overline{3}$ from the Gray Sand.

12.   Camel canine 3 inches west of the skull of Mammoth No. 1 in the Gray Sand.

13.   Large horse tooth from the Gray Sand.

14.   Miscellaneous bones, bison, bear (?), wolf, rodent.

15.   Dirt with small bones, from a burrow in the Diatomite.

16.   Turtle bones from the Gray Sand.

STRATIGRAPHY

The geologic beds overlying the mammoth bone bed (the north bank) were exposed in an excellent profile cut by the bulldozers as part of the stripping operation. This profile exposed the sediments at the edge of the pond over a distance of more than 100 feet, with an average height of 12 feet. Limited excavations were conducted along this bank resulting in the discovery of Folsom artifacts in the Massive Brown Sand unit (Diatomite equivalent) and Parallel Flaked artifacts in the overlying Laminated Diatomaceous Tan and Gray Silt and Sand (Carbonaceous Silt equivalent) (Fig. 76).

The sediments record the limits of a fluctuating pond as follows: Episodes of low pond level are represented by shore side alluvial deposits of sand and caliche nodules. Periods of high pond level are characterized by fine grained laminated and sometimes diatomaceous silts and sands.

A detailed description of each of these geologic units exposed in the North Bank is presented below. The location of the described section is immediately adjacent to pollen profile CL-VII (Fig. 76). In addition, descriptions are also given for the Caliche Bedrock (located on the left hand side of Fig. 76) and a contorted section of the Gray Sand unit on the west side of the mammoth pit (Fig. 77).

A permanent record of these beds was obtained through the removal of soil monoliths by Roald Fryxell. Specimens were collected for Eastern New Mexico University, Washington State University, and Fort Burgwin Research Center. These monoliths preserve the original stratigraphic relationships and character of the sediments. They are useful as a historical record of sediments now destroyed by gravel mining and also are available for use in future museum exhibits.

Detailed Description of Beds, North
Bank, El Llano Dig. 1

By Roald Fryxell

Stratum of subunit: Red brown (5 Yr. 4/4 M) fine sand; firm; massive, breaking to moderate coarse angular blocky; very widely scattered flecks of charcoal to 3 mm. maximum diameter; occasionally very poorly defined Krotovinas; abrupt undulating to irregular, unconformable boundary to--

(Major Stratigraphic Break)

Depth, 24 to 33 inches: Very dark gray to black (10 Yr. 3/1--2/1 M) fine sandy silt; friable; very coarse prismatic, breaking to weak medium subangular blocking; slightly sticky, very slightly plastic when wet; many very fine rootlet channels with mycecial lime filling; strong, consistent carbonate coating on surface of major prisms extends downward into unit to 16 inches plus with fill locally reaching 2 mm. in thickness and in places grading upwards into small clastic dikes up to 1 inch thick produced by downward migration of the overlying oxidized sand along joints bounding the prisms; abrupt wavy boundary to--

Depth, 33 to 40 3/4 inches: Very dark gray (10 Yr. 3/1 M) silty fine sand; as above, except surface of unit marks lower limit of elastic sand joined fillings; abrupt but transitional boundary to--

Depth, 40 to 41 3/4 inches: Grayish brown (2.5 Y 5/2 M) fine sand massive; firm, abrupt but transitional boundary to--

Depth, 44 to 45 3/4 inches: Grayish brown sand; massive; firm; abrupt smooth boundary to--

Depth, 45 3/4 to 48 1/2 inches: Black (10 Yr. 2/1 M) fine sandy silt; fine subangular blocking; firm; lime filled rootlet channels as described above; includes abundant very small fragments of organic detritus; contains common fine (1-2mm.) hard black concretions which may be MNO_2; includes discontinuous 1/2 inch thick lenses of light brownish gray (2.5 Y 6/2 D) friable, massive, fine sand and irregularly distributed pockets of grayish brown fine sand approximately 10 mm. across, abrupt smooth boundary to--

Depth, 48 1/2 to 53 1/2 inches: Light grayish brown (2.5 Y 6/2 M) fine sand; loose; massive; locally very weak cementation to fine subangular blocks; at 2 and 4 inches below its surface, unit includes 1/4 to 1/2 inch thick dark gray laminae similar to dark layers above; lower 1-1/2 inch has a completely incoherent single grained structure, abrupt smooth boundary to--

Depth, 53 1/2 to 57 inches: Dark grayish brown (10 Yr. 3.5/1 M) very fine sand; firm; massive breaking to moderate medium subangular blocking; abundant whitish fine rootlet fillings, and scattered very fine (1 mm.) flecks of organic detritus; 1 inch from surface contains discontinuous 1/4 to 1/2 inch thick light brownish-gray firm, massive sand lense; abrupt smooth boundary to--

Depth, 57 to 69 inches: Light gray (2.5 Y 7/2 M) fine sand; loose; single grain, locally has very weak indistinct (10 Yr. 7/2 M) FE stains resulting in slightly coherent massive

areas 4 cm. maximum diameter; 5 inches below top of unit is a 1/2 to 1 inch thick discontinuous zone of mixed very dark gray silt, fine organic fragments and firm pale brown (10 Yr. 6/3 M) fine sand; abrupt smooth boundary to--

Depth, 69 to 71 inches: Dark gray (10 Yr. 4/1 M) to grayish brown (2.5 Y 5/2 M) fine sand; firm; coarse moderately angular blocky; locally shows mixing and replacement filling of coarse rootlets or twig fragments up to 12 mm. in diameter with staining of friable sand fill in coarse and fine rootlet channels to pale brown (10 Yr. 6/3 M); 1/4 inch thick layer of broken black (10 Yr. 2/1 M) silt forms base of layer; abrupt smooth boundary to--

Depth, 71 to 74 1/2 inches: Light gray (10 Yr. 7/1 M) fine sand, with local indistinct staining (2.5 Y 7/2 M) loose; single grain; scattered small bone fragments and abundant bone flecks to 5 mm. maximum diameter; abrupt smooth boundary to--

(Major Stratigraphic Break?)

Depth, 74 1/2 to 84 inches: (Base of upper monolith at profile CL-VII) Grayish-brown (2.5 Y 5/2 M) sand; extremely firm, compact; breaks to medium or coarse very strong angular blocks at sample site includes numerous large mammal bones and very abundant fine bone flecks, abundant fine and medium (3 mm.) open rootlet channels. Occasional Krotovinas, mostly filled with very firm light gray sand from layer above; includes irregularly distributed granule to pebble sized white (10 Yr. 8/1-8/2 M) caliche fragments increasing in size and abundance irregularly downward; base of unit not exposed in upper step; the following description continues on the lower step at the pollen profile and monolith sample site.

Depth, 86 1/2 to 95 1/2 inches: Light gray (2.5 Y 7/2 M) sand; firm to very light; (light brownish gray 2.5 Y 6/2 M) coarse to very coarse moderately angular blocking; abundant very fine and medium rootlet channels some with whitish carbon (?) lining; abundant flecks of bone to 5 mm. maximum diameter coarser fragments include very coarse sand-sized subangular pieces of quartzite, and granule to pebble sized angular to rounded caliche fragments to 5 cm. (rare) maximum diameter; occasional Krotovinas filled with firm sand, lighter or darker in color than the matrix from horizon above and below; on drying entire section of this major unit shows vertical drying cracks marking joints bounding major very coarse prisms; collapsed and partially filled animal burrow 6 inches maximum diameter, in west monolith at this point; caliche pebbles show random orientation, abrupt smooth boundary to--

Depth, 95 1/2 to 102 1/2 inches: Light gray (2.5 Y 7/2 M) to gray (5 Y 6/1 M) sand as above with rootlet channels and randomly oriented caliche fragments in very firm matrix breaking to moderately medium angular blocking, but with discontinuous pinching, swelling, and slightly contorted zones of slightly lighter or darker sand, abrupt smooth boundary to--

Depth, 102 1/2 to 106 3/4 inches: Light olive gray (5 Y 6/2 M) coarse sand with granule sized subangular to subrounded quartzite fragments and abundant granule to pebble sized angular to rounded caliche fragments, most concentrated and crudely aligned near top of unit; unit is lense shaped, pinching out at both ends over a lateral distribution of 5 ft. - into unit above; friable; massive; abrupt undulating boundary to--

Depth, 106 3/4 to 111 1/4 inches: Varigated or irregularly laminated grayish brown to light grayish brown (2.5 Y 5/2 to 6/2 M) fine sand; firm; massive breaking to medium moderate blocking; similar to second unit above, into which it grades beyond limits of included coarse sand lense, but includes irregular discontinuous 1/8 to 1/4 inch laminae of very dark gray to dark gray (10 Yr. 3/ to 4/ M) silty fine sand; abrupt smooth boundary to--

Depth, 111 1/4 to 143 1/4 inches: Irregular alternating discontinuous thin lenses of coarse sand, sand and silty fine sand as follows (with intermediate gradations); light gray (2.5 Y 7/2 M) sand; friable to firm, massive, well sorted, maximum measured thickness 2 1/2 in.;

Light gray (10 Yr. 7/2 M) coarse sand to granule sand with subangular to subrounded quartzite fragments friable (very) massive; crude graded bedding; (maximum measured

thickness 8 in.) dark gray, fine sandy silt (10 Yr. 4/1 M) firm; usually thinner than 1/2 inch, usually grading upward to lighter fine sand; medium to very fine rootlet channels continue through sequence decreasing in abundance downwards, lower 2 inches include a lense of caliche and reddish brown sandstone subrounded to rounded pebbles, reworked from stratum below, abrupt unconformable wavy boundary to--

(Major Stratigraphic Break)

Depth, 143 1/4 to 157 1/4 inches: Light brownish gray (10 Yr. 6/2 M) pebbly sand, very firm; massive, with very coarse prisms breaking to strong medium angular blocky fragments, occasionally fine rootlet channels; abundant subangular to rounded caliche fragments, and reddish brown sandstone granules with random orientation scattered through matrix; gradual undulating boundary to--(Presence of mammal bone fragments equivalent to the stratigraphic position of the mammoths adjacent to this cut.)

Depth, 157 1/4 to 170 1/4 inches: Light brown (7.5 Yr. 6/4 M) pebbly sand; as above, but with coarser caliche and quartzite fragments, with occasional 3-inch cobbles; matrix is firm to very firm; massive to very coarse prismatic; boundary with horizon above is a color break probably controlled by oxidation related to water table level, abrupt undulating boundary to--

Depth, 170 1/4 to 179 3/4 inches: Reddish brown (5 Yr. 5/4 M) sand; very friable; massive; abrupt smooth unconformable boundary to--

(Major Stratigraphic Break)

Depth, 179 3/4 to 185 3/4 inches: Yellowish red (5 Yr. 4/6 M) pebble gravel; very firm to extremely firm; compact; poorly sorted, subangular to rounded caliche and indurated sandstone pebbles and cobbles; subangular to subrounded quartzite pebbles in a sand matrix; gravel surface marks unconformity exposed on face west of mammoths.

Detailed Description of Beds, West Edge, Mammoth Pit, El Llano Dig 1

The contorted sediments on the west wall of the mammoth pit (Fig. 76) are of considerable interest because of their evidence suggesting mixing of sediments and possible intrusion of implements into the lower portions of the Gray Sand as a result. A description of these beds follows. The exact locus of this section is shown on Figure 73.

Horizon or Unit

Depth, 0 to 11 inches: Grayish brown (10 Yr. 5/2 D, 4/1 M) sand; occasionally very fine carbonate lined rootlet channels; soft discontinuous thin laminations locally; occasionally very coarse sand (quartzite) fragments and subangular to subrounded quartzite granules; non-sticky, non-plastic when wet; comprises major portion of matrix around mammoth bones in Clovis level, reaching total thickness of 12 inches plus; includes and generally overlays (or is interstratified with) dark gray (10 Yr. 4/1 M, 2/1 W) organic silt, massive breaking to very fine weak subangular blocky, friable; non-sticky, slightly plastic when wet; forms thin discontinuous lense or pod-like deposit less than 3 inches thick, with lateral extent generally less than 2 or 3 feet, gray (10 Yr. 6/1 to 5/1 D, 5/2 M) fine sandy silt; friable; distinct very thin discontinuous laminations; non-sticky, very slightly plastic when wet, has abundant very fine rootlet channels with light yellowish brown (10 Yr. 6/4 D) limonite stains; thickness consistently 2 inches, marking base and unconformity with underlying sediment, brown (10 Yr. 5/3 M) sand; friable; massive; includes numerous fragments of sand and muck matrix; occurs as irregular roughly elipsoidal pockets, probably represents partially filled animal burrow of much later age distorted by partial collapse, sediments within this unit are extremely disturbed and locally mixed with repeated examples showing injection of lowest gray layer into overlying sediments, with internal distortion of bedding within all units; abrupt, broken unconformable irregular boundary with surface relief of 1 foot plus to--

Depth, 11 to 23 inches: Grayish-brown (2.5 Y 5/2 M) sand; firm; very coarse prismatic breaking to medium, moderate angular blocky; includes occasional granule or pebble sized caliche fragments; numerous very fine and occasionally medium size rootlet channels; broken

discontinuous irregular bedding showing contortion and intrusion of slightly lighter and darker layers into each other, abrupt irregular boundary with 18 inches plus vertical relief to--

Depth, 23 to 32 inches: Light gray (2.5 Y 7/2 D, 6/2 M), pebbly sand; very firm; massive breaking to very coarse prisms of medium angular blocks, irregular pale yellow (2.5 Y 7/4 M) oxidation around caliche pebbles and in numerous fine and occasionally medium rootlet channels; shows mixing and intrusive relationships with gray sand above; abrupt wavy to irregular (relief to 12 inches) unconformable boundary to--

(Major Stratigraphic Break)

Depth, 32 to 50 inches: Exposed reddish brown (2.5 Yr. 4/4 M) poorly sorted cobble gravel; very firm; massive with weak, very coarse prismatic jointing; matrix slightly sticky and plastic when wet, caliche cobbles are angular to rounded, up to 5 inches maximum diameter subangular to subrounded quartzite granules or pebbles, random orientation; less recognizable distortion, except for surface of unconformity, local lense-like bodies of brown (7.5 Yr. 5/4 M) sand or pebbly coarse sand; friable; massive entire unit represents base of section; depth undetermined.

Description of Caliche Bedrock and Underlying Sand, El Llano Dig 1

To west of pond sediments profiled (Fig. 76)

Stratigraphic Unit

Depth, 0 to 18 inches: Pinkish white (7.5 Y) caliche; extremely hard; indurated; massive with very coarse (18 to 24 inches) prismatic joint system; original sand matrix includes occasional quartzite subrounded granules; many fine rootlet channels; but in contrast to pebbly gray sand above there are no medium rootlet channels, diffuse (12 inches) wavy boundary to: light reddish brown (5 Yr. 6/4 D, 4/4 W) silty fine sand to clayey fine sand; very firm to hard; slightly sticky and plastic when wet; moderate coarse angular blocky breaking to very fine angular blocks, abundant very fine rootlet channels; occasional manganese dendrites on ped surfaces and many pink (5 Yr. 7/4 D) carbonate mottlings; base not exposed.

Archaic Age Well, El Llano Dig 1

Another stratigraphic discovery of importance and interest found at this time was a hand-dug well exposed in the North Bank similar to those reported by Evans (1951) and Green (1962) (Figs. 78, 79). This well was originally dug from the top of the Carbonaceous Silt stratum and extended some five feet into the Folsom horizon to the water table at that particular time. A second well in the vicinity, situated just south of Mammoth No. 2, is shown on the El Llano site plan published by Warnica (1966, Fig. 1). Unfortunately, the erosional surface from which this latter well was dug cannot be determined as the entire area was stripped down to the mammoth bone bed level before the well was discovered.

ARTIFACTS

Eighteen artifacts were recovered from the Folsom horizon and twenty-five artifacts were recovered from the Carbonaceous Silt, which contains material of the Parallel-Flaked Horizon. The recovery of these artifacts adds

Fig. 79. Photo of Archaic well illustrated in Figure 76, North Bank, El Llano Dig 1.

new information to that already known about these cultures. One hundred and sixty-six artifacts were recovered from the mammoth bone bed in the course of salvage excavations (Warnica, 1966, p. 349); however only 117 of these implements were available for study at the time the artifact section of this report was prepared (Appendix I). The projectile points associated with the mammoths identify the complex respresented as being of Clovis age, radiocarbon dated between 11,040 B.P. ± 500 years and 11,630 B.P. ± 400 years (Haynes, et al., 1966). An additional six artifacts were recovered from the back dirt and may not be assigned cultural provenience.

Following Hester's participation in the excavations, a number of artifacts were recovered from the El Llano dig and adjacent areas. The artifacts from those excavations sponsored by Eastern New Mexico University will be reported by Agogino and Hester in a separate publication.

Some of the additional artifacts collected by the El Llano Archaeological Society have been described by Warnica (1966). It is not known what reporting is planned for the artifacts collected by Texas Technological College.

Details of specific artifacts and their association with the mammoth remains may be obtained by comparing the artifact locations by number in Figure 80 with the descriptions by those artifacts in Appendix I. A list of these

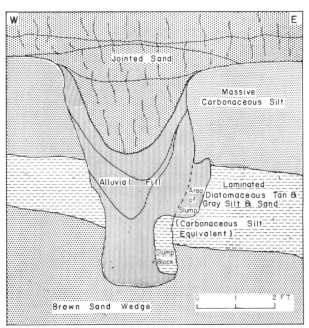

Fig. 78. Profile of Archaic well, North Bank, El Llano Dig 1, January 1963.

artifacts by type is presented in Table XXXV.*
Summary statements concerning the artifacts
from the Gray Sand presented by Warnica (1966)
are reproduced below.

TABLE XXXV

ARTIFACTS RECOVERED FROM EL LLANO DIG 1
BY TYPE AND LEVEL

Type				Bed			
	JS	CS	CSE	BSW	GS	NIP	GS*	Total
Flakes		18	10		35	5	30	98
Flake scrapers			1		6		1	8
Folsom points			1					1
Clovis points					4		3	7
Parallel flaked points		1						1
Indeterminant points		1						1
Side-scrapers		1			9	1	11	22
End-scrapers			1		2		1	4
Unifacial knives		1	1		4		2	8
Bifacial knives					7			7
Gravers					4		1	5
Flake knives					6	1	1	8
Bone tools			1		5		2	8
Hammerstones			3		1	2		6
Grinding stones					1		1	2
Cores	1		2				4	7
Broken pebbles					4		2	6
End- and side-scrapers					5	2	1	8
Scrapers					2			2
Flake scraper-knife					2			2
Chopper					1			1
Chips					4			4
Graver-flake knives					2			2
Hollow edge scraper					2		1	3
Shell artifact		1						1
Possible artifact					1			1
Burin on Clovis point**					1			1
Grooved caliche nodule						1		1
Burin and scraper					1			1
Knife fragment					1			1
Graver-scraper					1			1
Total	1	1	22	20	111	12	61	228[†]

* These artifacts were recovered by the El Llano Archaeological Society subsequent to the compilation of Appendix I. These artifacts are described in Warnica (1966).

** Jeremiah Epstein (in Warnica, 1966, p. 353) believes this specimen possesses a natural break rather than an intentionally struck burin blow.

† This total includes fragments of six broken artifacts, thus approximately 222 individual specimens are represented in the collection.

JS--Jointed Sand, CS--Carbonaceous Silt, CSE--Carbonaceous Silt Equivalent, BSW--Brown Sand Wedge, GS--Gray Sand, NIP--Not in Place.

---

*Table XXXV contains 63 artifacts which were not utilized in the description of artifact complexes presented in the artifacts section as these artifacts were recovered after analysis was completed.

"Many artifacts were found lying on their edges or on their ends. This suggests deposition by a fairly rapid movement of water. It will probably never be known how many of the artifacts were washed into the pond and how many were actually used in killing and cutting up the mammoths; but from the evidence available, it is believed that Mammoth No. 2 was definitely killed and butchered. All indications point to secondary deposition for most of the artifacts recovered from the Gray Sand stratum.

"The tools in the Clovis artifact assemblage were predominately unifacial and were manufactured from blades and primary flakes. Only projectile points and bifacial knives were flaked on both faces" (Warnica, 1966, p. 335).

"Most of the gravers from the Clovis horizon had two or more graver points. This specific characteristic will possibly not hold true for all gravers of Clovis age, but it does suggest that multiple-pointed gravers were preferred by the Clovis people.

"At least one stone used for grinding was recovered from the Gray Sand. This suggests a way of life that was not entirely dependent upon the procurement of game as a means of subsistence. During periods of heavier rainfall, grasses were undoubtedly luxuriant and produced edible seeds that could be utilized for food. Nothing has been found in the Gray Sand to indicate the use of true milling stones; but a small milling stone was recovered from Elida, a nearby Folsom campsite (Warnica 1961), which suggests that milling stones were in use not too long after Clovis times.

"Small Clovis points recovered from the Clovis bed strongly suggest normal occurrence of these small points in the weapon inventory of the Clovis people, but it is still not known whether small points were utilized for specific sizes of game. It is fairly certain that some of the large projectile points and associated tools were used to kill and to butcher the mammoths, but the problem of the relationship of the other artifacts to the bone bed still remains. Why were bone artifacts, gravers, hammerstones, cores, broken pebbles, chips, flakes, and grinding stones also found in association with the mammoths? The answer probably lies in the close proximity of the bone bed to the pond

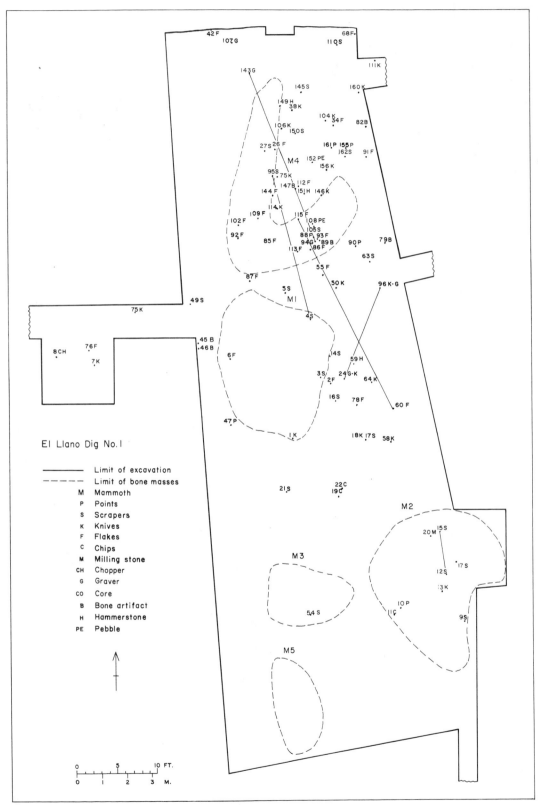

Fig. 80.   Map of El Llano Dig 1 showing distribution of artifacts.

margin and the fact that a stream flowed into the pond at a point just north of the bone bed (Fig. 2) [Fig. 76]. It is believed that a large number of artifacts from campsites on the margins of the pond were washed into the pond and came to rest among the bones in the Gray Sand. The movement of artifacts by stream action is supported by the fact that most of the artifacts were deposited along a general north-south axis that parallels the channel fill on the east margin of the bone bed (Fig. 1)" [Fig. 73] (Warnica, 1966, p. 355).

It should also be pointed out in connection with Warnica's statements above that the distribution of campsite debris extended throughout the bone bed. Artifacts associated with Mammoth 2, the farthest out in the pond, included scrapers, chips, and a milling stone, good evidence for secondary distribution through water action. Owing to this problem it is not possible to obtain much information concerning the butchering activities from study of the associated artifacts (Fig. 80).

SUMMARY

"Excavations in the Gray Sand (Fig. 9) at the Clovis site in 1962-63 by the El Llano Archaeological Society produced articulated remains of four mammoths and one bison, along with scattered remains of mammoth, bison, horse, camel, antelope, deer, wolf, peccary, turtle, rodents, and birds. These four mammoths and the bison were lying on their right sides with their heads pointing downstream and their backs parallel to the shore. The evidence seems to indicate that these animals were systematically hunted near a water hole. Haury (and others 1959:28) has drawn the same conclusion from the faunal and archaeological materials found at the Lehner site.

"Green's interpretation of a camel bone (Fig. 7a) as possibly being derived from a basin deposit of early Pleistocene age may complicate the faunal picture at the Clovis site. Bones of other animals recovered from the Gray Sand could also be derived from this earlier basin deposit " (Warnica, 1966, pp. 354-55).

"All of the bones, whole or fragmentary, were closely examined in order to be sure that no piece of human bone was overlooked. No

fragment could be identified as human. The absence of human bones is somewhat surprising in view of the fact that so much material was washed into the pond. If a human burial occurred on the pond margins, heavy rainfall should have washed parts of the skeleton into the pond. It is only by painstaking and thorough search that we can hope to find skeletal remains of Clovis man " (Warnica, 1966, p. 356).

CONCLUSION

Negotiations concerning preservation of the El Llano site were conducted between the State of New Mexico and Sam Sanders. The terms of the proposal were that two acres including the remains of the mammoths in situ and the stratigraphic section termed the North Bank be preserved. The plans were that the State of New Mexico would erect a museum building over the site with the mammoth remains and associated artifacts being preserved as an in situ exhibit. This exhibit was to be part of the New Mexico State Park system and was to be administered from Oasis State Park some two miles away.

Unfortunately, it was never possible for the two interested parties to reach agreement. Mr. Sanders believed that if the property had any value scientifically, it must also have great economic value. Therefore, he requested a price of $400,000 for the two acres. The state legislature appropriated $100,000 to purchase the property and erect the museum building. Negotiations over the price broke down and the only opportunity for the state to acquire the property lay in the exercise of the right of eminent domain, a right the Governor, Jack M. Campbell, was afraid to exercise owing to the possible unfavorable effect this action might have on his political popularity in the Portales region.

As the negotiations faltered it became increasingly difficult to deal with Mr. Sanders. Local interest groups were able to sway his opinions. As a result, various groups of excavators were permitted to work at the site and scientific coordination was not maintained. Eventually, Sanders reached the decision that the site should be destroyed and the remains removed. The best of the mammoths were

given to Texas Technological College and
Eastern New Mexico University, to be removed
in plaster jackets for future exhibit purposes.

The net result was disheartening. The
site was destroyed, the finds were dispersed,
and an opportunity to preserve these extra-
ordinary finds as an in situ museum was lost.

Concurrently with the removal of the
mammoths, Eastern New Mexico University
conducted additional salvage excavations in
which approximately 100 artifacts were recovered. These artifacts are described in
another publication (Agogino and Hester, n.d.).
As part of this research, radiocarbon samples
were collected by C.V. Haynes Jr. and dated
at the University of Arizona Radiocarbon
laboratory.

As part of the High Plains Ecology Project,
the pollen profile CL-VII from the North Bank was
processed and is reported in the second volume
on that project (Wendorf and Hester, n.d.).

EXCAVATIONS IN THE CAMPSITE AREA
EL LLANO DIG 1

A large portion of the campsite area
adjacent to the mammoth kill site was tested
by the Museum of New Mexico (Fig. 15, location 19). James Warnica had reported finding numerous Folsom artifacts indicative of a
campsite within the thin cover of modern dunes
overlying the caliche bedrock adjacent to El
Llano Dig 1. It was decided to test this area
after excavation at the mammoth kill demonstrated that a former campsite lay to the northwest. A bulldozer and operator were provided
by Sam Sanders and the area investigated was
cleared down to within a few inches of bedrock.
These remaining few inches of reddish brown
sand were then removed by hand and the underlying bedrock swept.

The major result of the excavation was
that no artifacts were located in situ. The
Folsom material was proven to be reworked
into an Archaic-age dune sand, the "Jointed
Sand." This unit lay on bedrock which had
been swept clean by wind and water subsequent
to the Paleo-Indian occupations. Blackened
areas on this bedrock were faintly visible, but
no formal hearths were located. These blackened areas also lacked significance as they
could have represented any or all occupations
between the Clovis and Archaic cultures.
While an area 45 by 105 feet was cleared, no
plan is published here as nothing was found.
The caliche bedrock had a seven degree dip
from west to east. The excavation did reveal
the north edge of a tributary arroyo to the
former pond, the arroyo that distributed the
campsite debris found in the mammoth bone bed.

Miscellaneous Data from the Gravel Pit

Additional finds of all types of data have
been made by numerous individuals during the
removal of sediments as part of the gravel mining. With respect to artifacts such finds have
been ignored unless some type of provenience
data could be established. Other finds include
bones and the outline of wells. Two of the latter have been recorded in cross-section drawings presented in Figures 81 and 82. Well P
was located at the north end of the North Pit
(Fig. 15) and was visible in 1962 when it was
recorded as part of the High Plains Ecology
Project research. Well 0 is shown with adjoining sediments as they appeared on the east
wall of the North Pit in 1956 (Fig. 15). This
profile was photographed in color by Fred
Wendorf on one of his periodic visits to the
site. The well and adjoining area have since
been removed by the gravel mining. It is clear

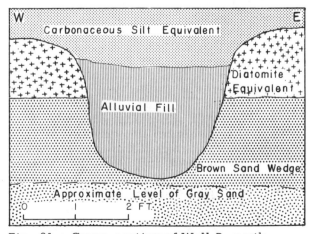

Fig. 81. Cross-section of Well P, north
wall of North Pit (see Fig. 15 for location)
as visible in 1962.

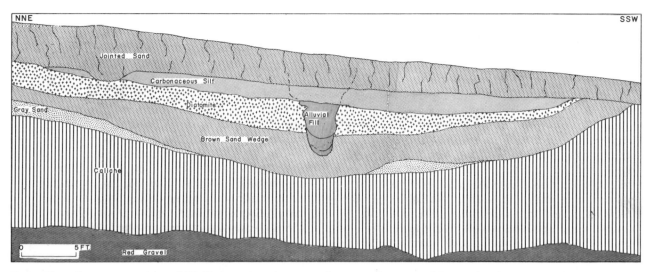

Fig. 82. Cross-section of Well 0 and sediments deposited in an old arroyo channel, east side, North Pit (see Fig. 15 for location). Note possible second well in the left upper portion of the diagram. Section prepared from color slide taken by Fred Wendorf, May 1956.

from the profile that the well was dug into sediments filling a former arroyo which had drained into the pond. At the time the well was dug, about 6,000 years ago, the arroyo was probably no longer visible as a defined drainage. However, it likely formed part of the depression at the site which ponded surface water after rains. During the dry seasons it must have been necessary to dig to reach the water table. The arroyo was also noted by Sellards in his 1955 field notes.

THE ARTIFACTS

The artifacts discussed in this section are those that are listed in Appendix I. These specimens include the finds made by the Texas Memorial Museum between 1949 and 1956 and finds made in 1961-63 by a variety of individuals and institutions. This sample has been selected for detailed analysis because valid provenience data has been established and the author has had the opportunity to study and compare the specimens. While this has reduced the total number of specimens studied by approximately 300 (from the total claimed to be from the site) the resultant group of 1073 artifacts represents an immeasurably more valid sample. These artifacts fall into three major categories: Folsom (534), Clovis (223), and Portales (100). A fourth category, Unknown (136), consists of those artifacts which are not distinctive in type and do not have provenience assigned to any specific stratum. It is assumed that the majority of these implements are Paleo-Indian in age, but an exact cultural affiliation cannot be assigned. A minor category includes implements assigned to the Archaic culture (80). As Recent Indian materials are poorly represented, it is assumed that the site was used sporadically after the pond dried up some 6,000 years ago.

The artifacts have been studied as individual specimens by listing all attributes present. The frequency of artifact types present in each culture is presented in Figure 83. A series of graphs have also been prepared to illustrate the frequency of occurrence of each attribute (Fig. 84) within each culture. These graphs constitute a summary of the nature of the industries and serve as the basis for all interpretive statements. It is obvious that many of these artifact types occur in too small numbers to constitute a true statistical sample. However, these artifacts are treated with the same methodology so that they may be available for comparison with other collections at a later date. Stone artifact types represented by a single example are not graphed on Figures 83 and 84, as all attribute occurrences would necessarily be 100%. These artifacts are discussed as individual specimens. In addition, the bone artifacts will be discussed individually owing to their unique character.

Analysis of the artifacts has suffered from a certain irregularity owing to the fact that collections borrowed from amateurs often were not available for reexamination. This meant that attributes detected late in the analysis could not be quantified. Another problem was the measurement of edge angles. The first method used was a visual estimate; rechecking with an angle measuring implement indicated that the original estimates were too high. However, as some of the collections were not available for reexamination, it was decided to reproduce the visual measurements of edge angles in Appendix I so that they could at least be internally consistent.

Artifact types will be described for each cultural period so that it will be possible to determine which tool types exhibit continuity and which exhibit change through time.

Definition of Terms Used in Analysis of Stone Artifacts

It seems appropriate to define the terms utilized so that their meaning will be consistently understood. These terms are primarily used to describe attributes exhibited by the various artifacts as used in the text and Appendix I. Their meanings are as follows:

Core tool--an implement made from the nodule from which flakes have been removed.

Primary flake--a flake removed by percussion from a core. The flake scars on the upper face of the flake being the result of the removal of earlier primary flakes.

Secondary flake--a flake removed during the retouch of a flake.

Prepared core--a core from which the exterior cortex has been removed preparatory to

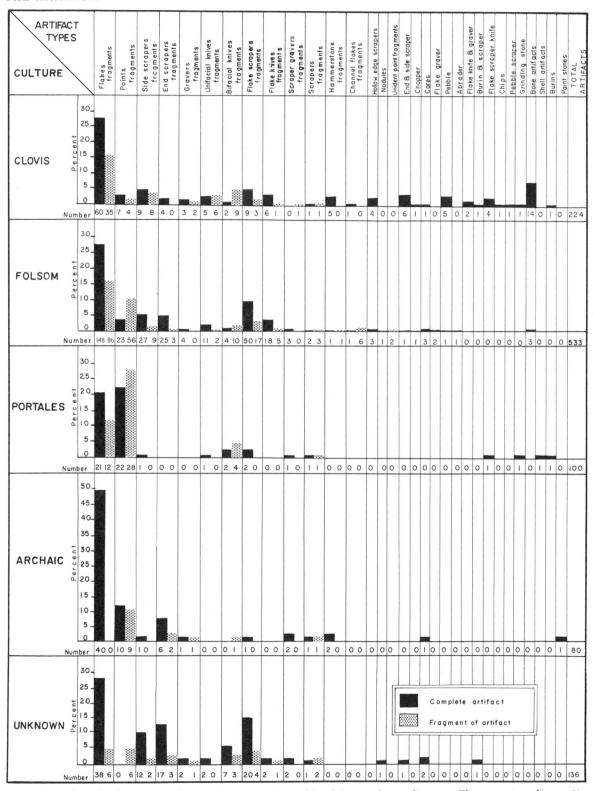

Fig. 83. Graph showing relative frequencies of tool types by culture. The greater diversity in the Clovis and Folsom assemblages is probably due to the inclusion of campsite debris in those collections. Archaic and Portales components are known primarily from killsites.

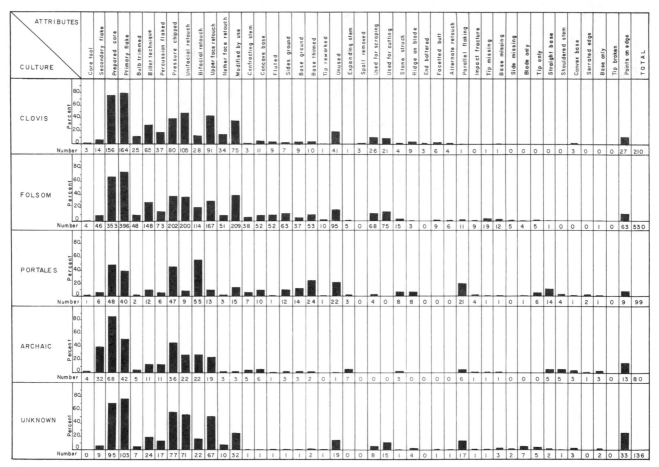

Fig. 84. Attribute frequency within the entire stone tool assemblage plotted by culture period. The differences between the graphs reveal attribute change through time. Bone and shell artifacts tallied in Figure 83 have been omitted.

the removal of primary flakes to be manufactured into implements. These cores are not shaped for the removal of a single specific flake; in other words, they are not of "Levallois" type.

Striking platform--the surface at one end of the flake representing the point on the core where the force was applied to remove the flake.

Bulb of percussion--a bulbar prominence on the nether face of a flake, near the end where the force was applied, resulting from the impact necessary to strike off the flake.

Bulb of percussion trimmed--the bulb has been reduced in size by striking off an additional flake from the nether face of the primary flake.

Billet technique--a distinctive striking platform present on the flake indicates the flake was struck with a billet or cylinder hammer. Characteristics are the low angle of the striking platform relative to the axis of the flake,

a lip or sharp edge to the striking platform, and the small size of the striking platform relative to flake size.

Percussion flaked--the artifact exhibits evidence of the removal of secondary flakes by use of a hammer of some type.

Pressure chipped--the artifact has had small chips removed through the application of pressure to the edge of the implement.

Unifacially worked--chips or flakes have been removed from one of the faces of the implement.

Bifacially worked--chips or flakes have been removed from both faces of the implement along the same edge.

Upper face worked--all chips or flakes have been removed from the upper face of the primary flake--the face of the flake that lay on the exterior of the core at the time the flake was removed.

Nether face worked--all chips or flakes have been removed from the nether face of the primary flake--the face toward the interior of the core at the time the flake was struck off.

Modified by use--the edge of the implement exhibits scars of chips removed through use.

Contracting stem--the stem of a projectile point narrows towards the base.

Concave base--the base of a projectile point is indented.

Fluted--the faces of a projectile point exhibit one or more longitudinal percussion-struck flake scars of such magnitude as to give the point a concave cross-section.

Grinding on sides--the edges of projectile points near the base have been dulled by grinding.

Base ground--the base of a projectile point has been dulled by grinding.

Basal thinning--numerous flakes or chips have been removed from the base of a projectile point in order to reduce the thickness of the artifact, presumably for hafting. These flakes or chips are parallel to the long axis of the projectile point.

Tip reworked--the point of a projectile has been resharpened by chipping.

Unused--flakes exhibiting no flake scars resulting from use.

Expanding stem--the stem of a projectile point widens toward the base.

Spall removed--a trimming flake has been sheared from the edge of a primary flake.

Used for scraping--scars on the edge suggest the flake was utilized for a scraping function. Normally, such scars are unifacial.

Used for cutting--scars on both faces of a flake along the edge or dulling of the edge suggest the flake was used for cutting.

Stone struck--the flake was struck from the core with a hammerstone. This is identified by small fractures on the striking platform, the crushing of the striking platform, the angle of striking platform near 90°, and the relatively large size of the striking platform.

Side flake--the striking platform is on the side of the flake when the greatest dimension is considered to be the length.

Median ridge on blade--a ridge present on the face of an implement. This ridge is the meeting point of convergent flaking from nearly parallel edges.

End flake--the striking platform is on one end of the greatest dimension of the flake.

End battered--one end of the implement possesses a frosted appearance resulting from use in pounding.

Chipped striking platform--the striking platform exhibits pressure chip scars indicating that it was shaped before the flake was struck off. Another suitable term for this is "faceted platform."

Worked to opposing faces--the implement has been unifacially worked to different edges. One of these edges has flakes removed from the nether face.

Parallel flaking--flake or chip scars meet in the middle of the faces of the artifact forming a series of scars running across the entire width of the face.

Impact break at tip--the tip of a projectile point has been broken through having struck a resistant object.

Tip missing--the tip of a projectile point has been broken off.

Base missing--the projectile point has the base broken off.

Side missing--the side of a projectile point has been removed.

Blade only--both the tip and base of the implement are missing.

Tip only--the blade and base of an implement are missing.

Straight base--the base of a projectile point is perpendicular to the axis of the point.

Shouldered stem--the stem of a projectile point possesses a slight indentation on each side near the base, which results in the stem being narrower than the blade.

Convex base--the base of a projectile point is rounded.

Serrated edges--the edges of the blade have been chipped so that they possess a series of small teeth or points similar to those on a saw blade.

Base only--the blade and tip of the artifact are missing.

Edges chipped--the edges of an artifact have been retouched by chipping.

Clovis Complex

The 223 Clovis artifacts described herein represent the largest assemblage of artifacts from this culture period studied to date. Previous descriptions of Clovis material (Cotter, 1937; Sellards, 1952; Haury, Sayles, and Wasley, 1959) were limited to much smaller collections, the 30 specimens from the Lehner site being the largest. In addition, these collections are limited to tool types represented at killsites. The present collection includes campsite debris from two excavations, Locality 4 and El Llano Dig 1. As a result, we have the opportunity for the first time to describe a wider range of stone and bone implements utilized by these people in their everyday life.

GENERAL CHARACTERISTICS

General characteristics of the assemblage are: Stone implements were manufactured from large primary flakes struck from prepared cores of fine grained cherts. Tools made from these flakes were primarily formed by percussion flaking with a cylinder hammer to remove flakes from the upper face. This flaking was limited in most cases to the edges with the remainder of the flake exhibiting the unaltered surface of the primary flake. Pressure retouch was also used along the edges of 37% of the stone implements. Although the sample is small, a total of 24 different implement types has been recognized. In addition, with the exception of flakes, no tool type occurs with greater frequency than 7.9% (Fig. 83). This random aspect of the assemblage may imply experimentation in the manufacture of tools.

Recognizable components of the assemblage include flakes, points, side-scrapers, end-scrapers, hollow edge scrapers, flake scrapers, gravers, unifacial knives, bifacial knives, flake knives, core struck blades, scrapers indeterminant in form, choppers, cores, hammerstones, broken pebbles, channel flakes, chips, a pebble scraper, and a grinding stone. The flakes may be considered as intentional tools as 43% show use. Several types represent dual-use implements. These include scraper-gravers, end- and side-scrapers, flake knife-gravers, burin (?)-scrapers, and flake scraper-knives.

Interesting new additions to the previously known Clovis assemblage are the presence of true core struck blades (also reported by Green, 1963), a grinding stone, and possibly burins.

The grinding stone is the earliest known in the New World. Its presence is significant in documenting a varied economy at this early date, with at least some emphasis on the gathering of plant foods.

While this is not a true core-blade industry in the European sense, the presence of blades, numerous bone implements, and possibly burins at this early time level suggests that the Clovis culture was much more closely related (in a typological sense) to an Old World predecessor than is the subsequent Folsom culture. These traits with Old World affinities are almost totally absent in the later Folsom culture thus indicating an increasing adaptation to the New World environment.

Stone types utilized listed in order of frequency are as follows (Fig. 85): Alibates chert (45.7%), Edwards chert (18.5%), quartzite (11.9%), other chert (6.0%), chalcedony (4.7%), Dakota quartzite (3.9%), basalt (2.8%), Tecovas jasper (2.3%), unknown (1.9%), shale (1.4%), and sandstone (0.9%). The specific quarries from which these materials were obtained are located at a distance of 100 to 200 miles (Fig. 86) with the two most prevalent types representing both ends of this range. The presence of chips indicates that some flaking was done at the site. The near absence of cores suggests that the imported stone was used up. A second possibility is that the primary flakes were struck off at the quarry with the cores being left at the quarry site.

The bone artifacts are more varied than those known previously and include implements which may have been used for the punching of holes (in hides?), the scraping of hides, the pressure flaking of stone tools, the manufacture of primary flakes by indirect percussion, and the foreshafts or points of spears. An interesting omission is the lack of any bone tools suggestive of being used as cylinder hammers.

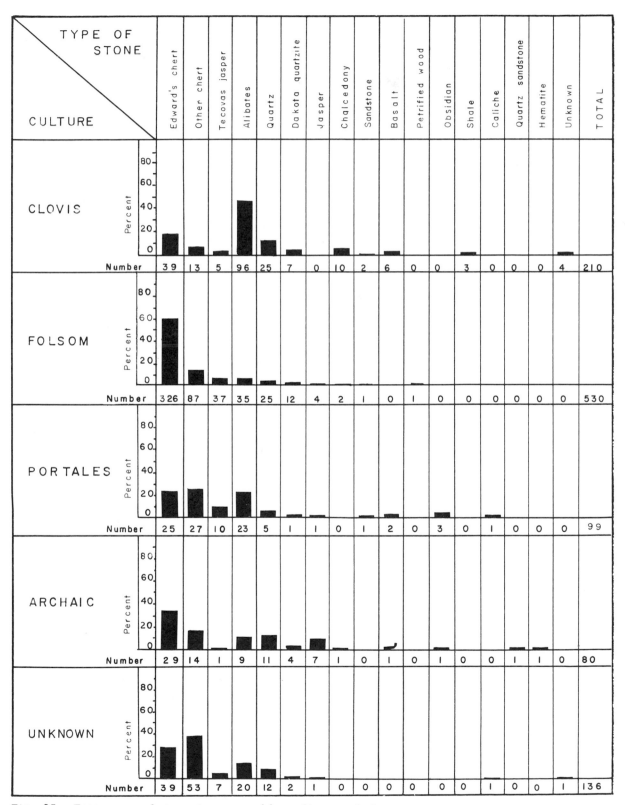

Fig. 85. Frequency of stone types used by culture period.

It is possible that the striking off of primary flakes was all accomplished by indirect percussion using the pointed bone tools as punches. The Old World Paleolithic character of these Clovis bone implements has been outlined by Cotter (1962) and Hester (1966). An important aspect of the bone tools is their frequency of occurrence, 6.2% of the total tool inventory. This percentage is in excess of any individual stone tool type with the exception of flakes and side-scrapers. This is an important fact as it contrasts strongly with the incidence of bone tools recovered from the succeeding Folsom period, a low 0.3%.

The specific artifact types identified for the Clovis complex are itemized below (Table XXXVI). These types will be described individually by attribute in the section to follow.

TABLE XXXVI

CLOVIS ARTIFACT FREQUENCIES BY TYPE

Type (whole specimens and fragments)	No.	Percentage
Flakes	95	42.6
Points	11	4.9
Side-scrapers	17	7.6
End-scrapers	4	1.8
Gravers	5	2.2
Unifacial knives	11	4.9
Bifacial knives	11	4.9
Flake scrapers	12	5.3
Flake knives	7	3.1
Hollow edge scrapers	4	1.8
Scraper-gravers	1	0.4
Indeterminant scrapers	2	0.8
End- and Side-scrapers	6	2.7
Choppers	1	0.4
Cores	1	0.4
Hammerstones	5	2.2
Pebbles	5	2.2
Channel flakes	1	0.4
Burin (?) and scraper	1	0.4
Flake scraper-knives	1	0.4
Flake knife-gravers	2	0.8
Chips	4	1.8
Pebble scrapers	1	0.4
Grinding stones	1	0.4
Bone artifacts	14	6.2
Total	223	99.0

MANUFACTURING TECHNIQUES

The Clovis industry has most of the stone implements manufactured from flakes struck from prepared cores. The method of percussion used was either indirect with the bone punches or rarely direct with hammerstones. As 74.2% of all artifacts exhibit no cortex, it may be inferred that outside trimming flakes were removed at the quarries, and only the high quality stone

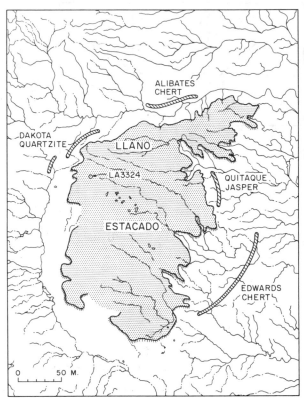

Fig. 86. Map illustrating location of stone quarries utilized by Paleo-Indian peoples on the Llano Estacado.

was transported back to the home camp. The primary flakes exhibit plain (unfaceted) striking platforms. It seems probable that the cores were hand held rather than being held on an anvil, as no bi-polar flakes were indentified. Modification of the flakes into implements was accomplished primarily by the removal of pressure chips (38.0%) and/or percussion flakes (17.6%) from the upper face (43.3%). Bifacially worked specimens occur with a frequency of 13.3%. Only 2.8% of the implements were worked unifacially to the nether face. Other characteristics of interest include the removal of a secondary flake from the nether face by hitting the striking platform in order to reduce the size of the bulb of percussion. Small use chips removed from the edges of 35.7% of the implements reveal modification through use. Other attributes occur in limited frequency. One attribute of interest is the removal of a trimming flake along the edge of a primary flake parallel to its long axis. This practice

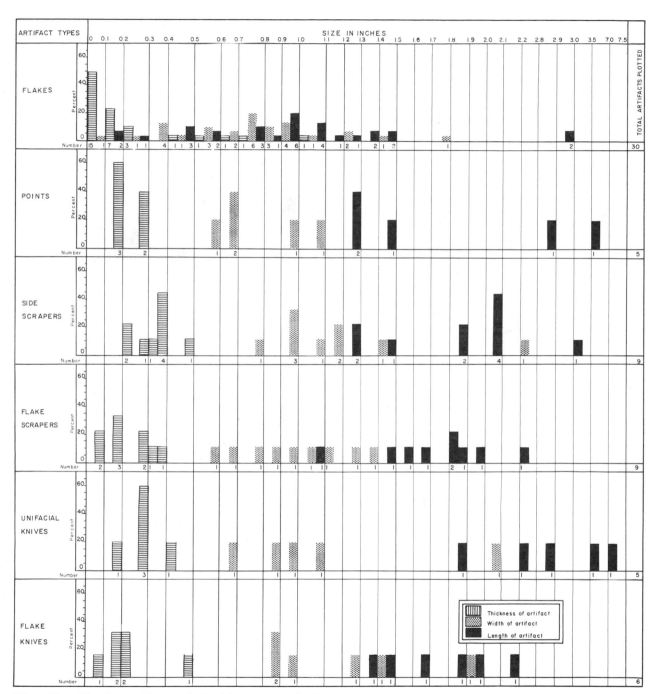

Fig. 87. Clovis artifacts plotted by type and size.

served to dull or back the edge so that it might be more easily held, or to steepen the edge so that it could be fashioned into a scraper.

The size range of implements varies somewhat by artifact type. The distribution of these artifacts by type and size is presented in Figure 87.

ARTIFACT TYPE DESCRIPTIONS

Flakes (95)* (Fig. 88)

Primary flakes and flake fragments are the most prevalent artifacts of which 53.5% show use. The used specimens have tentatively been classed by type of use as follows: 27% used for scraping; 22% used for cutting; and 4.5% show use which could not be classified. Criteria for type of use are chips removed unifacially--used for scraping; chips removed bifacially--used for cutting.

In form, the flakes are rectangular, triangular, or ovate, with all specimens tending to be irregular in outline. Typical transverse cross-sections are either a scalene triangle or a trapezoid with low angle sharp edges. The anterior-posterior cross-section tends to be of similar form, but curving, thus exhibiting a concavo-convex section. The ratio of average flake length to average flake width is 1:1, which is well within the flake range. The frequency of blades is 10.9%; however, this count includes several specimens which are quite irregular in outline. The incidence of nicely-made blades similar to European specimens is approximately half of the total number of blades (5.2% of the total number of stone artifacts). Size range of whole specimens: length 0.2 to 2.2 inches, average 0.80; width 0.1 to 1.8 inches, average 0.80; and thickness 0.1 to 0.8 inches, average 0.25.

---

*Number of artifacts in sample.

Projectile Points (11) (Figs. 89, 90)

The projectile points fall into two distinct categories which will be defined here as separate variants. These points include the classic Clovis type as illustrated by Wormington (1957, Fig. 68). This variant has been designated in this report as "Clovis Type 1." A type description of these points cannot be derived in detail from the small sample reported herein. However, the type is well known elsewhere as represented at the Naco (Haury, 1953) and Lehner killsites (Haury, Sayles, and Wasley, 1959).

Attributes of this type include leaf shaped blade, concave base, short flutes from the base on both faces, grinding on base, ground edges near base, basal thinning, slightly contracting stem, and bifacially worked utilizing both flaking and chipping. The points are typically thick and heavy with a lenticular cross-section. Size range: length 2.0 to 6.0 inches; width 1.0 to 2.0 inches; and thickness 0.2 to 0.4 inches. The flutes range in length from one-third to two-thirds the length of the point.

The other Clovis point variant is here described for the first time. This group has been designated "Clovis Type 2," (Figs. 89b, c; 90f, g). These projectiles possess the attributes described for the Type 1 points with the following distinctions: Type 2 points are much smaller with overall length ranging from 1.2 to 2.0 inches. The other basic difference is that these points possess a triangular blade which is widest at the base. Other attributes include the same chipping style, fluting, edge grinding, etc., as described above. The small size of these points and the small flutes result in their having a generalized resemblance to later points of the Portales and Archaic cultures. However, these points have now been found in definite association with other Clovis artifacts; thus, their cultural affiliation is established.

Fig. 88. Clovis flakes and blades: a, M-41; b, EL-19; c, 2-200; d, W-156; e, 2-216; f, 2-135; g, M-39; h, M-31; i, CO-1; j, EL-140; k, 2-212; l, EL-25; m, EL-26; n, EL-53; o, K-11; p, W-152; q, M-34; r, W-153; s, 2-126; t, M-35; u, EL-37; v, EL-77; w, EL-118; x, 2-124; y, EL-96/24; z, EL-102; aa, M-27; bb, 2-211; cc, EL-158. Specific provenience of these and all other artifacts illustrated may be obtained by reference to Appendix I.

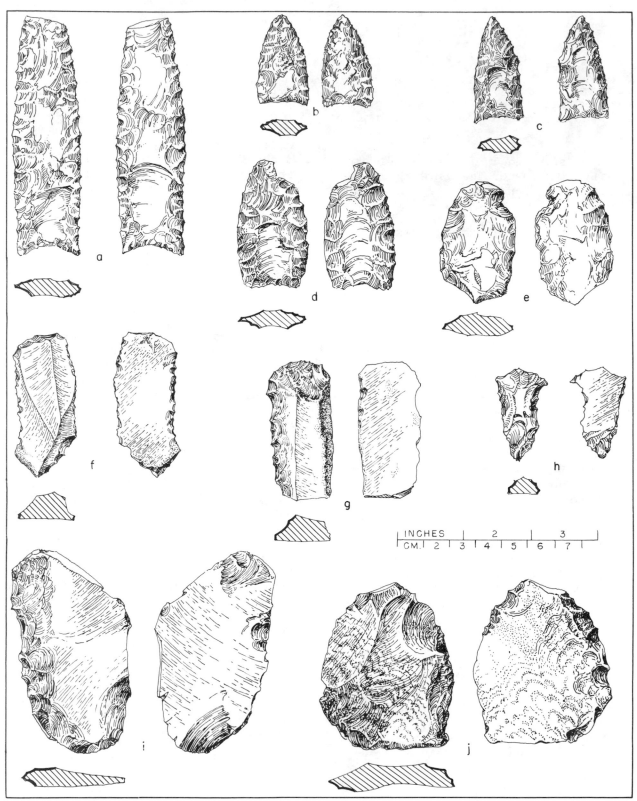

Fig. 89. Drawings of Clovis artifacts, illustrating details of flaking: a and d, Clovis points Type 1; b-c, Clovis point Type 2; e, bifacial knife; f, flake scarper; g, end-scraper on blade; h, spurred end-scraper; i-j, side scrapers. a, EL-10; b, EL-30; c, EL-47; d, EL-90; e, 2-205; f, EL-63; g, EL-23; h-EL-116; i, EL-16; j, EL-3. Drawing by Phyllis Hughes and Mrs. Alice Wesche.

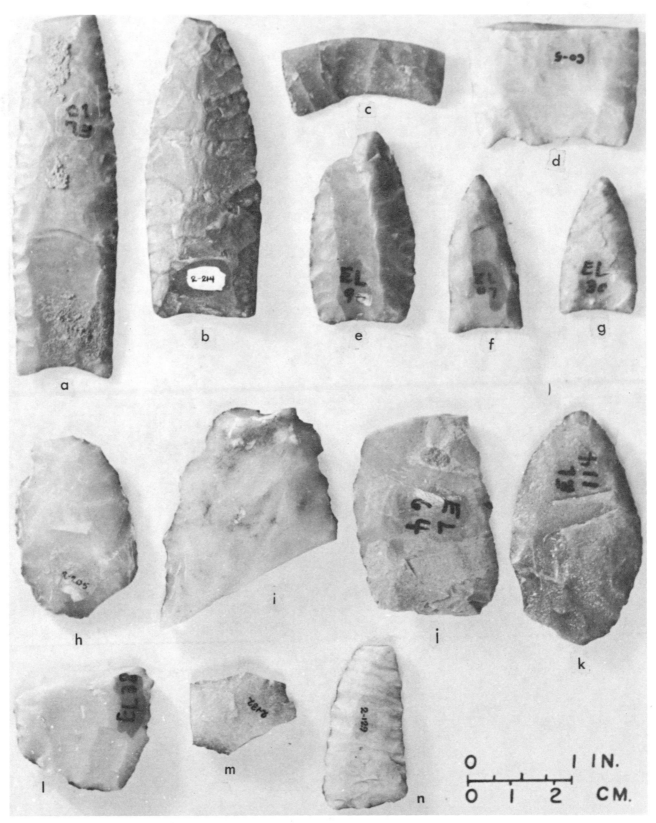

Fig. 90. Clovis bifaces: a-e, Clovis points Type 1; f-g, Clovis points Type 2; h-n, bifacial knives. a, EL-10; b, 2-214; c, 2-221; d, CO-5; e, EL-90; f, EL-47; g, EL-30; h, 2-205; i, EL-75; j, EL-64, k, EL-114; l, EL-38; m, 2-132; n, 2-129.

Fig. 91. Clovis side-scrapers: a, side-scraper of Enterline form; b and f, side-scrapers on blades; j-k, side-scrapers of human ear form, a type dating back to the Mousterian. a, EL-62; b, EL-9; c, EL-95; d, EL-103; e, unknown; f, EL-105 and 159; g, EL-17; h, EL-162; i, K-8; j, EL-3; k, EL-16; l, EL-110.

Fig. 92. Clovis end-scrapers and flake scrapers: a-j, end-scrapers; c and d are end-scrapers on blades, and e is the spurred variety; k-r, flake scrapers; a, M-40; b, EL-21; c, EL-23; d, EL-27; e, EL-116; f, EL-145; g, EL-83; h, CO-4; i, 2-206; j, 2-204; k, EL-63; l, 2-187; m, EL-36; n, EL-163; o, EL-49; p, 2-191; q, 2-202; r, K-12.

Both point types have been found in association with mammoth remains and presumably
were used to kill them. One Clovis Type 1
point was recovered by Sellards in association
with a bison scapula (Fig. 51) documenting
their use in the killing of other kinds of game.

Side-scrapers (17) (Fig. 91)

Side-scrapers are of varied form as a
result of the shape of the primary flake utilized.
Major attributes include primary flake (94%),
struck with billet technique (22%), flake from
prepared core (88%), retouch along edge to
upper face (94%), unifacially worked (88%),
and pressure retouch (100%) which is much
more common than percussion flaking (60%).
Most side-scrapers were made on end-flakes
(88%) indicating no deliberate selection of
side-flakes. Unusual attributes include a
high incidence of trimming of the bulb of percussion (28%), suggesting that this was an
intentional practice in the formation of the
artifact. Another attribute of interest is the
presence of trimming flake scars (16.5%) along
the edge of the scraper indicating the removal
of spalls to steepen or back the edge. The
transverse cross-section tends to be plano-
convex and the anterior-posterior section is
either the same or concavo-convex.

In general, the side-scrapers are a highly
variable artifact class. Within the group are
two forms of interest, a form with converging
sides (Fig. 91) similar to the Enterline side-
scraper described from Pennsylvania (Witthoft,
1952) and a form similar in shape to a human
ear (Fig. 91j, k) also known from the Bull Brook
site in Massachusetts (Byers, 1954). The removal of spalls from the edge of the scraper is
also a trait represented at Bull Brook. Size
range: length 1.3 to 3.1 inches, average 1.9
inches; width 2.3 to 1.0 inches, average 1.4
inches; thickness 0.5 to 0.25 inches, average
0.35 inches.

Flake Scrapers (12) (Fig. 92k-r)

Flake scrapers consist of primary flakes
modified by pressure chipping to the upper face
along a portion of the perimeter. This chipping
did not modify to any appreciable degree the
outline or cross-section of the original flake.
In general, these are more casual artifacts than
the side-scrapers although presumably they were
used to perform the same functions, namely, the
scraping of hides or woodworking.

Major attributes are   from prepared core
(84%), primary flake (84%), billet technique
(53%), pressure chipped (92%), unifacially
worked (100%), upper face worked (100%), and
modified by use (45%). Size range: length 1.1
to 2.3 inches, average 1.7 inches; width 0.8
to 1.4 inches, average 1.1 inches; thickness
0.1 to 0.4 inches.

Hollow-Edge Scrapers (4) (Fig. 93)

Scrapers with a concave working edge .
have been termed "hollow edge." This group
is limited in number and may properly be considered as a variety of side-scrapers. This
sample is too small to yield valid attribute
percentages. However, attributes recorded
include   primary flakes from prepared core,
billet technique, bulb of percussion trimmed,
pressure chipped unifacially to the upper face,
nether face also worked and modified by use.
The cross-sections are not appreciably different
from those of side-scrapers. One presumed
function is for the shaping of spear shafts.
Size range: length 1.3 to 2.1 inches; width 1.1
to 1.7 inches; thickness 0.1 to 0.4 inches.

End-scrapers (4) (Fig. 92a-b, e-j)

End-scrapers of a snub-nosed variety
occur in the collection. These specimens have
been manufactured from a thick bulbar flake by
flaking and chipping of the upper face around

Fig. 93. Drawings of Clovis artifacts: a, Enterline side-scraper; b, hollow edge-scraper;
c, side-scraper on blade; d, double graver; e, burin; f, unifacial knife; g, Folsom sandstone
edge grinder.   a, EL-62; b, EL-162; c, EL-105; d, EL-107, e, EL-110, f, EL-13, g, 2-26.

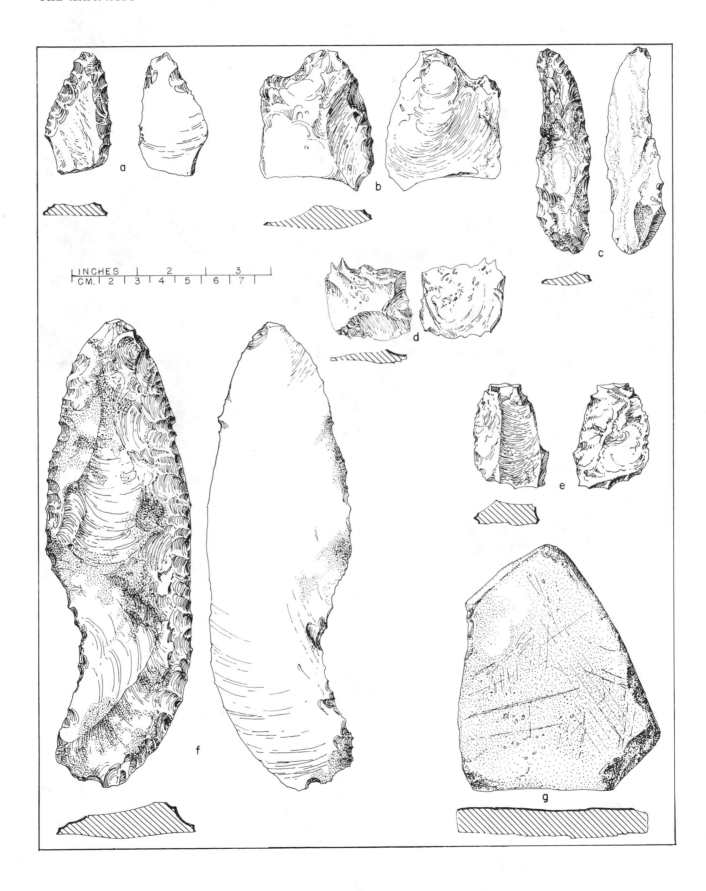

Fig. 94. Clovis unifacial knives: a, EL-14; b, 2-119; c, EL-111; d, W-165; e, M-30; f, EL-165; g, EL-12; and EL-15 (fragments found separately), h, EL-106; i, EL-13; j, EL-146.

Fig. 95. Clovis stone artifacts: a-e, gravers; f-s, flake knives. a, EL-107; b, EL-166;
c, M-33; d, 2-127; e, CO-3; f, EL-18; g, M-28; h, EL-7; i, 2-198; j, CO-110; k, 2-121;
l, EL-58; m, CO-109; n, EL-56; o, 2-183; p, EL-115 and EL-60 (pieces found separately);
q, EL-104; r, EL-50; s, EL-32.

the perimeter. The resultant form is a generalized tear drop with the large end opposite the
striking platform. The bulb of percussion is
frequently trimmed. The transverse cross-
section is plano-convex or trapezoidal in form.
The anterior-posterior cross-section is a scalene
triangle or trapezoid with the steepest angle at
the working edge. The small sample eliminates
percentile definition of attribute frequencies.
Additional attributes present include from prepared core, primary flake, bifacially worked
(one specimen) modified by use, and points on
perimeter. The latter resemble the graver spurs
reported on end-scrapers from the Bull Brook
site (Byers, 1954). The function of these tools
is presumed to have been for the scraping of
hides. Size range: length 1.5 to 2.1 inches,
width 0.8 to 1.0 inches, thickness 0.25 to 0.4
inches.

End- and Side-scrapers (6) (Fig. 92c-d)

This group of artifacts consists of end-
scrapers possessing secondary scraping edges
along one or both sides. The artifacts are made
from primary flakes or core struck blades by
flaking and chipping to the upper face around
the perimeter. The main working edge of the
implement tends to be on the end opposite the
bulb of percussion. This is normally the edge
with the steepest angle. The scraping edges
along the side are less steep. The small sample prohibits use of attribute percentages as
meaningful indices. However, in general,
this group possesses many characteristics in
common with end-scrapers. The function of
these tools could have been for the scraping
of hides or for the manufacture of wooden implements. Size range: length 1.5 to 2.4 inches,
width 0.8 to 1.9 inches, thickness 0.1 to 0.45
inches.

Bifacial Knives (11) (Fig. 90h-n)

Bifacial knives are manufactured from
primary flakes (100%) struck from prepared
cores (100%). The method of manufacture consisted of the removal of percussion flakes (100%)
from both faces around the perimeter. These
flaked edges frequently had been retouched with
pressure (33%). The form of the knives ranges
from triangular to oval. No appreciable differences were noted between whole specimens and
fragments. Cross-sections tend to be lenticular.

The function of these implements was presumably
for cutting. Size range: length 1.6 to 2.6 inches,
width 1.0 to 1.7 inches, thickness 0.15 to 0.4
inches.

Unifacial Knives (11) (Fig. 94)

Unifacial knives were made from primary
flakes (100%) struck from prepared cores (100%).
These flakes were then modified by pressure
chipping (91%) along the edges to the upper face.
In every case, however, the primary working
edges were unifacially retouched. Only one
specimen shows evidence of percussion flaking.
The form of the artifacts conforms to the shape
of the original flake. This implies that naturally
sharp flakes were selected and were not appreciably altered to a desired form. Additional
attributes include trimming of the bulb of percussion (99%), evidence of a billet technique
of striking off the original flake (36%), and
modification through use (9%). Cross-sections
are identical to those of the original flakes,
either scalene triangular or trapezoidal. The
function of these implements is presumed to
have been for cutting. Size range: length 1.9
to 7.2 inches, width 0.7 to 2.1 inches, thickness 0.15 to 0.45 inches.

Flake Knives (7) (Fig. 95)

Flake knives consist of primary flakes
with naturally sharp edges struck from prepared
cores. Their edges show modification from
pressure chipping and from use. In most cases
chips have been removed from the upper face.
While this removal causes the implements to
superficially resemble scrapers, the use marks
are bifacial implying a cutting function. Minor
attributes include billet technique and the trimming of the bulb of percussion. The sample is
small, thus percentages of attribute frequency
are not given. The artifacts possess the same
form as the original flakes although there appears to have been selection for flakes with
long sharp edges. Cross-sections are identical to those of the original flakes. Two specimens also possess graver points chipped on
the edges. Size range: length 1.4 to 2.2 inches, width 0.8 to 2.0 inches, thickness 0.1
to 0.25 inches.

Gravers (5) (Fig. 95)

Gravers are made from primary flakes struck from prepared cores. The modification consists of pressure chipping to the upper face in two converging arcs to form a short point. Some of these points show additional modification from use. The flakes are otherwise unmodified. They appear to have been selected for small size possibly to facilitate their being held. One specimen is made on a thick flake, all others are on thin flakes. Cross-sections are identical to those of the original flakes. The function of gravers is uncertain, possible uses include the engraving of bone, the drilling of small holes in wood or bone, the separation of fibers such as sinew, or tattooing. Size range: length 1.2 to 1.8 inches, width 1.0 to 1.4 inches, thickness 0.1 to 0.3 inches.

Chips (4)

Secondary flakes exhibiting a bulb of percussion typical of cylinder hammer-struck flakes are present in the Clovis assemblage. While not common, these chips are indicative of a fine control of percussion flaking. These flakes tend to be oval or circular in form and concavo-convex or plano-convex in cross-section. All chips are unused and presumably discarded, as they did not serve any known function. Size range: length 0.3 to 0.6 inches, width 0.2 to 0.5 inches, thickness 0.05 to 0.2 inches.

Hammerstones (5) (Fig. 97f-i)

Three hammerstones consist of oval pebbles modified by pecking on their ends. A fourth hammerstone is a pebble of shale which has been bifacially flaked around 3/4ths of the perimeter to form a sharp edge suitable for fine controlled pecking. The hammerstones are of a convenient size for hand holding. They are oval to circular in plan and oval in cross-section. Their use was presumably for percussion flaking of stone implements. However, evidence from the debitage suggests that approximately 90% of all flaking was done with cylinder hammers. As we have no cylinder hammers in the collection, it is possible they were made of wood and have not been preserved. Size range: length 2.4 to 3.6 inches, width 1.4 to 3.2 inches, thickness 1.4 to 2.0 inches.

Pebbles (5) (Fig. 97)

Several small oval pebbles with broken edges are present in the collection. These small stream pebbles do not appear to have been deliberately fashioned into implements. On the other hand, the fact that the pebbles have been broken suggests they are artifacts as other pebbles in the same formation have not been broken. In any event, there is no evidence that these stones were used. Size range: length 1.3 to 1.8 inches, width 0.8 to 1.3 inches, thickness 0.3 to 0.7 inches.

Chopper (1) (Fig. 96)

A chert nodule has been bifacially flaked all over, resulting in an oval form. The perimeter is bounded by a sinous edge due to the removal of flakes from alternate faces. Cross-sections are bi-convex. The edges are not battered and it is possible the implement actually is a simple core. Use could have been for cutting or chopping. Size range: length 1.7, width 2.2, thickness 0.7 inches.

Grinding Stone (1) (Figs. 96c, 97e)

This small mano consists of a natural sandstone cobble used for grinding. The cobble is of an oval form with oval cross-sections. One face has been flattened through use and exhibits striations indicative of a reciprocal motion. The two ends show use in pounding. This specimen may have been used for the cracking and grinding of wild seeds. An alternative use could have been as a hammerstone for the manufacture of stone implements. Size: length 2.9 inches, width 1.9 inches, thickness 1.6 inches.

Other Stone Artifacts

Additional stone artifacts include two scrapers of indeterminant type, a core, a channel flake, and a combination burin (?)-scraper. The scrapers and burin (?)-scraper are unique and, therefore, have little cultural meaning except to document variability of artifact manufacture. The core and channel flake represent typical items of campsite debris which are poorly represented at this site. These artifacts are not adequate for a type

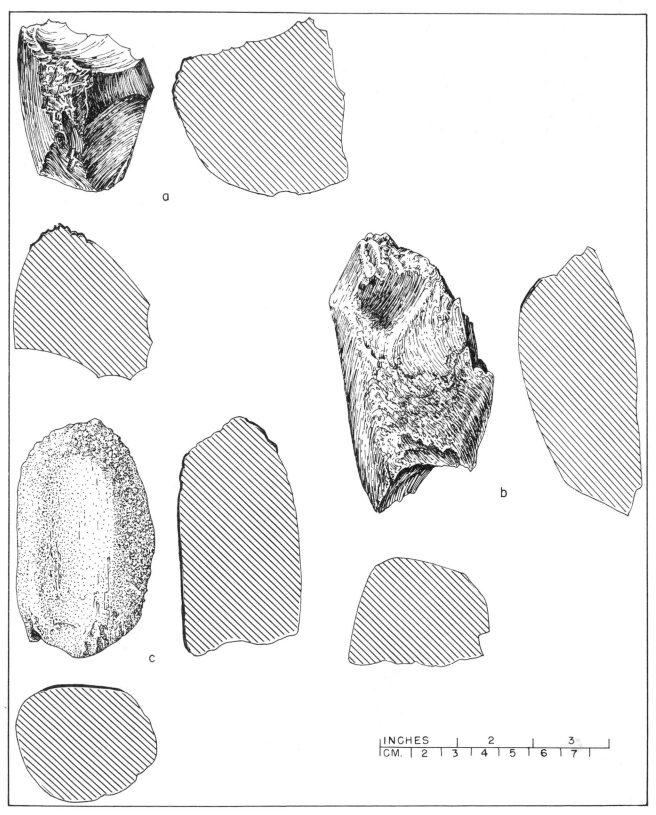

Fig. 96. Drawing of Clovis and Folsom core tools: a, Clovis hammerstone; b, Folsom hammerstone; c, Clovis grinding stone. a, EL-151; b, 2-116; c, EL-20.

Fig. 97. Additional Clovis stone artifacts: a, core; b, problematical object; c–d, broken pebbles; e, grinding stone; f, flaked hammerstone; g–i, pebble hammerstones. a, EL-8; b, EL-99; c, EL-161; d, EL-150; e, EL-20; f, EL-151; g, LA 3324-7; h, El -57; i, EL-149.

Fig. 98. Paleo-Indian bone and shell artifacts: a,c,d,e,h,i are Clovis bone artifacts; b, f, g are Folsom bone artifacts; i is a Portales shell artifact. a, 2-123; b, LA-3324-8; c, EL-147; d, EL-46; e, EL-45; f, EL-41; g, EL-82; h, EL-79; i, EL-43.

description but their presence denotes aspects of tool manufacture which may best be understood from analysis of stone assemblages from other Clovis campsites.

BONE ARTIFACTS

Artifacts of bone are an important and varied portion of the artifact assemblage.

Representing 6.2% of the total material culture, they are more abundant than any specific stone tool type with the exception of flake side-scrapers. However, this statement is somewhat misleading as to the bone implements represent a complex of tools rather than a single tool type. Another aspect is the fact that many of these tools are represented by single specimens. As the nature of this complex is extremely important for purposes of cross-cultural comparisons, we will describe each artifact individually.

K-13 Bone Flesher (Fig. 117a)

This is a split rib, perhaps elephant, which was split lengthwise and then ground along the edges. The tool has the original bone exterior remaining on only one face. One end has been ground on both faces to produce a thin flattened edge. This edge is round in plan view and beveled in cross-section. Use of this implement may have been as a flesher. Size: length 10.3 inches, width 1.3 inches, thickness 0.5 inches.

2-123 Bone Awl (Figs. 98a, 99)

This artifact may have been used as an awl or needle. It was formed from a portion of a split mammal bone. The exact type of bone is unidentifiable owing to the modification. The original portion selected could have been a fragment of a large bone or a small mammal bone. One half of its length has been ground on all sides and tapers to a sharp point. This point is round in cross-section. Size: length 1.1 inches, width 0.2 inches, thickness 0.1 inches, length of point 0.6 inches.

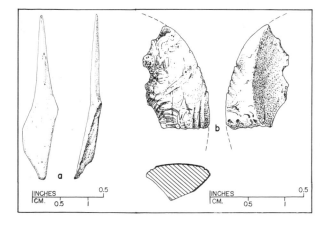

Fig. 99. Drawing of unusual Clovis and Folsom bone artifacts: a, 2-123 Clovis-Age awl; b, LA-3324-8 Folsom-Age ornament. Drawing by Phyllis Hughes.

EL-45 Bone Tool (Fig. 98e)

This artifact is a portion of a split mammal longbone. The exact bone is not identifiable, but the bone possessed a ridge on the shaft similar to that on a tibia. The modification consisted of grinding the two edges at one end to a blunt point. The portion utilized consisted of this ridge plus portions of the adjacent sides resulting in a form similar to that of a piece of angle iron. Modification consisted of grinding the two edges at one end to a blunt point. The grinding on one edge was concave, the other convex. Use of this implement is unknown although it might possibly have been a flaker. Size: length 2.7 inches (incomplete), width 0.6 inches, thickness 0.5 inches, length of grinding on point 1.2 inches.

EL-46 Bone Tool (Fig. 98d)

A portion of split mammal bone has been ground to a blunt point at one end. This artifact is similar in form to EL-45 and may have been utilized for the same purpose. The exact bone cannot be identified. The shaping was confined to the edges at one end with both edges ground to a convex form. Size: length 2.3 inches (incomplete), width 0.8 inches, thickness 0.6 inches, length of point 0.4 inches.

EL-79 Bone Point (Fig. 98h)

This specimen has been fashioned from a solid piece of bone, presumably a portion of a mammal long bone. As the entire surface has been modified by grinding, the original bone cannot be identified. In form the artifact is long and slim with a rounded point. In cross-section, it has two opposing flat faces and two opposing convex faces. The specimen is broken so its true length and hafting are unknown, but presumably is the same type of bone projectile point or foreshaft as those found by Cotter and Sellards. Size: length 3.9 inches (incomplete), width 0.7 inches, thickness 0.5 inches.

EL-82 Bone Knife or Point (Fig. 98g)

A portion of a split mammal long bone, presumably bison, shows evidence of grinding on both edges. In form the artifact is an isoceles triangle with a blunt point. The cross-section is trapezoidal with a convex base. Grinding was confined to the edges and appears to have been done to sharpen them for cutting. The artifact could have been hafted for use as a projectile point or knife. The specimen appears to be purposefully cut on the end opposite the point suggesting that the entire artifact has been recovered. Size: length 3.8 inches, width 1.1 inches, thickness 0.4 inches.

EL-147 Bone Tool (Fig. 98c)

This implement is fragmentary with only the tip remaining. In form it is similar to EL-45 and EL-46 having been made from a ridged portion of a long bone shaft. One face and one edge have been ground to a common sharp point with a short chisel-like edge. The edge is slightly hollow ground to a concave form, the ground face has a convex form. The complete specimen is triangular in cross-section. Only the tip of the specimen has been preserved. The function of this artifact is unknown although it could have been used as a flaker. Size: length 1.7 inches (incomplete), width 0.6 inches, thickness 0.4 inches, length of grinding on edge 1.1 inches, length of grinding on face 0.3 inches, width of point 0.3 inches.

EL-169 Bone Scraper or Knife (Fig. 100g)

A large portion of a split bison long bone,

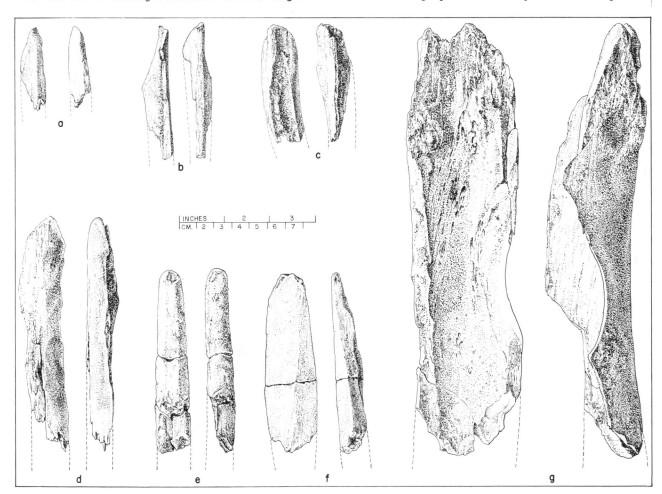

Fig. 100. Drawing of typical Clovis bone artifacts: a-d, f, pointed implements; e, bone projectile or foreshaft; g, scraping or cutting tool. a, EL-147; b, EL-45; c, EL-46; d, EL-41; e, EL-79; f, EL-82; g, EL-196. Drawing by Phyllis Hughes. El-41 is of Folsom Age.

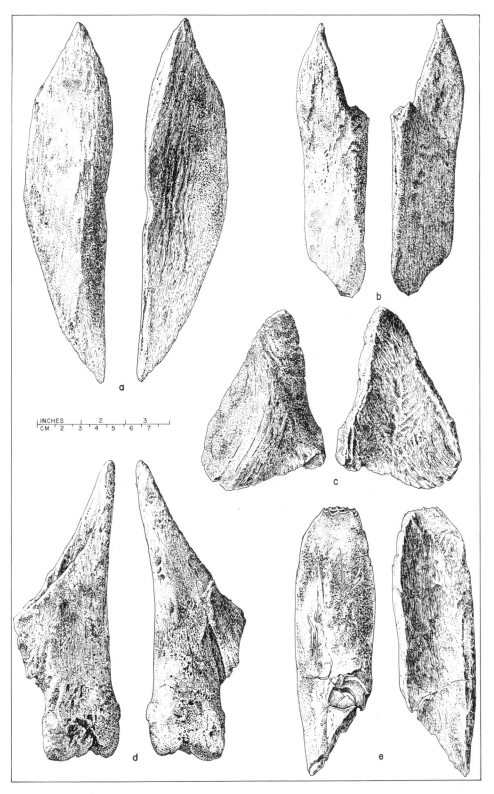

Fig. 101. Drawing of typical Clovis bone artifacts: a,b,d, pointed tools, possible flakes; c,e, digging or scraping tools. a, 937-94; b, 937-95; c, 30-3214; d, 937-688; e, 30-3215. Drawing by Alice Wesche.

probably a tibia, has been modified by the grinding of one edge. The grinding was performed to the interior of one of the edges of the bone. This grinding resulted in a sharp concave edge which would have been suitable for cutting or scraping. The remainder of the worked edge exhibits a slight polish from use. Otherwise the bone is unaltered. Size: length 9.3 inches, width 2.2 inches, thickness 1.5 inches, length of worked edge 3.5 inches, depth of concavity on worked edge 0.5 inches.

EL-89 Bone Flesher (Fig. 117d)

A section of a split mammal rib, probably mammoth, has been worked to a sharp edge at one end. This edge is the full width of the implement and may have been used for the scraping of hides or in digging. The form of the implement is long and narrow with a slight curvature. The worked end is slightly convex, the opposite end is irregularly broken. The cross-section is lenticular. Only one end shows any evidence of shaping. Size: length 11.2 inches, width 1.5 inches, thickness 0.7 inches.

30-3214 Bone Tool (Fig. 101c)

This implement is a triangular portion of a large mammal long bone taken from a point near the articular end of the bone. The specific bone utilized is not definite but it could have been a bison tibia or humerus. The surface of the bone is badly eroded, and it is difficult to determine the degree of modification. The specimen appears to have had two edges ground to form a point at one end. In general, this point is of similar form to those of artifacts EL 45 and EL 46, suggesting that the present specimen is indeed an artifact. The point is rounded and slightly shovel-shaped with one of the convergent edges straight and the other rounded. The artifact is of convenient size for grasping and could have been used in digging or scraping. The cross-section is identical to that of the original bone, a rounded triangle. Size: length 4.4 inches, width 3.0 inches, thickness 1.7 inches, width of point 1.0 inches. Illustrated in Dittert (1957, Fig. 3).

30-3212 Bone Tool (Fig. 103d)

A fragment of split mammal long bone

(probably bison) has been worked to an oval form by flaking. The flaking resulted in a thin steep edge suitable for use in scraping or cutting. No other modification is present. The worked edge constitutes about 40% of the perimeter. Size: length 2.1 inches, width 1.6 inches, thickness 0.6 inches. Illustrated in Dittert (1957, Fig. 3).

30-3213 Bone Tool ? (Fig. 103a)

This specimen probably is an artifact although it cannot definitely be established as such. It consists of a portion of split mammal long bone, presumably bison, which appears to have been modified at one end. This end has two concave arcs which converge to form a blunt point. The method of forming this point appears to have been by flaking or crude grinding. The remainder of the specimen is unaltered. It is roughly rectangular in form with a concavo-convex cross-section. Such a blunt pointed tool could have been used as a flaker or punch. Size: length 3.0 inches, width 1.6 inches, thickness 0.4 inches, length of converging arcs 0.6 and 0.4 inches, width of point 0.3 inches. Illustrated in Dittert (1957, Fig. 3).

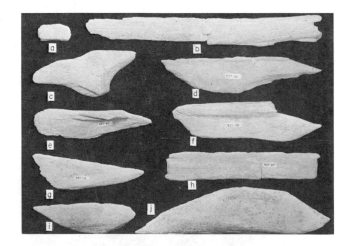

Fig. 102. Photo of Clovis bone tools from excavations of E.H. Sellards: a, 937-89; b, 937-86; c, 937-99; d, 937-84; e, 937-91; f, 937-95; g, 937-98; h, 937-87; i, 937-96; j, 937-94. Length of a, 1 1/4 inches. Artifacts 84 thru 91 are from the Gray Sand, Station A; the remainder are from the Gray Sand, Station H.

937-61 Bone Tool (Fig. 105a)

    This is a long pointed bone tool probably made from a bison rib. It appears to have been ground on all sides to a rounded rectangular cross-section, and to a blunt point. The anterior-posterior cross-section is concavo-convex. A possible use for this implement is as a bone point as it has an identical form and cross-section as EL-79 with the exception of the slight longitudial curvature. Size: length 9.8 inches, width 0.8 inches, thickness 0.5 inches, amount of curvature 0.5 inches. Illustrated in Sellards (1952, Fig. 14).

937-84 Bone Tool (Figs. 102d, 104b)

    This tool is a split section of a mammal longbone, probably bison. It has been ground to a point at one end. Both ends are pointed, one naturally. The man-made point was formed by grinding from one edge to meet the converging opposite edge. The resultant point has one straight side (man-made) and one hollow edge (the result of a natural break). The tool could have been used as a flaker or a punch, or possibly for digging. The cross-section is concavo-convex and is identical to that of the original bone. Size: length 1.3 inches, width 0.7 in-

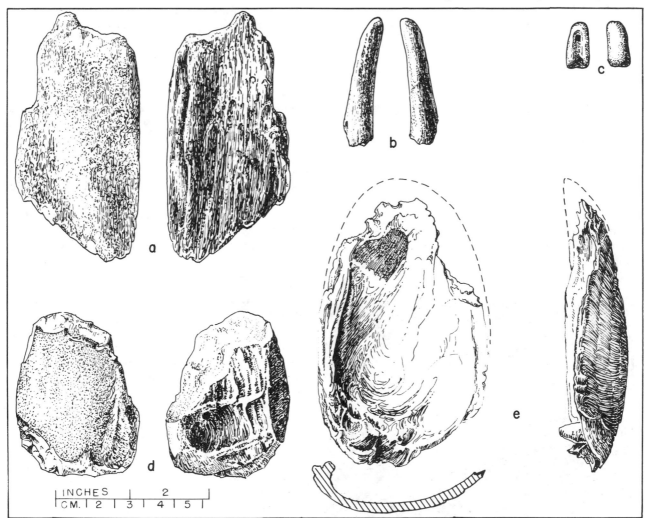

Fig. 103. Drawing of unusual Clovis bone implements and a Parallel Flaked horizon shell artifact: a, flaker or punch; b, ornament or flaker; c, bead; d, scraper?; e, shell knife? a-d, Clovis bone tools; a, 30-3213; b, 937-682; c, 937-680; d, 30-3212. Parallel flaked horizon shell artifact; e, EL-43.

ches, thickness 0.5 inches, depth of cuts 0.05
inches. Illustrated in Sellards (1952, Fig. 13).

937-94 Bone Tool (Fig. 102j)

This is a section of a split long bone,
possibly a bison tibia, which has been ground
to a point on one end. The opposite end is
naturally pointed and the specimen is very
similar to 937-84. The implement is triangular
in cross-section. The modification consisted
of grinding one edge till it met the opposing
natural edge. The point so formed has an angle
of approximately 30°, with the long axis of the
tool. The tool could have been used as a flaker,
a punch, or a digging implement. Size: length
8.0 inches, width 1.9 inches, thickness 0.9
inches, length of grinding on edge 1.9 inches.

937-89 Cut Bone (Figs. 102a, 104a)

This is a short section of bone of a rounded rectangular form with cross-sections of the
same form. One face of the bone exhibits six
engraved cuts. These cuts are in no identifiable design; however, the artifact appears to
have been broken since the cuts were made.
Although the object does not fit into any artifact class the cuts are almost certainly man
made. In a general sense the cuts are similar
to those on Upper Paleolithic bone tools from
Europe reported by Marshak (1964). It is not
intended here to imply that the object at hand

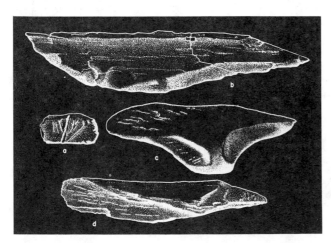

Fig. 104. Drawing of typical Clovis bone
tools: a, cut bone; b-d, flakers or punches.
a, 937-89; b, 937-84; c, 937-99; d, 937-91.
After Sellards (1952, Fig. 13).

represents a lunar calendar of any type (the
purpose inferred by Marshak). However, it is
suggested here that engraving of bone by Clovis
peoples may be derived from the Upper Paleolithic tradition of bone working. Size: length
1.3 inches, width 0.7 inches, thickness 0.5
inches.

937-95 Bone Tool (Fig. 102f)

This implement is almost identical to
937-94. It is a split long bone with a point
formed at one end by grinding from one side.
The opposite end is also bluntly pointed and
the specimen has a triangular cross-section.
Use was probably identical to that of 937-94.
Size: length 6.1 inches, width 1.5 inches,
thickness 0.9 inches, length of grinding on
edge 1.1 inches.

937-680 Bone Bead (Fig. 103c)

This is a cylindrical piece of bone which
has a hole drilled from one end on a bias and a
second hole drilled from the opposite end. The
second hole was not finished. The type of bone
is unknown. The specimen may have been used
as an ornament. The bead is a rounded rec-
tangle in plan and oval with one flat face in
cross-section. Size: length 0.5 inches,
width 0.3 inches, thickness 0.2 inches.

937-682 Bone Tool (Fig. 103b)

This is a polished section of what appears
to be a canine tooth. The polish is confined to
one section of the object along one edge. It is
oval in the transverse cross-section and triangular in plan. The anterior-posterior cross-
section is concave-convex. Use may have been
as an ornament or as a flaker. Size: length 1.6
inches, width 0.4 inches, thickness 0.3 inches.

937-688 Bone Tool (Fig. 101d)

This is a split metapodial (distal end) of
a large bison or camel. It has been ground
from one side to produce a point on the end
opposite the articular surface. This point is
at an angle of approximately 30° to the long
axis of the tool. Use was probably as a flaker
or a punch. The implement is otherwise unmodified. In form the artifact is rounded on one end
and pointed on the other with a rounded rec-

tangular cross-section. Size: length 6.3 inches, width 2.0 inches, thickness 1.6 inches, length of ground edge 4.0 inches.

9-9 Bone Point (Fig. 105c)

This is a cylindrical shaft of bone worked all over so that the original bone cannot be identified. The point is beveled at both ends, having been ground from one side to achieve the bevel on the basal end and ground from all sides to form the point at the tip. One end is slightly thicker than the other. The remainder of the shaft is oval in cross-section. The point was found in association with a mammoth ulna and phalanx which suggests that it was utilized as a projectile point. Size: length 10.1 inches, diameter 0.6 inches. Illustrated in Cotter (1937, Pl. 6, Fig. 1; p. 7).

9-10 Bone Point (Fig. 105b)

This bone point is cylindrical in form with a slight taper. The basal end has a long bevel made by grinding from one side. The tip is pointed but does not possess a distinct bevel. The cross-section is oval with two contiguous flat facets. The bevel at the base possesses oblique transverse scratches indicating the direction of the grinding strokes. The artifact was located eleven inches from a mammoth tusk. Size: length 9.35 inches, diameter 0.68 inches. Illustrated in Cotter (1937, Pl. 2; Pl. 5, Fig. 3).

937-99, 937-91, and 937-88 Dubious Bone Implements (Figs. 102c, e; 104c, d)

Several of the split bones in the collection at the Texas Memorial Museum including those illustrated by Sellards (1952, Fig. 13, c, d) are considered by him to be artifacts. Examination of these specimens by the present author has led to doubt that they are true artifacts. Their form is identical to other specimens which are undoubted artifacts. However, the specimens at hand could be the result of natural splintering of bone. In any event, these specimens add little to our knowledge of the Clovis bone industry.

In addition to the specimens described in this section there are perhaps as many more which fall into the dubious artifact category. Most of these are pointed specimens similar

to the possible flakers or punches described. In most cases, erosion of the surface of the bones has removed all traces of any grinding or polishing that might have been present.

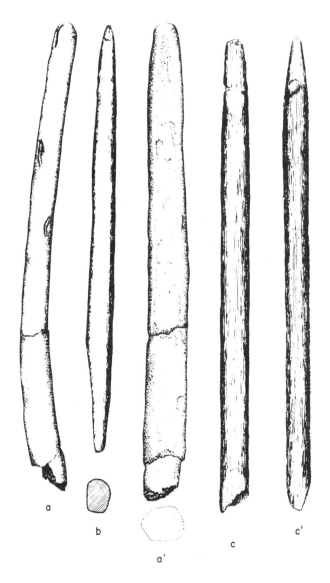

Fig. 105. Clovis Age bone projectile points or foreshafts: a, 937-61 is from the Gray Sand, Station A; b, 9-10 and c, 9-9 are from Cotter's 1936 excavations at the south end of the South Pit (after Sellards, 1952, Fig. 14).

Discussion

The significance of the Clovis bone industry can perhaps be realized for the first time
as a result of the descriptions above. The bone
tools were an important portion of the entire
artifactual assemblage with almost as many
uses as the stone implements. These uses
probably included flaking, scraping, cutting,
piercing, ornamentation, digging, and the killing of game. Another use, the straightening of
spear shafts with a shaft wrench, may have
been a part of the culture as such a tool has
been found in a Clovis site at Murray Springs,
Arizona (Haynes and Hemmings, 1968).

The manufacture of bone tools was a
rather simple process emphasizing the splitting
of large mammal long bones and then grinding
portions of these to the desired form with the
remainder of the bone being unaltered. Minor
manufacturing techniques included allover
polishing and scoring.

Perhaps the most important aspect of this
bone industry is its prevalence on this early
time level. This fact leads to the inference
that this industry must have been derived from
the Upper Paleolithic bone industry of the Old
World.

NOMENCLATURE OF CLOVIS MANIFESTATIONS

Nomenclature of Early Man materials is
in some confusion owing to overemphasis on
minor attribute differences between projectile
points and to a general inadequacy of data.
The result is the definition of a large number
of projectile point types with little emphasis
on describing the total cultural complex associated with these points. A conspicuous exception to this is Sellards' definition of the "Llano
Complex" (Sellards, 1952, p. 17-18).

"The terms Llano complex and Llano man,
taken from the Llano Estacado, or Staked Plains
of Texas and New Mexico, are new and are proposed to include both a complex of artifacts
found in place in association with extinct animals in the Southern High Plains region of the
United States and the people who made and used
those artifacts."

Unfortunately, Sellards' definition seems
too narrow geographically as within a short time
artifacts of this same culture were found at Naco
and Lehner, Arizona (Haury, 1953; Haury, Sayles,
and Wasley, 1959). In addition, artifact types
now known from Blackwater No. 1 have close
counterparts in the eastern United States at the
Bull Brook (Byers, 1954) and Shoop (Witthoft,
1952) sites. Formerly, these eastern sites were
considered as variants of the Clovis culture but
now, with our larger sample from the type site,
it can be seen that these collections approach
cultural identity. As a result, it is the author's
opinion that the geographic term "Llano" has too
restricted a meaning, as defined by Sellards, to
be continued in use.

Although the term "Clovis" is also geographical, it has been used over the past thirty
years in the same manner as the term "Folsom",
a name similarly derived but used to denote a
widespread cultural manifestation. In view of
the above considerations it seems appropriate
to continue use of the older term "Clovis" as
it has established priority in the literature.

Folsom Complex

Artifacts of the Folsom complex possess
specific characteristics which distinguish them
from the preceding Clovis complex and the later
Portales complex. In addition, the Folsom
assemblage, because of the large sample,
enables us to describe more accurately the
nature of the Folsom complex.

The data have been obtained from two
types of sites: (1) killsites within the pond
margin and (2) campsites located just outside
the pond margin or debris from those campsites
washed into the pond. The combined artifact
frequencies by type from all Folsom localities
has been graphed in Figure 83. This sample
includes 534 specimens considered as artifacts.
The breakdown by tool types is listed in Table
XXXVII below. This sample contains considerable campsite debris.

TABLE XXXVII

FOLSOM ARTIFACT FREQUENCIES BY TYPE

Type (whole specimens plus fragments)	No.	Percentage
Flakes	234	43.8
Points	79	14.8
Side-scrapers	36	6.7
End-scrapers	28	5.2
Gravers	4	0.7
Unifacial knives	13	2.4
Bifacial knives	14	2.6
Flake scrapers	67	12.5
Hollow edge scrapers	3	0.5
Flake knives	23	4.3
Scraper-gravers	3	0.5
Scrapers	5	0.9
Nodules	1	0.1
Unidentified point fragments	2	0.3
End- and side-scraper	1	0.1
Choppers	1	0.1
Cores	3	0.5
Hammerstones	2	0.3
Pebbles	1	0.1
Channel flakes	7	1.3
Abraders	1	0.1
Bone artifacts	4	0.7
Total	534	98.4

Of the twenty-three tool types identified, only nine occur in frequencies greater than 1.0%. This contrasts with the Clovis industry which has fifteen tool types occurring with frequencies greater than 1%. This difference may be due to the greater control of tool manufacture by the Folsom peoples. This technological control suggests a greater adaption to the environment than was present in the preceding Clovis culture.

At this point, it seems appropriate to describe the differences in artifact assemblages between the killsites and the campsites. The sample from the killsites is rather small, therefore detailed comparisons cannot be made. It is sufficient to note that the campsite debris from the surface site at the northwest corner of the pit, a total of 237 specimens, contained 55 artifacts (23%) and 182 secondary waste flakes (77%). This contrasts strikingly with the killsite debris which contained less than 1% secondary waste flakes. Apparent differences include greater frequency of gravers, projectile point bases, hammerstones, and cores in the campsite debris while killsites feature flakes, projectile points, knives, and scrapers.

The Folsom artifact type frequencies are similar to those of the Clovis assemblage with the following exceptions: Flake scrapers, flake knives, and projectile points occur with greater frequency in the Folsom culture. By contrast, core struck blades and bone implements are much less common in the Folsom culture than in the preceding Clovis material.

MANUFACTURING TECHNIQUES

Folsom stone flaking is clearly derived from the Clovis tradition with types and specific attributes of artifacts occurring with almost identical frequencies in the two assemblages (Figs. 83, 84). However, the Folsom industry possesses a few attributes not present in the earlier Clovis material. These features include a chipped striking platform, unifacial implements worked to opposing faces, retouch on the nether face of flakes, and parallel flaking. All these characteristics occur in minor percentages.

Characteristics of the Folsom industry not amenable to percentage tabulations may be compared with the Clovis materials in general terms. The Folsom material is better made with greater emphasis on finer chipping. The implements are also smaller on the average. Greater control in both flaking and chipping is evident. There is a suggestion of a modified Levallois technique with flakes of a desired form for manufacture into specific artifact types, such as end-scrapers, being struck from the prepared core.

The predominant stone manufacturing technique consists of primary flakes struck from prepared cores with a cylinder hammer, being worked by flaking (with a cylinder hammer), and then retouched with pressure. Tools are of two major varieties listed in order of prevalence: unifacial, with only a portion of the perimeter of the upper face worked, and bifacial. The cores are deliberately prepared by the striking off of trimming flakes to remove the cortex prior to the removal of flakes to be made into implements. These trimming flakes were probably removed at the quarry as they are not found in the present collection. The striking platform was prepared in most cases by the removal of such a trimming flake so that the striking platforms on the flakes are of a plain unfaceted type. The other type of platform, the faceted type prepared by pressure chipping, which sometimes is dulled by grinding, is rare. The Folsom industry is based more

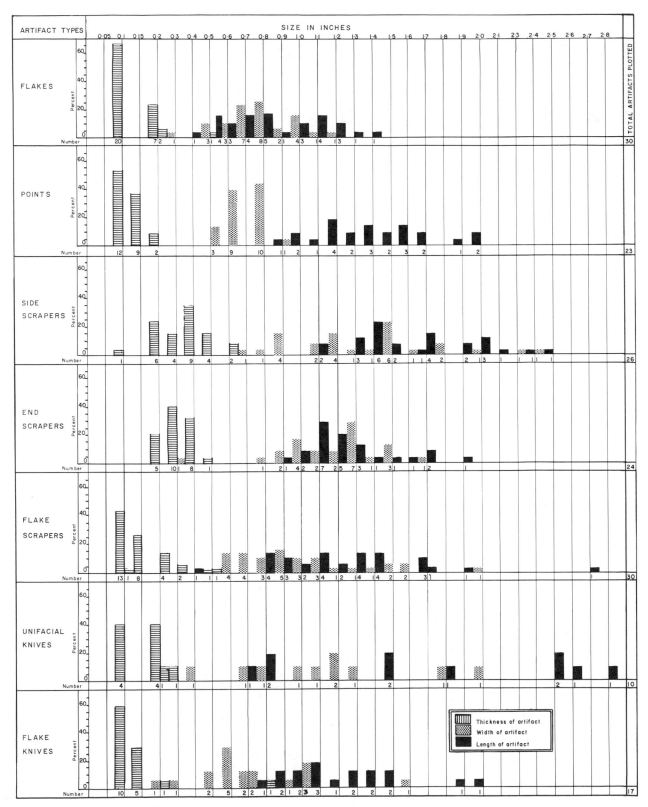

Fig. 106. Folsom artifacts by type and size.

specifically on flakes than is the Clovis industry. Average Folsom flakes range from 72% to 85% as wide as they are long with blades being almost nonexistent.

The types of stone utilized are the same as those used during Clovis times with the major change being a shift in preference. The favorite Folsom material was Edwards chert (61.5%) in contrast to the Clovis preference

for Alibates chert (Fig. 85). The reason for this change in preference is not apparent. Other stone types utilized include other chert (16.5%), Tecovas jasper (6.9%), Alibates chert (6.6%), quartzite (4.7%), Dakota quartzite (2.2%), jasper (0.7%), chalcedony (0.3%), sandstone (0.1%), and petrified wood (0.1%).

Folsom artifacts tend to be smaller than Clovis implements and cluster more tightly

Fig. 107. Details of Folsom chipping and flaking: a-1, secondary flakes; p-v, primary flakes; a-f, upper face shown; g-1, nether face shown; m-o, details of billet flake striking platforms; m, plain; n-o, prepared platform; p-q, typical billet flakes; r-s, stone struck flakes; t-v, flakes with bulb of percussion. a, W-186; b, W-30; c, W-397; d, W-318; e, W-276; f, 2-87; g, W-207; h, W-225; i, W-370; j, W-286; k, W-27; l, W-183; m, W-62; n, CO-79; o, 7; p, 2-41; q, F; r, CH-6; s, CH-9; t, W-355; u, 2-173; v, M-47.

Fig. 108. Folsom points, primarily from the 1962 excavations (Localities 4 and 5): a, K-5; b, W-142; c, W-7; d, W-129; e, W-108; f, CO-7; g, CO-6; h, W-4; i, W-122; j, K-2; k, W-121; l, W-6; m, W-55; n, 2-6; o, 1A; p, 5A; q, 2-3; r, W-144; s, M-74; t, 8A; u, W-109; v, W-143; w, K-1.

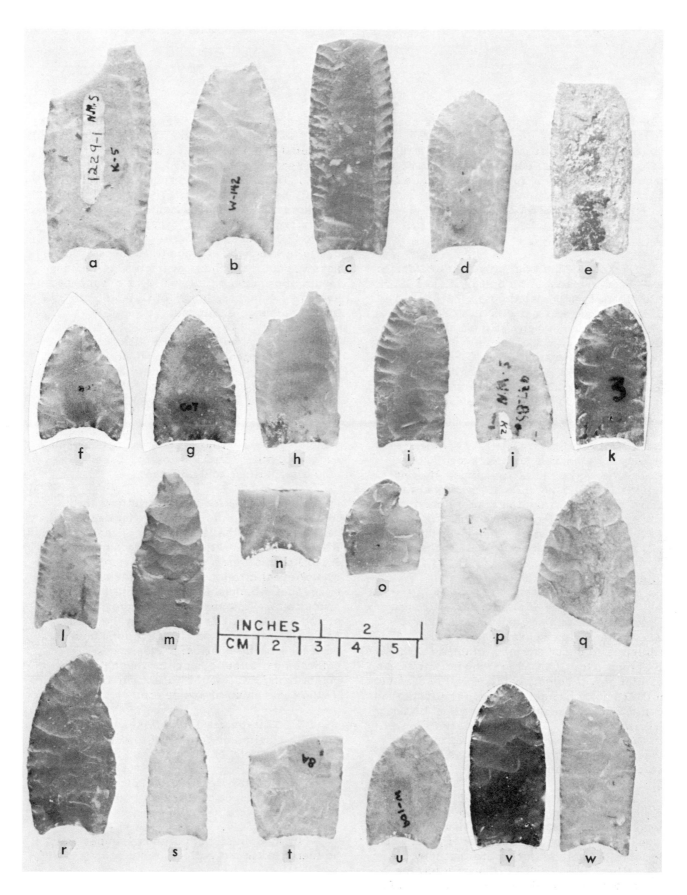

Fig. 109. Folsom points; illustrating opposite side of artifacts shown in Figure 108.

around the median measurements. It is possible this clustering is a result of the larger Folsom sample, but it is also probably a result of finer technological control. The size of these artifacts by type is plotted in Figure 106.

ARTIFACT TYPE DESCRIPTIONS

Flakes (234) (Fig. 107)

Flakes are the most prevalent artifacts in the Folsom industry. The primary flakes (81.1%) were struck from prepared cores (76.2%). A billet technique was used on 45% of the whole flakes and although many of the flakes are fragmentary (86%) 23.9% of these exhibit a cylinder hammer scar. Numerous flakes show evidence of use with 31.4% being used for cutting and 30.3% used for scraping. One inference derived from these data is that many flakes were deliberately struck off to be used as flakes. Minor attributes include bulb of percussion trimmed (7.5%), unifacially worked (17.3%), bifacially worked (1.2%), upper face worked (11.1%), nether face worked (6.6%), chipped striking platform (3.0%), and unifacially worked to opposing faces (2.6%). Size range: length 0.3 to 2.3 inches, average 0.95 inches; width 0.2 to 2.3 inches, average 0.77 inches; thickness 0.05 to 0.8 inches, average 0.15 inches.

Projectile Points (79) (Figs. 108, 109)

Folsom points are extremely well known to professional and amateur archaeologists alike. The basic emphasis in the present description is to document the variability within this group (Fig. 106). Too frequently it seems descriptions of Folsom points dwell excessively on their exotic characteristics. The result has been the development of a skewed public image of Folsom points. The present description will attempt to describe the typological range of these artifacts with little emphasis on the establishment of an abstract type.

Folsom points are presumably made from primary flakes struck from prepared cores, although evidence of this usually has been destroyed by the subsequent allover bifacial working. Major characteristics are that they are bifacially worked (100%) although a few are only retouched around the perimeter on one face, are pressure chipped (94.6%), possess a slight-

ly contracting stem (53.1%) and a concave base (78.2% in whole specimens, 60.7% in fragments), are fluted (65.4%), have ground edges on the sides near the base (84.4%), have basal grinding (65.3% in whole specimens, 39.2% in fragments), have basal thinning (86.9% in whole specimens, 58.9% in fragments), and may have the tip reworked (7.9%). Size range: length 1.0 to 2.0 inches, average 1.42 inches; width 0.6 to 0.8 inches, average 0.71 inches; thickness 0.1 to 0.2 inches, average 0.14 inches; length of grinding on sides 0.3 to 1.3 inches, average 0.8 inches; length of flutes 0.3 to 2.0 inches, average 0.9 inches.

It is apparent that while all of these attributes might appear in a "type" description, their incidence is variable by attribute. Conclusions to be drawn from this fact are that there existed a cultural norm typified by these attributes but that suitable projectile points which lacked some of these attributes were made and used. Minor attributes include an expanding stem, parallel flaking, basal thinning after fluting, and unfluted.

The reasons for these variations in the form of Folsom points cannot be determined here because of the limited size of the sample. It is assumed that study of a wide range of Folsom points from a number of different sites would reveal differences in manufacturing techniques which might be referable to differences in time and space. In the present sample, the opposite has been proven the case. Folsom points widely different in form have been found with identical provenience. Hypotheses as to the reasons for these disimilar points being made at the same time and place by the same group of people are:

1. Differences in the flakes utilized limited or controlled to some degree the form of the point.

2. The sample contains Folsom points representing different stages of manufacture.

In my opinion both of these causes may be identified in the collection studied.

Side-scrapers (36) (Fig. 110)

Side-scrapers are made from primary flakes (100%), struck from prepared cores (70.3%), which have been modified by pressure chipping (100%) along the edge to the upper face (94.4%). A sizable proportion (44.4%) has also been initially modified by percussion before the pressure retouch. The form of the side-scrapers tends to approximate that of the original flake with alterations being confined to the steepening of the edge. Elongate flakes with nearly parallel sides tended to be selected for manufacture into side-scrapers. Evidence of a billet technique is present on 25% of the specimens, and 22.2% have had the bulb of percussion trimmed, possibly to facilitate use or hafting of the scraper. Minor attributes include a slight degree of bifacial working (5.5%) and some modification from use (7.7%). Size range: length 0.9 to 2.5 inches, average 1.73 inches, width 0.7 to 2.4 inches, average 1.38 inches, thickness 0.1 to 0.7 inches, average 0.36 inches.

Flake Scrapers (67) (Fig. 111)

These artifacts differ from side-scrapers in being more casual in form although they are very similar in basic attributes. Presumably, their function was identical to that of side-scrapers. Flake scrapers have been differentiated from side-scrapers on the basis of less formal retouch along the edges and more modification by use. In many instances, no retouch is present and the artifact is in reality a utilized flake. Attributes include primary flake (97.0%), from a prepared core (83%), unifacially worked (92.6%), to the upper face (72.0%), by pressure chipping (54.4%), and modified by use (64.7%). Minor attributes are percussion flaked (7.3%), bifacially worked (8.8%), nether face worked (30.8%), billet technique (33.8%), and bulb of percussion trimmed (8.8%). Size range: length 0.5 to 2.8 inches, average 1.33 inches; width 0.5 to 2.0 inches, average 0.95 inches; thickness 0.1 to 0.5 inches, average 0.21 inches.

Hollow Edge Scrapers (3) (Fig. 112o-r)

Hollow edge scrapers occur in too small a frequency to permit percentage tabulation of attributes. The artifact type may be considered a variant of either a side-scraper or a flake scraper characterized by one hollow scraping edge. Form and cross-section are identical to those of the original flake. Attributes include primary flake from prepared core; unifacially worked to either the upper or lower face by pressure, percussion, or through use. Size range: length 1.6 to 1.7 inches, width 1.0 to 1.3 inches, thickness 0.3 to 0.5 inches.

End-scrapers (28) (Fig. 113)

A major category of Folsom implements is the end-scraper. These tools rank fifth in frequency and are typologically the most sensitive Folsom indicators after projectile points. End-scrapers typically have a triangular to tear-drop form with the working edge being the widest edge on the tool, normally the end opposite the bulb of percussion. A minor variant includes scrapers made of elongate flakes with parallel sides. In cross-section, the implements are either trapezoidal or triangular with steep edge angles. The thickest portion of the tool is normally near the working end. Typically, the end has an edge angle steeper than those of the sides. A secondary feature of typological importance is the presence of graver spurs on the perimeters. These spurs range from one to three in number and are normally located at the intersection of two edges. These spurs are present in the earlier Clovis end-scrapers but are much more common and more precisely formed on the Folsom specimens. It would appear from the consistent form of these artifacts that they were made from selected flakes. This form may be the result of a modified Levallois technique where the desired flake form was prepared on the core prior to being struck off. This inference is reinforced by the fact that most end-scrapers have the retouch confined to the edges. Major attributes are primary flakes (100%), from prepared core (92.9%), pressure chipped (100%), unifacially worked (100%), upper face worked (96.4%), percussion flaking (46.4%), bulb of percussion trimmed (28.5%), and billet technique (39.0%).

Minor attributes are bifacially worked, chipped striking platform, nether face worked, modified by use, stone struck, and worked to opposing edges. Tallies on the flake form (side or end flake) were not started at the beginning of the analysis. A tentative opinion on this point is that flakes selected were end flakes with a wide edge opposite the striking platform.

Fig. 110. Folsom side-scrapers: a, 19-A; b, 2-21; c, 2-20; d, 2-22; e, d-10; f, d-1;
g, 23a; h, 12A; i, 2-43; j, 2-18; k, CO-87; l, 28A.

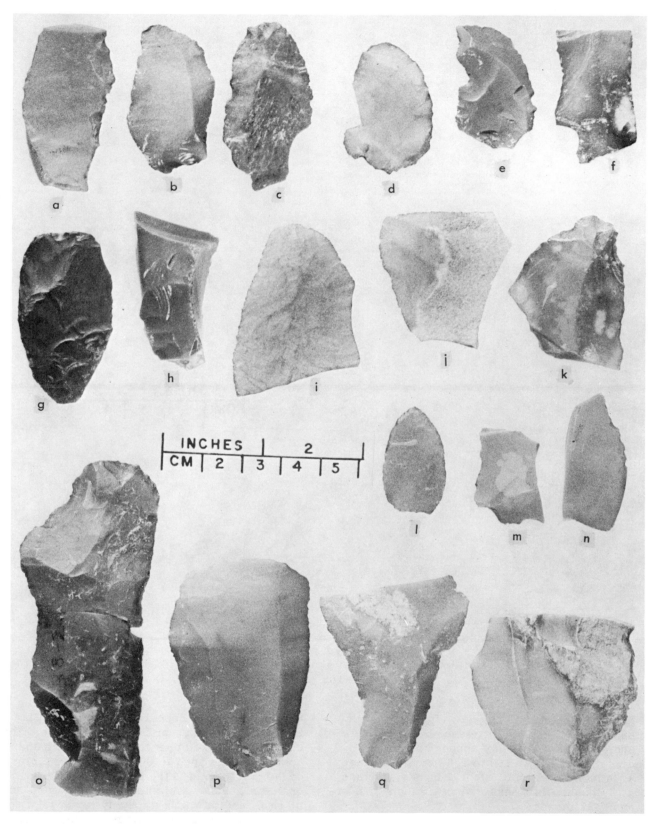

Fig. 111. Folsom flake scrapers: a, 24A; b, 2-68; c, 2-36; d, CO-76; e, 2-51; f, 2-54; g, 11; h, 2-34; i, 18A; j, 32A; k, 31A; l, CO-51; m, CO-36; n, 46A; o, W-5; p, 2-160; q, 2-157; r, 27A.

Fig. 112. Folsom artifacts of limited frequency: a-g, channel flakes; h-m, gravers; n, scraper-graver; o-r, hollow edge-scrapers. a, W-27; b, 2-90; c, W-24; d, W-21; e, W-202; f, 2-102; g, 2-102; h, 2-53; i, W-188; j, W-202; k, W-83; l, D-2; m, 2-105; n, 2-32; o, 4B; p, W-160; q, 53A; r, W-402.

As these implements have a width-length ratio approaching 1:1, the difference between side- and end-flakes does not appear meaningful. Size range: length 1.0 to 1.8 inches, average 1.36 inches; width 0.3 to 1.7 inches, average 1.17 inches; thickness 0.2 to 0.5 inches, average 0.32 inches.

Gravers (4) F (Fig. 112h-m)

Gravers are flakes, retouched by pressure, to form one or more small, sharp points at the intersection of arcs chipped into the edge. This chipping is to the upper face of the flake and normally is confined to the immediate vicinity of the graver point. The rest of the flake is unaltered. Flakes selected for gravers tend to be small and thin with a roughly rectangular outline. Use is problematical but may include the drilling of small holes, engraving of bone, tattooing, or the separation of fibers. Size range: length 1.1 inches, width 0.3 to 1.4

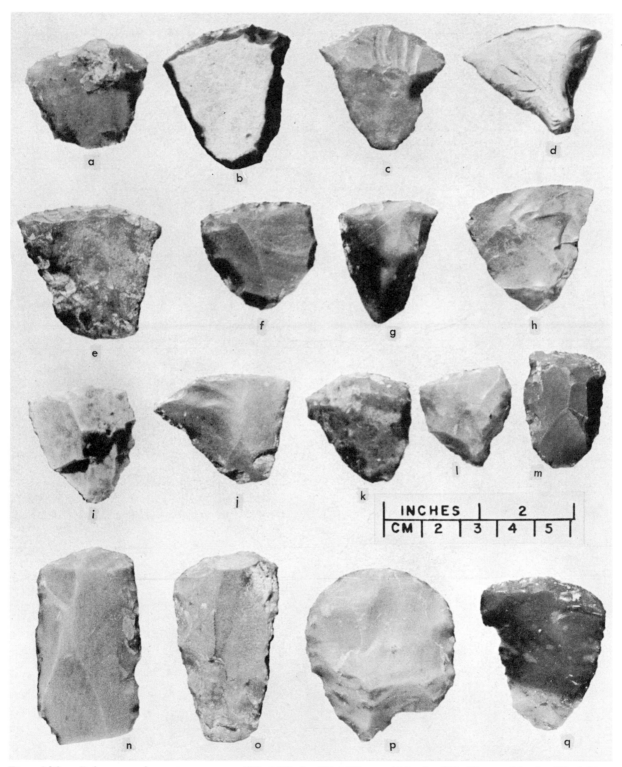

Fig. 113. Folsom end-scrapers: a, CO-106; b, W-178; c, 42A; d, CO-89; e, 9A; f, CO-100; g, 2-13; h, W-177; i, d4; j, 2-33; k, 41A; l, W-242; m, M-64; n, 5-1; o, 2-13; p, 1B; q, 2-14.

Fig. 114. Folsom knives: a–g, bifacial; h–m, unifacial. a, T; b, 2–25; c, CO–60; d, 2–24; e, W–162; f, CO–59; g, 2–169; h, CO–108; i, G–79; j, HA–1; k, 2–153; l, CH–14; m, CH–2.

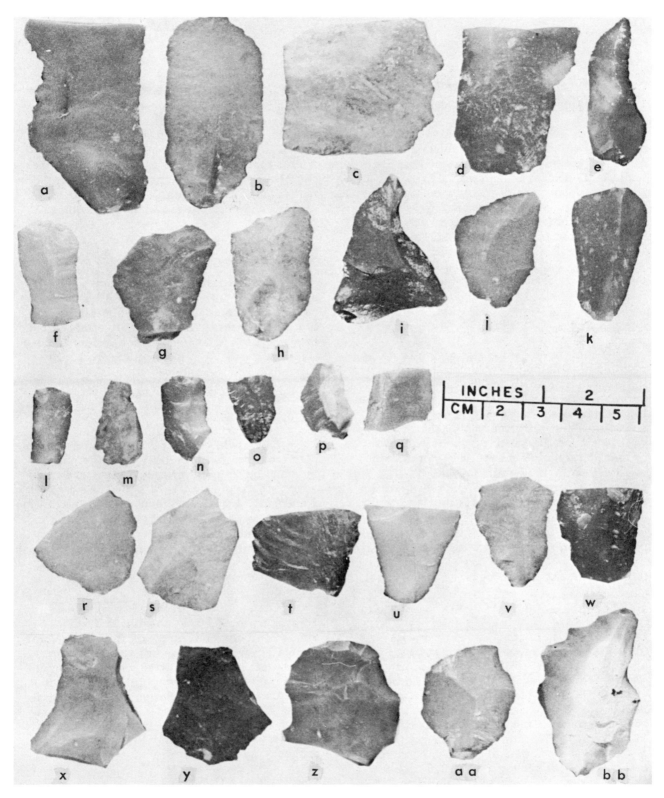

Fig. 115. Folsom artifacts: a-k, flake knives; l-bb, utilized flakes. a, M-46; b, 2-29; c, CO-61; d, 2-46; e, 2-39; f, 2-181; g, 2-45; h, 29A; i, 2-50; j, 2-77; k, 2-30; l, CO-40; m, CO-102; n, 57A; o, 59A; p, 47A; q, 38A; r, CO-84; s, 45A; t, P; u, CO-64; v, CO-94; w, CO-65; x, CO-20; y, CO-19; z, CO-66; aa, 6p; bb, CO-57.

inches, thickness 0.1 to 0.2 inches.

Unifacial Knives (13) (Fig. 114h-m)

Billet flakes altered by pressure chipping along the edge to the upper face were occasionally used as knives. In appearance, these implements are quite similar to flake scrapers. However, inspection of the working edge reveals the edge angle to be normally less than that of the scrapers. In addition, use marks normally occur on both faces. Size range: length 0.8 to 2.9 inches, average 1.91 inches; width 0.4 to 1.8 inches, average 1.15 inches; thickness 0.1 to 0.3 inches, average, 0.17 inches.

Bifacial Knives (14) (Fig. 114a-g)

Bifacial knives are distinctive in possessing bifacial flaking or chipping along the working edge, other attributes are similar to those of unifacial knives. As most of the specimens are fragmentary, it is not possible to describe adequately the form of these implements. Some are worked around the entire perimeter to a triangle or teardrop form; others are only worked along one long edge, the form being the result of the shape of the original flake. Another variant possesses allover flaking. It is possible that some of these implements are blanks for the manufacture of projectile points. The typical cross-section is lenticular. Size range: length 1.3 to 2.4 inches, width 0.8 to 1.2 inches, thickness 0.1 to 0.3 inches.

Flake Knives (23) (Fig. 115a-k)

Flake knives consist of primary flakes from prepared cores, utilized for cutting. Most of these flakes (95.6%) have bifacial use chips removed from the edge. Deliberate modification of these flakes is rare, either through percussion (8.8%) or pressure (8.8%). A high percentage have a cylinder hammer scar on the striking platform (60.8%). The form and cross-section of flake knives are identical to those of the original flake. Size range: length 0.8 to 2.0 inches, average 1.3 inches; width 0.3 to 0.6 inches, average 0.77 inches; thickness 0.1 to 0.9 inches, average 0.19 inches.

Scraper-Gravers (3) (Fig. 112n)

These implements consist of artifacts with a dual purpose. One or more edges have been modified by flaking and chipping to form a scraping edge. In addition, a graver point has been chipped on the edge. The implements are made from typical primary flakes struck from prepared cores. An unique aspect is that two of the three specimens are worked on the nether face. Size range: length 0.7 to 1.0 inches, width 1.1 to 1.5 inches, thickness 0.2 inches.

Scrapers (5)

These artifacts possess a scraping edge but are not of definite form. As a result, it is not possible to assign them to specific scraper types. As these artifacts are of variable form they add little to our knowledge except to document the presence of such variability. Size Range: 1.9 to 3.5 inches, width 1.6 to 2.7 inches, thickness 0.3 to 0.5 inches.

Choppers (1) (Fig. 116c)

The single chopper present consists of a core tool modified bifacially by stone percussion and by pressure to form a sinuous cutting edge. The implement is of large size (by Folsom standards) and a convenient size to hold in the hand. Use was presumably for the cutting of meat or other soft materials. Size: length 3.4 inches, width 2.3 inches, thickness 1.2 inches.

Cores (3) (Fig. 116)

Cores are rare in this assemblage of Folsom artifacts. One possibility is that, because of the local scarcity of stone, the cores were discarded at the quarry site. The cores present are bifacially flaked with percussion. In contrast to the numerous billet flakes, these cores do not exhibit negative bulbs indicative of use of a cylinder hammer. Some show use as hammerstones. Size (one measured): length 3.5 inches, width 2.7 inches, thickness 1.8 inches.

Hammerstones (2) (Fig. 116b,d)

Hammerstones are core tools with percussion flaked bifacial edges. They were probably used to strike flakes off cores. The

Fig. 116. Folsom core tools: a, core; b,d, hammerstones; c, chopper; e, abrader. a, 2-117; b, 2-112; c, 2-115; d, 2-116; e, 2-26.

use resulted in battering of the hammerstone edges. These artifacts are oval to round with an oval cross-section. Size (one measured): length 2.5 inches, width 1.5 inches, thickness 1.1 inches.

Channel Flakes (7) (Fig. 112a-g)

Flutes removed from the faces of Folsom points possess allover unifacial working on the upper face through a combination of both percussion flaking and pressure chipping. In form, the flakes are oval to boat shaped, and have a plano-convex cross-section. All may be considered as secondary flakes as they were struck from a prepared artifact. Several of the channel flakes show evidence of subsequent use in cutting and scraping. Size (one measured): length 0.9 inches, width 0.5 inches, thickness 0.1 inches.

Abraders (1) (Fig. 116e)

A small piece of fine grained tabular sandstone exhibits a number of short scratches on one face. It is presumed that this stone was used for the grinding of the edges of Folsom points. In form, the stone is roughly rectangular with a rectangular cross-section. Size: length 3.7 inches, width 2.9 inches, thickness 0.6 inches.

Other Artifacts

Present in the collection are several implements of different form. These artifacts include a jasper nodule, a quartzite pebble, a combination end- and side-scraper, and two unidentifiable (to type) projectile point fragments. These artifacts, while present, give little additional information about the Folsom Complex. Perhaps of most importance is the fact that end- and side-scrapers are more common in the preceding Clovis period.

Summary of Stone Artifacts

The Folsom assemblage at the Clovis site presents few artifacts not already known from other Folsom sites, notably Lindenmeier. Specific differences and similarities between this industry and others from this site will be discussed at the end of this section. The major emphasis in this section has been on document-ing the frequency of attribute occurrence by type.

BONE ARTIFACTS

Artifacts of bone are not common in this Folsom assemblage. A contributing factor may be the poorer preservation of bone in the Diatomite (as compared with the Clovis level, the Gray Sand). This poorer preservation is a fact as it is well demonstrated by the condition of the vertebrate specimens. Nonetheless, this low incidence of bone artifacts (0.7%) appears to be a reality. This statement is supported by the large sample at hand, 534 artifacts. Owing to the small sample of bone artifacts each will be discussed individually.

EL-41 Bone Tool (Figs. 98f, 100d)

A portion of split mammal bone has been altered by grinding the two edges to form a blunt point. The remainder of the implement is unmodified except for a few scratches along one edge. As both edges have been fractured, it is possible these scratches represent the remains of a former ground edge. The form of the tool is long and slim with a half round-triangular cross-section. Use of this implement could have been as a flaker or a punch. Size: length 4.9 inches (incomplete), width 0.9 inches (probably incomplete), thickness 0.5 inches, length of point 0.6 inches.

S - Bone Tool (Fig. 117)

This implement appears to be a split bison rib smoothed slightly on the cancellous side. Both edges show grinding and they converge at one end to a blunt point. The original length is unknown as the end opposite the point appears to be snapped off. The use of this implement is unknown--it could have been a spear point, a flesher, or a flaking tool. Size: length 4.8 inches (incomplete), width 1.4 inches, thickness 0.4 inches.

10 - Bone Tool (Fig. 117)

This artifact is a portion of a bison rib broken at its widest (possibly distal) end. The opposite end has been split for a short distance, which removed one half of the rib. The remaining portion of the split end has been ground on

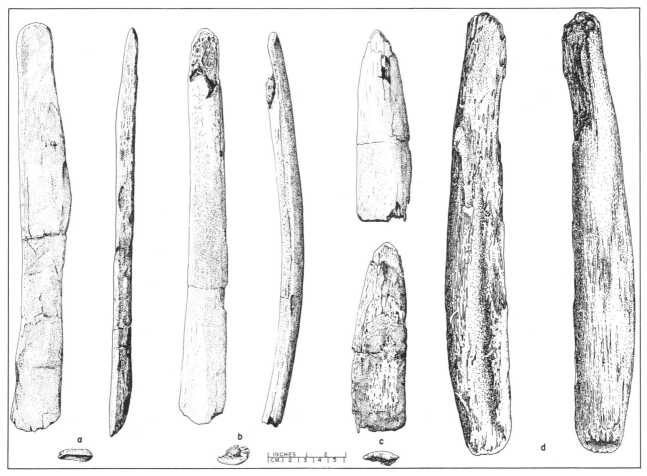

Fig. 117. Folsom and Clovis Age bone tools: b and c are of Folsom Age; a and d are from the Clovis level. a, K-13; b, 10; c, S; d, EL-89.

both edges to a blunt point. The function of this tool is uncertain but most probably it was used as a flaker. The implement retains the natural curvature of the rib it was made from. Size: length 10.0 inches, width 1.1 inches, thickness 0.5 inches.

LA 3324-8-Bone Ornament (Fig. 99b)

A portion of a bone disk ornamented with straight line incisions on one face was recovered. This small disk resembles superficially the engraved disks from the Lindenmeier site. Use was presumably as an ornament. It is especially interesting to note the similarities between this bone disk and those from Lindenmeier to similar artifacts from the Upper Paleolithic of the Old World. Schuster (1963) has noted the similarities between the Folsom speci-

mens and artifacts from the Brno II level in Czechoslovakia (24,000 B.C.), those from the Magdalenian culture of Western Europe (15,000-10,000 B.C.), and late paleolithic materials found near Krasnoyarsk in Southern Siberia. It is Schuster's opinion that such objects may be fertility symbols. In a recent article, Vertes (1965) reports a similar artifact made of lime-stone from the East Gravettian site at Bodrog-keresztur, Hungary. He interprets the edge grooves on this artifact as representing a lunar calendar, an upper Paleolithic culture trait first postulated by Marshack (1964). Size: length 0.6 inches (incomplete), width 0.3 inches (incomplete), thickness 0.2 inches.

Summary of Bone Artifacts

The four bone tools described above are

important primarily as evidence of the decline in the relative frequency of bone tools between Clovis (6.2%) and Folsom (0.7%) time. This decline in the use of bone tools is here interpreted as a lessening in importance of the Upper Paleolithic tradition because of increasing adaptation to the New World environment.

The form of these artifacts and their presumed uses are similar to those of the Clovis bone industry. They could have been used as flakers, projectile points, or ornaments. Slight differences in form (as compared with Clovis bone tools) are represented by the engraved disk (LA 3324-8) and the flat point (S).

Portales Complex

Unfortunately, artifacts assignable to the Portales Complex are too few to enable us to describe accurately the full range of the assemblage. This fact is the result of two factors: (1) The Portales use of the site seems to have been less extensive than that of the two earlier cultures. (2) Many of the excavations in the Portales horizon were carried out during the Texas Memorial Museum work between 1953-57, the period from which we have the least reliable provenience data.

If we only accept those artifacts with valid provenience data other than projectile points, our sample is limited to 49 specimens. The projectile point group alone is as large. As a result, although many points have no provenience, owing to their typological distinctiveness, they may be included in our study sample with justification. A list of the artifacts in this sample is as follows:

TABLE XXXVIII

PORTALES ARTIFACT FREQUENCIES BY TYPE

	No.	Percentage
Projectile points	50	50
Flakes	33	33
Bifacial knives	6	6
Scrapers	2	2
Side-scrapers	1	1
Flake scrapers	2	2
Flake scraper-knives	1	1
Scraper-gravers	1	1
Unifacial knives	1	1
Burin bec de flute	1	1
Grinding stones	1	1
Shell artifacts	1	1
Total	100	100

The scanty nature of our data makes it difficult to arrive at any general statements concerning the industry. It is apparent, however, that aspects of the assemblage, especially flaking techniques and some tool types, are derived from the Folsom tradition (Figs. 83, 84).

A specific problem concerns the assumed contemporaneity of the various distinctive projectile points as described by Sellards (1952, pp. 72-74). Of 50 points in the present sample, 25 have no provenience. The remaining 25 are identified to the geologic stratum from which they came as follows: Jointed Sand, (2), Carbonaceous Silt, (21), white sand under Carbonaceous Silt (2).

The specimens from the white sand are not typologically distinct, so are of no use in the present inquiry. The Jointed Sand is a fossil sand dune level; therefore, the specimens in this level may well be redeposited. The 21 specimens from the Carbonaceous Silt include the following named point types: Milnesand, Scottsbluff, Eden, Angostura, Plainview (?), and Portales. As these specimens form the basis of Sellards' definition of the "Portales Complex" we will examine their association with each other in some detail (Table XXXIX).

The association of these particular point types does not clearly, in my opinion, validate Sellards' definition of the "Portales Complex," as only eight of the above points have both a definite assigned type name and some provenience within the Carbonaceous Silt unit. The best association seems to be with the artifacts from the "upper bone bed" of Station E. If we may assume this occurrence to be the result of one bison kill, then we have established contemporaneity for Scottsbluff, Eden, and Milnesand points. As all these points were found within a radius of about 15 feet (Fig. 44), this assumption would seem to be tenable. The other named point types known from the Carbonaceous Silt, Angostura, Plainview, Agate Basin, and Portales, cannot be assigned temporal position on the basis of the evidence at hand.

TABLE XXXIX

PROVENIENCE OF ARTIFACTS USED BY SELLARDS
TO DEFINE THE "PORTALES COMPLEX"

CAT.NO.	POINT TYPE	LOCATION*	PROVENIENCE WITHIN CS MEMBER (Bed thickness ranges from 1 to 3 feet according to accession record)
937-5	Reworked	Station E	8 inches below top of unit
937-13	Milnesand	Station E	8 inches below top
937-16	Plainview?	Station E	Elevation not given
937-21	Scottsbluff	Station E	Upper bone bed
937-22	Milnesand	Station E	Elevation not given
937-23	Indefinite	Station E	Upper bone bed
937-24	Scottsbluff	Station E	Upper bone bed
937-26	Eden	Station E	Upper bone bed
937-31	Eden?	Station E	Upper bone bed
937-32	Milnesand	Station E	Upper bone bed--6 inches from top of unit
937-33	Indefinite	Station E	Upper bone bed
937-34	Scottsbluff	Station E	Elevation not given
937-62	Milnesand	Station E	Elevation not given
937-63	Angostura	Station E	Elevation not given
937-65	Indefinite	Station E	8 inches below top of unit
937-67	Eden	Station E	5 inches below top of unit
937-68	Scottsbluff	Station E	Elevation not given
937-75	Portales	Station B	3 inches below top of unit
937-79	Milnesand	Station E	Elevation not given
937-80	Scottsbluff	Station E	Elevation not given
937-17	Eden	Station E	Elevation not given

* For exact location of specimens see Figures 39 and 44.

The Carbonaceous Silt represents that portion of time between approximately 9,000 years B.P. and 6,000 years B.P. This interval possesses the cultural materials termed "Portales Complex" by Sellards (1952, pp. 72-74). As we have demonstrated above, many of the projectile points assigned to this complex cannot be given specific provenience within this 3,000 year interval. As these points differ rather widely in form, it is quite probable that they differ in age also. The conclusion we have reached here is that any assemblage of artifacts covering this amount of time and including such diverse forms should not be considered as a true "complex" unless we have strong stratigraphic and associated evidence that such is the case. In the present case, these specimens appear to represent a geological association within a stratigraphic unit rather than a true cultural assemblage. The eight specimens with the provenience of the "upper bone bed" probably represent a true complex of related forms in contemporaneous use. These specific forms include two, Eden and Scottsbluff, which commonly occur together in other sites (Finley, Horner, and Claypool) in association with a specific form of hafted knife, the Cody knife, and other artifacts. The entire assemblage has been termed the "Cody Complex" (Jepsen, 1951). As this term precedes Sellards' definition of the Portales complex, it seems to us best to abandon the term "Portales Complex"

and recognize that this designation included some artifacts referable to the Cody Complex and other artifacts both earlier and later in time. If this view is acceptable it is possible to add the Clovis gravel pit to the list of sites with a Cody complex occupation and proceed to a discussion of aspects of this complex at this site which differ from manifestations elsewhere.

The major distinctions of the Cody Complex at the Clovis site are (1) the absence of Cody knives and (2) the presence of Milnesand points. The meaning of these differences cannot be assessed at this time. It is possible that components of this "complex" have slightly different geographical distributions. One aspect of typological importance is the style of flaking on the Milnesand points. This is the type of flaking known as "collateral horizontal parallel flaking" (Dick and Mountain, 1960, p. 226). The fact that this is also the style of parallel flaking on the Eden and Scottsbluff points suggests that these flaking styles may have temporal significance. Throughout the remainder of this report the artifacts from the Carbonaceous Silt will be termed "Parallel Flaked" as a cultural designation. These artifacts typologically fit into this general artifactual horizon. However, owing to the stratigraphic inadequacies in our data it would be fallacious to attempt to define any complex. For the same reason no use is made of the term "Plano" (Jennings, 1955).

The other artifacts from the Carbonaceous Silt are not distinctive in form and most have no provenience identified within the geologic unit. Only two specimens, 937-19 and 937-20, may be assigned to the "upper bone bed" and hence contemporaneous with the Cody Complex projectile points. Both of these specimens are fragmentary sections of either projectile points or bifacial knives. Approximately twenty flakes are known from the white sand unit of the El Llano dig but unfortunately the only associated projectile point is aberrant in form and cannot readily be assigned to type.

In spite of these discrepancies and omissions in our data, it has been possible to quantify attribute frequencies on three artifact classes, projectile points, bifacial knives, and flakes. While these attribute tallies have little

Fig. 118. Archaic and Parallel Flaked Horizon points from Carbonaceous Silt: a-e, Archaic;
f-g, Portales Points; h, Meserve Point; i, Eden; j,m, Agate Basin; k, Plainview; l, Scottsbluff.
a, W-68; b, W-32; c, W-43; d, W-39; e, W-21; f, W-2; g, W-67; h, W-73; i, W-10;
j, W-146; k, M-26; l, M-3; m, M-25.

typological significance, it may help us describe general trends in tool manufacture during the interval between the end of the Folsom period and the beginning of the Archaic.

ARTIFACT TYPE DESCRIPTIONS

Projectile Points (50) (Fig. 118f-m)

Basically all of the points in this group fall into the category "parallel flaked"; how-ever, a wide diversity is apparent within the group as indicated by the numerous type names assigned. It seems sufficient here to list these type names and reference their type descriptions (Wormington, 1957, pp. 264-9). Named types include Scottsbluff, Eden, Angostura, Milnesand, Plainview, Meserve, Portales, and Agate Basin. Diversity within this group is also apparent in the attribute frequencies. While these frequencies have limited meaning, they are listed here for reference purposes. Tallies on attributes

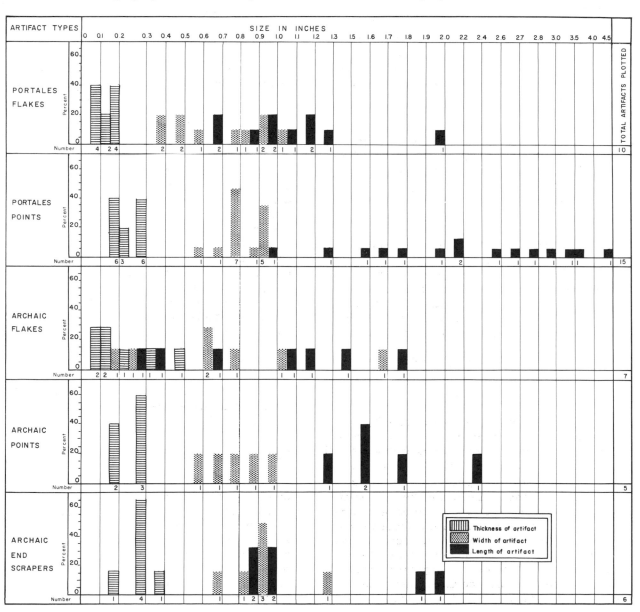

Fig. 119. Portales and Archaic artifacts by type and size.

are limited to 47 specimens as three specimens within blocks of matrix (937-17, 79, 80) were not available for attribute analysis.

The points presumably were manufactured from primary flakes struck from prepared cores; however, in most cases, evidence of this has been completely removed by subsequent working. Other attributes include pressure chipped (95.7%), bifacially worked (100%), straight base (57.8%), concave base (10.5%), parallel flaking (70.2%), grinding on sides (68.3%), base ground (52.2%), basal thinning (89.5%), shouldered stem (21.0%), contracting stem (15.7%), expanding stem (10.5%), and median ridge on blade (12.7%). As 21 specimens had the base missing, all attributes associated with the base are computed on the samples of whole specimens.

Minor attributes occurring with a frequency of less than 10% are percussion flaking, modified by use, fluted, tip reworked, serrated edges, impact flute at tip, impact break at tip, blade only, and tip only.

As compared with Clovis and Folsom points, the Parallel Flaked points are much more variable. Hypotheses which might explain this variability are (1) more time is represented by our sample, or (2) this was a period of greater experimentation in projectile point forms. A distribution of the size of these points is plotted in Figure 119. Size range: length 1.0 to 4.3 inches, width 0.6 to 1.0 inches, thickness 0.2 to 0.3 inches.

Bifacial Knives (6) (Fig. 120)

Bifacial knives are worked both by percussion and chipping of primary flakes struck from prepared cores. This working is either all over both faces or limited to the perimeter. It is possible that some specimens classified in this group represent blanks for the making of projectile points. No form preference is discernible. The specimens with allover working tend to be leaf shaped with a lenticular cross-section. Edge worked specimens are of similar form and section as the original primary flake. Size (1 whole specimen measured): length 3.1 inches, width 0.9 inches, thickness 0.4 inches.

Flakes (33)

Primary flakes from prepared cores account for 84.9% of the total number of flakes with secondary flakes representing the remaining 15.1%. A billet technique is apparent on 27.2% of the flakes. Compared with earlier flakes, a high percentage are used (66.6%). Another departure from earlier flake characteristics is the high proportion (30.3%) of stone struck flakes. Minor attributes are bulb trimmed, pressure chipped unifacially and bifacially, and nether face worked. The utilized flakes seem to have been primarily used for scraping. A graph of Portales flake sizes is presented in Figure 119. Size range: length 0.5 to 1.3 inches, average 0.9 inches; width 0.4 to 1.2 inches, average 0.8 inches; thickness 0.1 to 0.2 inches, average 0.15 inches.

Other Artifacts (4)

Artifacts other than those described above include forms of scrapers and knives known from the earlier cultures at the site. No apparent differences in the form or manufacture of these implements are discernible in the small sample at hand. An obvious lack is the absence of end-scrapers. This omission is curious as these implements are an integral part of the Cody Complex (Dick and Mountain, 1960, Fig. 8, SN-1-SN-7), which appears to be directly derived from the Folsom industry. It is assumed that absence of these implements at the Clovis site has no meaning, but is due to the small sample at hand.

Unique artifacts include a burin bec de flute, a grinding stone, and an artifact of mussel shell. These will be described separately.

937-300 Burin Bec de Flute (1)

This artifact is a small bifacially flaked core of teardrop form. The anterior-posterior cross-section is trapezoidal. The transverse section is a scalene triangle. There are two striking platforms on this implement with the secondary platform exhibiting scars from the removal of three burin spalls. The intersection of these spall scars forms a burin bec de flute. Presumably the implement functioned first as a core from which primary flakes were struck.

Fig. 120. Parallel Flaked Horizon artifacts: a-b, points; c, unifacial knife; d, flake scraper; e, flake knife; f, side-scraper; l, bifacial knife; g,h-u and w-z, flakes; v, end- and side-scraper. a, EL-133; b, EL-121; c, EL-128; d, EL-142; e, EL-130; f, EL-122; g, EL-135; h, EL-131; i, EL-127; j, EL-123; k, EL-126; l, EL-120; m, EL-124; n, 2-138; o, 2-143; p, 2-144; q, EL-141; r, EL-129; s, EL-125; t, EL-132; u, 2-145; v, EL-69; w, EL-136; x, EL-84; y, EL-137; z, 2-142.

After the core was exhausted for this purpose, it was then altered into a burin. The material is Edwards chert. Size: length 1.1 inches, width 0.8 inches, thickness 0.5 inches.

30/3211 Grinding Stone   (1)

This is a small piece of poorly consolidated sandstone. While fragmentary now, the original specimen may have been rectangular with a trapezoidal cross-section. Both faces show use and the edges appear to have been pecked into shape. The used surfaces differ, one being slightly concave along both axes (0.02 inches), the other slightly convex along both axes (0.04 inches). Size: length 2.4 inches, width 1.8 inches, thickness 0.5 to 0.8 inches. Illustrated in Dittert (1957, Fig. 3, No. 6).

EL-43 Shell Artifact   (1) (Fig. 103e)

A large fresh-water mussel shell, probably Anodonta cf. grandis Say, has been made into an artifact by the notching of the edge opposite the hinge. This edge is naturally sharp, and the artifact could have been used as a knife. When found, a portion of one end and approximately one half of the worked edge were missing. It is assumed that the artifact was broken during use and then discarded. Three notches are present on the remaining edge. This species of mussel inhabits quiet ponds with inlets and probably lived at the site. Paleontological identification by Robert J. Drake. Size: length 3.55 inches, width 2.2 inches, thickness 0.6 inches.

Stone Types Utilized

Stone types differ from those used earlier in preference of use of existing quarries. New quarries were not exploited to any degree (Fig. 86). Listed in order of frequency, the types are chert (26.0%), Edwards chert (25.0%), Alibates chert (22.9%), Tecovas jasper (10.4%), quartzite (5.2%), obsidian (3.0%) [a sizable difference from the earlier absence of obsidian], basalt (2.0%), Dakota quartzite (1.0%), jasper (1.0%), sandstone (1.0%), and shale (1.0%). In contrast to the Clovis and Folsom industries, no single quarry was favored; instead, four different stone sources were almost equally favored accounting for 85% of the total stone utilized.

Summary

Little is known about artifacts from the Parallel Flaked Horizon owing to the poor provenience on the specimens at hand. With this horizon producing the least known cultural assemblage of any horizon at the site, it seems to the author invalid to continue use of the term "Portales Complex." Instead, it has been demonstrated that within this assemblage, covering about 3,000 years, is to be found evidence of a "Cody Complex" occupation exhibiting some variation from other site collections of this complex. Earlier and later manifestations are also present but cannot be placed in exact chronological position because of inadequate provenience data.

Major manufacturing aspects are the continuation of techniques derived from the Folsom tradition plus the beginning of techniques which become dominant during the later Archaic period.

Archaic Complex

Artifacts assigned to the Archaic Complex have less valid provenience than the Paleo-Indian artifacts because of their method of deposition. The Archaic horizon is the Jointed Sand, a fossil sand dune deposit. Some artifacts within this layer are assumed to be secondarily deposited through the reworking of older deposits by wind. In at least two instances, this assumption is verified by the presence of parallel flaked points. However, the majority of the artifacts from this zone may be assigned to the Archaic Complex on the basis of the associated projectile points. The sample of artifacts is small and limited in types represented. As a result, it is not possible to describe a cultural complex. We can describe the artifacts present and draw some conclusions as to the changes that occurred between the Paleo-Indian and the Archaic horizons. The Archaic period was a time of aridity with reduced surface water, characterized by a more desertic flora and fauna than that present earlier. This environmental change was accompanied by a switch from a predominantly big game hunting economy to one of wild plant gathering and the hunting of small animals. This change is reflected in the artifacts. In addition, another cultural adaptation to this environmental change has been identified, the presence of hand-dug wells.

ARTIFACT TYPE DESCRIPTIONS

The 81 stone artifacts are limited to three types well enough represented to permit type descriptions; points, flakes, and end-scrapers. All other specimens are limited to one or two examples of each form. A list of these artifacts is given below.

While this group of artifacts does not constitute a total cultural assemblage, it does represent 11 of the types described for the Paleo-Indian tradition plus the addition of one new type, a hematite paintstone. Analysis of this material will be based on a comparison with the similar Paleo-Indian types. Similarities and differences will give us some idea of the degree of continuity and change between the Archaic Complex and its Paleo-Indian antecedents. Sufficient specimens were available to permit the plotting of size distribution of

TABLE XL

ARCHAIC ARTIFACT FREQUENCIES BY TYPE

Type (whole specimens plus fragments)	No.	Percentage
Projectile points	19	23.7
Flakes	40	50.0
Bifacial knives	1	1.2
Scrapers	3	3.6
Side-scrapers	1	1.2
End-scrapers	8	10.0
Flake scrapers	1	1.2
Scraper-gravers	2	2.4
Cores	1	1.2
Gravers	2	2.4
Paintstones	1	1.2
Hammerstones	2	2.4
Total	81	100.5

the flakes, points, and end-scrapers (Fig. 119).

Flakes (40)

The 8 primary flakes and 32 secondary flakes are distinguished by their small size. Otherwise they are similar to those from the Paleo-Indian levels. Attributes include prepared core (87.5%), partially prepared core (5.8%), bulb of percussion trimmed (2.5%), billet technique (25.0%), pressure chipped (2.5%), unifacially worked (5.0%), upper face worked (2.5%), nether face worked (2.5%), and modified by use (2.5%). Size range: length 0.3 to 1.2 inches, width 0.2 to 1.0 inches, thickness 0.1 to 0.4 inches.

Projectile Points (19) (Fig. 118a-e)

Typical projectile points include a variety of stemmed forms with a triangular blade. The change to these forms from the long parallel flaked varieties of the preceding period is the most striking change evident in the Archaic artifacts. While functional interpretations are fraught with pitfalls, this change is of such magnitude that we infer a change in the fauna hunted, with the major game perhaps being antelope or smaller animals rather than bison. Attributes include prepared core (79.0%), unifacially worked (5.2%), bifacially worked (94.8%), expanding stem (31.0%) shouldered stem (21.0%), contracting stem (26.1%), side notched (5.2%), straight base (26.0%), convex base (5.2%), concave base (31.0%), parallel flaking (31.0%), ground edges (15.5%), ground base (15.5%), basal thinning (10.3%), points on perimeter (5.2%), and serrate edges (5.2%).

As evidenced by the attributes above, the projectile points are quite variable in form. Reference to the Handbook of Texas Archeology reveals that most of these points may be referred to the Edwards Plateau Aspect of the Archaic Stage which has a time range of 4,000 B.C. to 1,000 A.D. Individual specimens are assigned as follows (all references are in Suhm, Krieger, and Jelks, 1954):

937-2   Darl Point 1-1000 AD (p. 414, Pl. 86s)
937-423   Pandale Point 2000 BC - 800 AD (p. 464,
              Pl. 111m)
937-425   Pedernales Point 4000 BC - 1000 AD
              (P. 468, Pl. 114 1)
937-429   Travis Point 4000 BC - 1000 BC
              (p. 484, Pl. 212 dd)
937-428   Williams Point 4000 BC - 1000 AD
              (p. 490, Pl. 124 1)

One exception is the Pandale Point which may be assigned to the Pecos River Focus. The temporal position is the same. Size range: length 1.4 to 3.4 inches, width 0.8 to 1.4 inches, thickness 0.1 to 0.3 inches.

End-scrapers (8)

End-scrapers continue the tradition established in Clovis times. The scrapers are made from thick plano-convex to trapezoidal (in section) primary flakes struck from prepared cores. Retouch is by pressure around 1/2 to 7/8ths of the perimeter to the upper face forming a working edge of 50° to 80° on the end opposite the bulb of percussion. In form the scrapers are more variable than their Paleo-Indian predecessors ranging from trapezoidal to almost round. A major difference is that the graver spurs common to the Paleo-Indian end scrapers are much less pronounced. Other attributes include the trimming of the bulb of percussion. Size range: length 0.9 to 2.0 inches, width 0.9 to 1.0 inches, thickness 0.3 to 0.4 inches.

Scraper-gravers (2)

These artifacts are also made on primary flakes from prepared cores. Working is limited to pressure retouch along two edges to the upper face. This retouch has produced both a scraping edge and one or two graver points. One specimen has limited chipping on the nether face to thin the flake. In plan, the artifacts are roughly rectangular. Cross-sections are triangular. Size range: length 0.9 to 1.1 inches, width 0.7 to 0.8 inches, thickness 0.2 inches.

Gravers (2)

This artifact is made from a small secondary billet flake. It is hexagonal in plan and plano-convex in the transverse cross-section and rectangular in the anterior-posterior section. It has been modified on one end by chipping to the upper face to form two converging hollow arcs terminating in the graver point. Size: length 1.2 inches, width 0.8 inches, thickness 0.2 inches, length of point 0.3 inches.

Scrapers (3)

This group of artifacts is quite variable with no type being discernible. They consist of primary flakes modified by flaking and chipping to the upper face to form a scraping edge. In form they tend to be ovoid with a plano-convex cross-section. Two specimens show thinning of the flake on the nether face. Size range: length 1.2 to 2.7 inches, width 0.9 to 1.5 inches, thickness 0.1 to 0.6 inches.

Hammerstones (2)

The hammerstones are of two forms. Both are river pebbles; but one has been modified by flaking on one end. The other hammerstone has been modified by use on both sides. These artifacts are oval in form and oval in cross-section. Size: length 3.1 and 3.9 inches, width 1.8 inches, thickness 1.0 and 1.4 inches.

Paintstones (1)

A small piece of hematite was ground on all sides and edges. The resultant artifact is triangular in form with a rectangular cross-section. Presumably, the grinding was performed to obtain paint. The source of the stone is unknown. Size: length 1.0 inches, width 0.7 inches, thickness 0.3 inches.

Other Artifacts

Additional artifacts represented by one specimen each include a bifacial knife fragment, a core, a side-scraper, and a flake scraper. As these specimens are only faintly indicative of artifactual "types," they will not be described in detail here. Reference to type descriptions of the Edwards Plateau Aspect should help us infer the nature of the additional artifact types which might have been represented at the site (Suhm, Krieger, and Jelks 1954, pp. 102-111).

Stone Types Utilized

Stone types are indicative of some change in preference of quarries utilized. Differences between the Archaic stone and the preceding Parallel Flaked Horizon is the addition of three new stone types and the absence of one used earlier. The major stone types are the same in both periods with some differences in frequency (Fig. 85). The greatest change is a reduction in the use of Tecovas jasper and an increase in the use of quartzite and Edwards chert. One possible meaning of these changes could be wider utilization of stone resources of the region. Stone types in order of preference are Edwards chert (39.9%), chert (17.2%), quartzite (13.5%), jasper (8.6%), Alibates chert (11.1%), and Dakota quartzite (4.9%). Tecovas jasper, chalcedony, basalt, obsidian, hematite, and quartzitic sandstone are represented by one specimen (1.2%) each.

Summary

The Archaic culture period is poorly represented at the gravel pit. The occupation coincided with a period of aridity marked by drying up of surface water and the formation of sand dunes. The prehistoric inhabitants adjusted to this habitat through the digging of wells to obtain water and a shift in the basic economy. Unfortunately, wind erosion and the subsequent formation of the sand dunes served to obliterate much of the evidence of occupation. The artifactual assemblage continues some of the Paleo-Indian stone working traditions with minor modifications. Ground stone tools indicative of a gathering economy, while known elsewhere for this period, unfortunately were not recovered. However, identification of the culture stage represented, the Edwards Plateau Aspect, permits a greater understanding of the culture during this period.

The Neo-American Period

The presence of a few late artifacts such as Harrell Points documents a late occupation of the site. No additional artifacts are known for this period. Although these points are few in number suggesting a very limited occupation, it is evident that the site was occupied at least intermittently during the Neo-American period.

Artifacts With Unknown Provenience

A number of artifacts from the gravel pit dumps could not be definitely assigned to a cultural period. These artifacts (136 in number) have been analyzed in the same fashion as the known specimens. The resultant tallies of artifact types represented, attribute frequencies, and stone type frequencies (Figs. 83, 84, 85) suggest that this group is predominantly of Folsom age with slight admixture (perhaps 10%) of artifacts from the Parallel Flaked Horizon. This evidence corroborates the evidence from the in situ sample that the Folsom culture was the major occupation of the site. While the information gained from this sample is not great, several artifacts (Fig. 121) represent types or variants not present in the identified series. Although we do not know their cultural affiliation, these artifacts are illustrated in order to further document the variety in Paleo-Indian artifacts.

Fig. 121. Unusual artifacts from the Dump, exact age unknown: a-b, gravers; c, Neo-American point; d-f,m, end-scrapers; g, side-scraper; h-i, hollow edge-scrapers; j-k,n, bifacial knives; l, burin; o, unifacial knife. a, W-120; b, W-11; c, W-126; d, M-16; e, W-134; f, W-15; g, 8; h, W-42; i, W-63; j, M-10; k, W-36; l, M-7; m, W-65; n, W-13; o, M-4.

Comparison of Artifact Assemblages

Differences between the various artifact assemblages are apparent. While these differences do not negate the fact that these assemblages belong to the same tradition, they are of sufficient magnitude to enable us to describe patterns of change. The patterns described here have been outlined in the preceding section. In this portion, we will attempt to describe changes in manufacturing techniques through time. A graphic presentation of these changes as reflected in attribute frequencies is presented in Figure 84. Exact comparison of attribute percentages is not valid, however, as the composition of each cultural assemblage is different. On the other hand, we know the nature of this skewing of the data and, therefore, can correct for it to some degree. In general, the trait attributes are seen as increasing in frequency through time, decreasing, or variable with no trend apparent. Attributes are listed by these trends as follows (Table XLI).

Perhaps the major importance of the above list is that it gives us an understanding of which attributes diminish through time and which increase. The primary reason for these changes is assumed to be an increasing adaptation to the environment. These changes through time are also indicative of techniques emphasizing finer control of flaking and chipping (with the exception of the Archaic), reduction in size of artifacts, and greater reliance on stone tools with a corresponding decrease in bone tools. Presumably, during this same time period, the functions of the artifacts remained constant. The new tool types introduced suggest an increasing variety in the economy.

TABLE XLI

CHANGES IN ATTRIBUTE FREQUENCY THROUGH TIME

Increasing	Decreasing	Variable
Core tools	Primary flakes	Secondary flakes
Pressure chipped	Bulb trimmed	Prepared core
Bifacially worked	Billet technique	
Contracting stem	Percussion flaked	
Concave base	Unifacially worked	
Expanding stem	Upper face worked	
Stone struck	Nether face worked	
	Modified by use	
	Fluted	
	Utilized flakes	

Peak in Clovis Period	Peak in Folsom Period	Peak in Parallel Flaked Period	Peak in Archaic Period
Primary flakes	Grinding on sides	Base ground	Shouldered stem
Bulb trimmed	Faceted platform	Basal thinning	Secondary flakes
Billet technique	Worked to opposing faces	Stone struck	Prepared core
Unifacially worked	Modified by use	Median ridge on blade	Expanding stem
Upper face worked		Parallel flaking	
Nether face worked		Straight base	
		Convex base	
		Serrated edges	
		Pressure chipped	

VERTEBRATE REMAINS FROM THE GRAY SAND

by Ernest L. Lundelius, Jr.

Introduction

The early man site in Blackwater Draw near Portales, New Mexico, is one of the most interesting and important sites in North America. The stratified deposits and abundant faunal material provide information on the faunal and climatic changes during part of late and post Pleistocene time.

This report is concerned with the vertebrate faunal material of the Gray Sand unit at the gravel pit. This is the oldest late-Pleistocene unit with abundant vertebrate fossils. It is overlain by a Diatomite with fossil material, and underlain by a coarse Red Gravel which has yielded little fossil material to date.

Early work on the fauna of this site was done by Stock and Bode (1937) who reported most of the species discussed here. Unfortunately, it is difficult to equate their stratigraphic units with those of Evans (1951). Only those specimens with provenience considered valid as a result of Hester's inquiries and checking of records are described herein.

The vertebrate fauna of the Gray Sand, the basal fossiliferous unit at the Portales, N.M., site, consists of Terrapene canaliculata, Aenocyon dirus, Canis lupis, Canis latrans, Vulpes velox, Smilodon californicus, Ondatra zibethica, Platygonus sp., Camelops sp., Tanupolama macrocephala, an antilocaprid, Bison antiquus, three species of equids, and Mammuthus sp.

Three of the skeletons of Mammuthus are semi-articulated and are intimately associated with flint implements. The animals were victims of human predation and were butchered on the spot without being dismembered. The remains of other potential human food animals are much more scattered, indicating more complete dismemberment during butchering.

The number of extinct species indicates an age in excess of 8,000 years B.P. The absence of gigantic bison indicates an age younger than Sangamon.

Ondatra zibethica and Terrapene canaliculata indicate the presence of permanent water and some wooded areas. This would demand more rainfall than at present and probably indicates a more even distribution of precipitation throughout the year.

Systematic Descriptions

Class REPTILIA

Order CHELONIA

Terrapene canaliculata Hay

Material: A skull (TMM 937-158); portion of the left side of carapace with bridge and anterior part of the posterior lobe of the plastron (TMM 937-206); an anterior lobe of the plastron and fragments of the carapace (TMM 937-899) and many isolated fragments of the shell.

Remarks: The skull is well preserved. Aside from size it shows few differences from the skull of its living near relative T. carolina. The braincase is less inflated, and the various ridges and processes marking areas of muscle attachment are more pronounced. These differences are probably a result of the difference

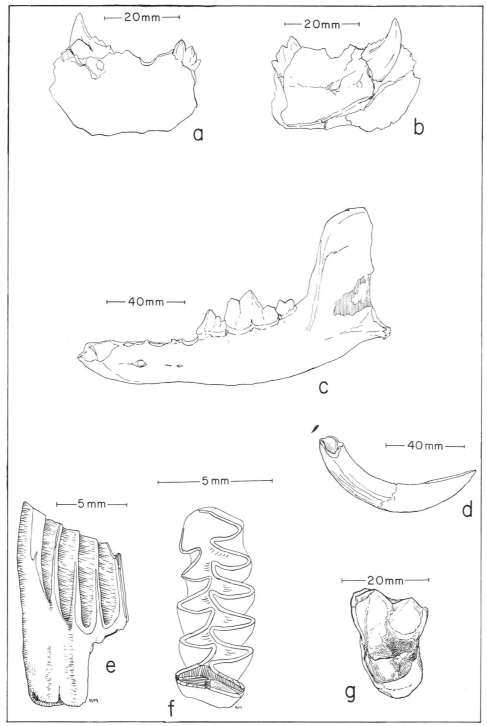

Fig. 122. Vertebrate remains from the Gray Sand: A–Medial view of mandible of juvenile _Smilodon californicus_ TMM 937-159; B–Lateral view of mandible of juvenile _Smilodon califor-nicus_ TMM 937-159; C–Lateral view of mandible of _Canis lupus_ TMM 937-895; D–Lower canine of _Platygonus_ sp. TMM 937-902; E–Medial view of M_1 of _Ondatra zibithecus_ TMM 937-162; F–Occlusal view of M_1 of _Ondatra zibithecus_ TMM 937-162; G–Occlusal view of M^1 of _Canis lupus_ TMM 937-885.

in size. The basal length of the skull is 46.2 mm., width across the quadrates 27.7 mm. This compares with width across the quadrates of 28.0 mm. of a specimen from Ingleside, Texas.

A comparison of the carapace and plastral material with material from Friesenhahn cave and Ingleside shows no differences. The width of the posterior lobe of the plastron is approximately 114 mm. which is within the range of variation given by Milstead (1956) for Terrapene canaliculata from Friesenhahn Cave.

Stock and Bode (1937) reported T. ornata from a "blue sand" unit in Anderson Basin, a few miles from the Sanders Gravel Pit. It is presumably associated with extinct late Pleistocene species. No trace of this species has been found in the Gray Sand. If it is associated with the extinct Pleistocene fauna, it is from some unit above the Gray Sand.

Reworked Turtle Material

There is a fragment of very thick turtle carapace from the Gray Sand that represents a turtle much larger than Terrapene and is probably referable to Testudo. This fragment is much more heavily mineralized and differently colored than any of the other bone material from the Gray Sand. It is the author's opinion that this fragment has been eroded from an older deposit and redeposited in the Gray Sand. For this reason it has not been considered in the ecological interpretation. Green (personal communication to Warnica, 1966) has also suggested that some of the bones from the Gray Sand have been reworked. This is discussed further in the section on the interpretation of the fauna. [An almost complete carapace of a very large turtle, probably Testudo, was found in the Red Gravel in 1960 just below the water table at that time. The specimen was badly damaged in removal but a photo taken by Gordon Greaves shows the specimen in situ, and there is no doubt of the validity of the find. The specimen is in the possession of J.D. Murray of Portales.]

Class MAMMALIA

Order CARNIVORA

Aenocyon dirus (Leidy)

Material: Anterior edge of right P^4 (TMM 937-884).

Remarks: Although the material is scanty there seems to be no doubt about its identity. The specimen is much larger than the corresponding tooth of Canis lupus. Comparison with Aenocyon dirus material from San Patricio County, Texas, shows no differences. [The Canis dirus jaw recovered by Green and Wendorf and identified by Green is referred to the same genus and species (Aenocyon dirus).]

Canis lupus Linnaeus

Material: left M^1 (TMM 937-885); left mandible with P_4-M_2 (TMM 937-895) (Fig. 122c, g).

Remarks: There is no doubt about the assignment of this material to Canis lupus. It is too small to be Aenocyon dirus and too large to be Canis latrans. The size of the teeth is within the range given by Young and Goldman (1944) for a large series of Canis lupus from North America. The horizontal ramus of the mandible is slightly less massive than a specimen from Michigan, but the Blackwater Draw specimen is a young adult and the Michigan specimen is an old adult. The difference could be due to age. Tooth measurements are P^4, length 15.5 mm., width 8.2 mm.; M_1, length 27.9 mm., width 10.9 mm.; M_2, length 10.4 mm., width 8.2 mm.

Canis latrans Say

Material: A right M_1 (TMM 937-896); a left lower canine (TMM 937-897).

Remarks: Neither the canine nor the M_1 can be separated from the corresponding teeth of Recent coyotes. The dimensions of the canine are anteroposterior length at the base of the enamel 10.0 mm.; width at base of the enamel, 6.4mm. The measurements of the M_1 are length 23.7 mm.; width at protoconid, 8.0 mm.; width of talonid 8.2 mm.

Vulpes velox (Say)

Material: Left mandibular fragment with P_3 (TMM 937-898).

Remarks: This specimen is referred to Vulpes velox on the basis of the structure of P_3. An examination of a number of specimens of Urocyon cinereoargenteus and Vulpes velox shows that the latter species has the more complicated premolars. The posterior edge of the main cusp and the anterior and posterior cingula are better developed. In addition all specimens of Vulpes velox which were examined have a distinct cuspule on the posterior cingulum. None of the specimens of Urocyon cineroargenteus and Vulpes velox shows that the latter species has the more complicated premolars. The posterior edge of the main cusp and the anterior and posterior cingula are better developed. In addition all specimens of Vulpes velox which were examined have a distinct cuspule on the posterior cingulum. None of the specimens of Urocyon cineroargenteus showed this cuspule. The Blackwater Draw specimen is too small and lightly built to be Vulpes fulva. The length of the P_3 is 7.5 mm. which is within, but at the higher end of, the range of size of a Recent sample of Vulpes macrotis.

Smilodon californicus Bovard

Material: Anterior portion of right mandible with deciduous canine and dP_3 (TMM 937-159) (Fig. 122a, b).

Remarks: The mandible is from a very young individual. The deciduous canine and dP_3 are not completely erupted. This is the only evidence of this species in the Gray Sand. The specimen has been compared with several very young specimens of Dinobastis serus from Friesenhahn Cave, Texas, and with figures of Smilodon californicus and Felis atrox given by Merriam and Stock (1932). The dP_3 in Dinobastis and Smilodon and the Blackwater Draw specimen are very similar. The deciduous canines show some differences. In Dinobastis it has a small cuspule on the anterior edge, while in Smilodon it has one on the medial side. Such a cuspule is reported by Merriam and Stock (1932) to be entirely lacking in Felis atrox. The specimen from Blackwater Draw has a cuspule on the medial side. The posterior edge of the deciduous canine is extended near the base and bears three small tubercules.

This is probably one of the more recent specimens of Smilodon known. Hester (1960) gives the most recent known data of Smilodon as about 14,000 years B.P. This may prove to be somewhat younger and is interesting in that it indicates that the species was widespread during the last few thousand years of its existence.

Order RODENTIA

Ondatra zibethica (Linnaeus)

Material: A mandible with molars missing (TMM 937-160); left M_1 (TMM 937-162) (Fig. 122e, f).

Remarks: The M_1 shows the six triangles between the anterior and posterior loops. The anterior edge of the anterior loop is a smooth triangle with a rounded apex and lateral angles which are not markedly turned backwards. In this character it resembles the M_1's from late Pleistocene deposits near Lubbock more than Pleistocene material from Florida or Recent material from Ohio or Alabama. The Blackwater Draw site is well out of the Recent range of this species which is an inhabitant of streams, ponds, and marshes with open water. Its presence at Blackwater Draw and other late Pleistocene sites on the High Plains indicates more water and more permanent bodies of water at that time than at present. This almost certainly indicates increased rainfall and probably lower temperatures during the late Pleistocene.

Order ARTIODACTYLA

Platygonus sp.

Material: Two lower canines (TMM 937-902, 903) and an M_3 (TMM 937-200) (Figs. 122d, 123f).

Remarks: The material available is insufficient to allow a positive specific identification. The dimensions of the M_3 are length 22.9 mm., anterior width 14.0 mm., and posterior width 12.8 mm. These measurements all fall within the observed ranges for a sample given by Simpson (1949) of P. compressus.

Camelops sp.

Material: A left M^1 and M^2 (TMM 937-737, 736); right M_1 and M_2 (TMM 937-736A,

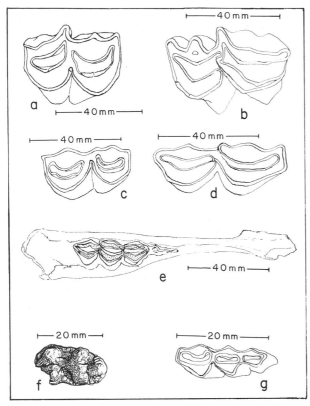

Fig. 123. Vertebrate remains from the
Gray Sand.

736B); a proximal phalanx (TMM 937-904); and
left M$_3$ (TMM 937-644) (Fig. 123a,b,c,d).

Remarks: It is probable that the teeth
are from the same individual. They apparently
were found in close proximity, and the facets
between the M^1 and M^2 and M$_1$ and M$_2$ fit very
closely. The teeth are very large and conform
to the size given by Merriam (1913), Hay (1913B),
and Lull (1921) for various specimens of C.
hesternus and C. huerfanensis. However, the
material is inadequate to permit a closer identification. The tooth measurements are given in
Table XLII; the phalanx is too badly broken to
measure reliably, but its assignment to Camelops
is certain.

TABLE XLII

TOOTH MEASUREMENTS OF CAMELOPS sp. (mm.)

	TMM 937-737 M^1	TMM 937-736 M^2	TMM 937-736A M$_1$	TMM 937-736B M$_2$	TMM 937-644 M$_3$
Length	43.9	52.9	39.5	52.2	57.7
Anterior Width	22.9	26.8	14.9	19.4	20.6
Posterior Width	24.8	25.3	18.9	17.9	18.5
W. Posterior Loop	----	----	----	----	11.5

Tanupolama macrocephala (Cope)

Material: Mandible with P$_4$-M$_3$ (TMM
937-874); mandible with M$_{1-3}$ (TMM 937-900);
juvenile mandible with dP$_4$ (TMM 937-901)
(Figs. 123e, 125d).

Remarks: The material from Blackwater
Draw resembles the Tanupolama material from
Rancho La Brea called T. stevensi by Stock
(1928). Hibbard and Dalquest (1962) have
shown that T. stevensi is probably the same as
T. macrocephala (Cope).

A P$_3$ is present but is single rooted. This
tooth is present in some but not all the Rancho
La Brea material. The P$_4$ is similar to the other
material referred to T. macrocephala by Hibbard
and Dalquest (1962) in that the anterior portion
is narrow and, although the tooth is deeply worn,
apparently lacked folds on the anterior part of
the tooth. These characters all distinguish it
from T. mirifica which has a two rooted P$_3$ and
a P$_4$ with folds on the anterior lobe. Unfortunately, not enough of the anterior part of the
jaw is preserved to determine the distance between P$_1$ and P$_4$. This is relatively short (55
to 66 mm.) in T. macrocephala and relatively
long (81 to 99 mm.) in T. mirifica. The M$_1$ of
TMM 937-900 has a small median external
pillar. This is uncommon in Tanupolama although a few specimens from Ingleside, Texas,
show one.

Table XLIII gives dental measurements of
the adult specimens. The measurements of the
dP$_4$ of TMM 937-901 are   length 32.6 mm.,
anterior width 9.0 mm., mid-width 10.6 mm.,
posterior width 10.5 mm.

TABLE XLIII

TOOTH MEASUREMENTS OF
TANUPOLAMA MACROCEPHALA (mm.)

	TMM 937-874	TMM 937-900
Length P$_4$	14.0	----
Width P$_4$	8.1	----
Length M$_1$	17.0	20.2
Anterior Width M$_1$	11.1 est.	12.5
Posterior Width M$_1$	13.5	14.1
Length M$_2$	23.2	25.7
Anterior Width M$_2$	13.9	13.9
Posterior Width M$_2$	----	15.3
Length M$_3$	----	35.6
Anterior Width M$_3$	----	13.4
Mid Width M$_3$	----	13.1
Posterior Width M$_3$	----	6.5

Antilocaprid

gen. et sp. indet.

Material: Left M$_3$ (TMM 937-879) (Fig. 123g).

Remarks: This tooth cannot be identified generically or specifically with any certainty. Its dimensions (length 19.8 mm., width anterior lobe 7.3 mm., width of mid-lobe 7.0 mm., width of posterior lobe 4.8 mm.) fall within the ranges of both Antilocapra americana and Stockoceras onusrosagris given by Skinner (1942). The M$_3$ of Stockoceras averages smaller than that of Antilocapra. The Blackwater Draw specimen is near the lower limit of the observed range for M$_3$'s of Antilocapra but is very close to the mean of Stockoceras.

There is no fourth lobe on the wear surface, but there is a slight elongation of the posterior end. This is more pronounced on the lower part of the tooth. This would result in the enlargement of the posterior elongation of the third lobe with wear. The M$_3$ of Stockoceras shows the same enlargement of the fourth lobe with wear. Skinner (ibid) shows that the presence and development of the fourth lobe is variable in both species and is useless as a means of differentiating them. More precise identification must await the discovery of horn-cores which are the principle basis of classification.

Bison antiquus Leidy

Material: A partial skull with complete cranium and horn cores (TMM 937-764); numerous isolated teeth, mandibles and skeletal elements (Fig. 124a, b).

Remarks: This is one of the most abundant species in the Gray Sand. The cranium is

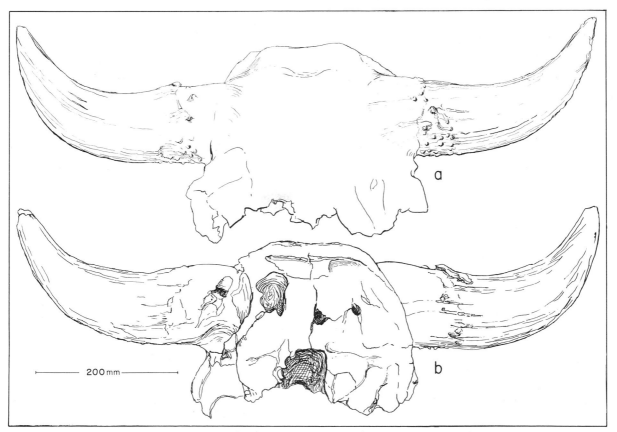

Fig. 124. Bison antiquus skull from the Gray Sand: A-Dorsal view of skull; B-Posterior view of skull.

broad. The horn-cores extend from the skull at right angles to the axis of the skull, and swing down slightly before turning up at the tips. The horn-cores are circular in cross-section and do not turn posteriorly. The length of the upper curve is less than the circumference at the base.

All measurements are within the range of variation given by Skinner and Kaisen (1947) for B. antiquus (Table XLIV).

TABLE XLIV

MEASUREMENTS OF A SKULL OF
BISON ANTIQUUS, TMM 937-764

Measurement	Size in mm.
Spread of horns, tip to tip	802
Greatest spread on outside	820 est.
Core length, upper curve	
tip to burr	245
Core length, lower curve	325
Length, tip to burr (cord)	232
Vertical diameter	89
Circumference	285
Width of cranium between	
horns and orbits	350

Sellards (1955) measured the size of astragali from various early man sites and showed a decrease in mean size from the older to the younger deposits. The largest individuals were from the Brown Sand Wedge which overlies the Gray Sand. No astragali are available from the Gray Sand for comparison.

Order PERISSODACTYLA

Family EQUIDAE

Genus Equus Linnaeus

The genus Equus in the broad sense includes the living horses, zebras, African asses, Asiatic asses, and various related Pleistocene species. Various authors have subdivided the genus into a number of genera or subgenera, but it is doubtful that our knowledge of the relationships of the Pleistocene species is sufficient to make meaningful subdivisions at this time. The genus is used here in the broad sense.

There appear to be three species of the genus Equus represented in the material from the Gray Sand. Stock and Bode (1937) recognized only one species of Equus E. excelsus. This is rejected here for reasons given below. Quinn (1957) recognized four taxa from the Gray Sand, E. conversidens, E. midlandensis, E.

caballos caballos and E. caballos laurentius. The occurrence of two subspecies of the same species in the quarry assemblage is extremely unlikely unless the quarry assemblage accumulated over a considerable period of time to allow time for evolution to take place or to allow ecologic zones to move. It seems doubtful that enough time is represented by the Gray Sand for either of these to have taken place (Haynes and Agogino, 1966).

Equus conversidens Owen

Material: A partial skull (TMM 937-504); one anterior first phalanx and one posterior first phalanx (TMM 937-228, 227); one second phalanx, one pes (TMM 937-229); one right metacarpal (TMM 937-917); six upper molars (TMM 937-195, 194, 203, 822, 918, 207); two dP^2 (TMM 937-919, 920); dP^3 or dP^4 (TMM 937-921); a right astragalus (TMM 937-185) (Figs. 125a, c; 126i,j,k,l,m,n).

Description: The partial skull (TMM 937-504) and a metacarpal (TMM 937-917) are the only specimens of horses of any significance to be recovered since Quinn's study. The skull consists of the brain case and the posterior part of the palate with M$^{1-3}$ on one side and M^3 on the other. The anterior edge of the internal nares lies at the level of the middle of M^2. In general, Recent specimens of Equus do not have the nares located as far anterior although this feature is variable. The Recent specimens of asses which have been examined have the nares at this point. The muscle scars on the supraoccipital are arranged in two groups, a dorsal pair consisting of a shallow depression on each side of the midline and a ventral pair that together make a sharply defined oval depression. The Recent ass has a similar arrangement, but the ventral depression is narrower.

Some recent specimens of Equus approach this condition but most have the ventral area expanded to cover almost all the exoccipital, and the shape is usually more triangular.

The anterior edge of the orbit is even with the posterior edge of M^3. In most recent specimens of asses and horses it is located well back of M^3.

The skull is proportionately deeper than

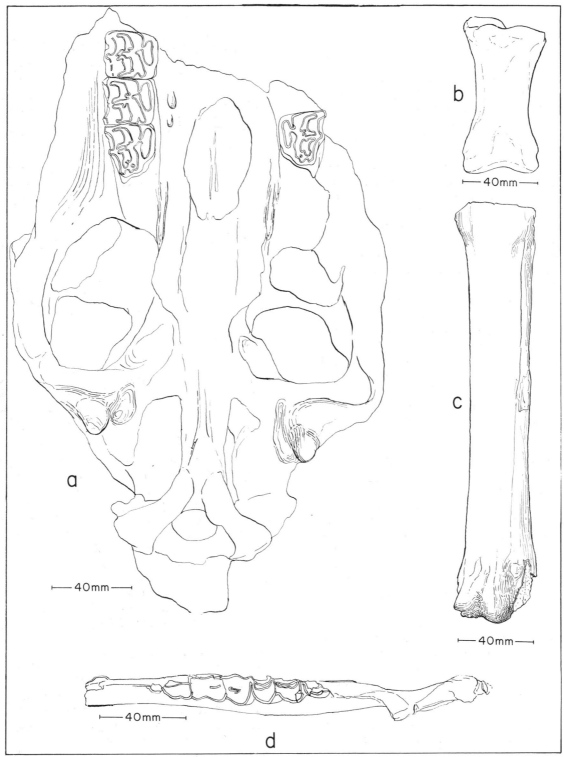

Fig. 125. Horse and camel remains from the Gray Sand: A-Ventral view of skull of Equus conversidens TMM 937-504; B-Anterior side of first phalanx, pes, of Equus niobrarensis TMM 937-876; C-Anterior side of metacarpal of Equus conversidens TMM 937-917; D-Occlusal view of mandible Tanupolama macrocephala TMM 937-874.

that of the Recent ass and resembles that of a horse in this respect.

The upper teeth are almost square in cross-section with a relatively simple pattern. The fossettes are small with three or four plications in the premolars and one or two in the molars. The hypoconal groove is shallow. In M^3 it is closed off to form a circular hypoconal fosette. The pli protoloph and pli hypostyle are reduced to absent on the molars and are moderately well developed in the premolars as in the type of E. conversidens. The post protoconal groove is relatively wide, parallel sided, and has a straight end. The pli caballin is not present in the molars but is present in premolars. The protocones of the molars are elongated, flattened on the lingual surface and lack well developed grooves. This is different from the recent asses available for comparison. The type of E. conversidens has the lingual grooves slightly better developed than the Blackwater Draw material. The uppers resemble those of the type of E. conversidens but have fewer plications on the fossettes. The teeth resemble E. conversidens in the size and shape of the pre-protoconal groove and the overall shape of the protocones.

The dP^2 and dP^3 or dP^4 (TMM 937-919, 920, 921) are referred to E. conversidens on the basis of their size. They are almost exactly the same size as the upper deciduous teeth of the Recent ass. The protocone of the dP^2 is more elongated and flattened lingually than in the Recent ass. The post protoconal groove is relatively wide in the unworn tooth but becomes narrow toward the bottom of the tooth. A pli caballin is present in the unworn tooth and absent on the worn tooth. The pli protoloph, pli protoconule, and the pli hypostyle are all larger than in the Recent ass but are uncomplicated. The fosettes are slightly smaller and more complicated in the fossil. The enamel borders between the mesostyle and metastyle are more strongly curved than in the Recent ass.

The dP^3 or dP^4 is worn and differs from a comparably worn tooth of the Recent ass in having a more elongate protocone, a relatively narrower post protoconal groove which is oriented at less of an angle to the long axis of the tooth, and in having a longer and better developed pli protoconule and anterior fold on

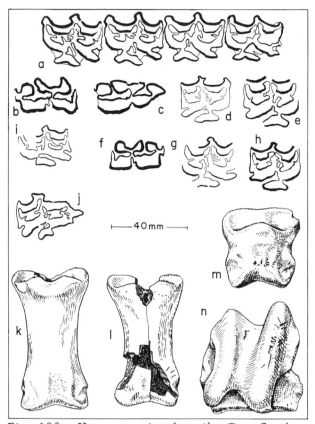

Fig. 126. Horse remains from the Gray Sand: A - Occlusal views of left P^3 - M^2 of Equus scotti TMM 937-170, 171, 172, 173 (Probably one individual); B - Occlusal view of right P_3 or P_4 of Equus scotti TMM 937-169; C - Occlusal view of right P_2 of Equus scotti TMM 937-192; D - Occlusal view of right upper premolar of Equus niobrarensis TMM 937-923; E - Occlusal view of right upper molar of Equus niobrarensis TMM 937-678A; F - Occlusal view of left lower molar of Equus niobrarensis TMM 937-252; G - Occlusal view of left molar of Equus niobrarensis TMM 937-738A; H - Occlusal view of right upper molar of Equus niobrarensis TMM 937-191; I - Occlusal view of left dP^3 or dP^4 of Equus conversidens TMM 937-921; J - Occlusal view of right dP^2 of Equus conversidens TMM 937-919; K - Anterior view of first phalanx, manus of Equus conversidens TMM 937-228; L - Anterior of first phalanx, pes, of Equus conversidens TMM 937-227; M - Anterior view of second phalanx, pes, of Equus conversidens TMM 937-229; N - Proximal view of astragalus of Equus conversidens TMM 937-185.

the postfossette.

The lower teeth referable to E. conversidens are assigned on the basis of size and enamel pattern. The lower teeth have rounded metaconids and oval metastylids whose long axes are oriented approximately 45° to the long axes of the teeth. The anterior faces of the metastylids are flattened, and their tips are compressed. The valley between the metaconid is present but small. They resemble the lowers of the type of E. francisi in the V-shaped valley between the metaconid and metastylid and V-shaped median valley.

The metacarpal (TMM 937-917) is slightly larger than one from Papago Springs Cave referred by Skinner (1942) to E. conversidens and is within the range of size of the metacarpals referred to E. conversidens by Dalquest and Hughes (1965).

The anterior first phalanx (TMM 937-228), posterior first phalanx (TMM 937-227), and second phalanx (TMM 937-229) figured by Quinn (1957, Pl. III, Figs. 3, 4, 5) are very similar to those of the Recent ass in size and proportion. They are somewhat smaller and more slender than the posterior first phalanx (TMM 937-876), here referred to Equus niobrarensis.

Discussion: This material is slightly larger than the types of E. conversidens and E. francisi. The length of M1-3 (71.8 mm.) is almost exactly the same as in the specimen from Papago Springs Cave (71.9 mm.)* assigned to E. conversidens by Skinner (1942). The patterns of the upper teeth of both the Blackwater Draw and Papago Springs Cave specimen are slightly less complicated than those of the type of E. conversidens and are more comparable to the specimen from Canyon, Texas, described by Dalquest and Hughes (1965). The material from Blackwater Draw and Papago Springs Cave appears to be similar and to differ in the same way from the type of E. conversidens. The differences are slight and are interpreted here as representing geographic differences.

---

*Measurement taken from Fig. 8, Skinner (1942).

Equus niobrarensis Hay

Material: Left upper premolar (TMM 937-738A); right upper premolar (TMM 937-678A); right upper premolar (TMM 937-923); left M$_1$ (TMM 937-252); right M^1 (TMM 937-191); first phalanx, manus (TMM 937-876); distal end of a metapodial (TMM 937-876) (Figs. 125b; 126d, e,f,g,h).

Description: The recognition of this species is based on the upper cheek teeth. The upper teeth are slightly larger and more complicated than those of E. conversidens from Blackwater Draw (Table XLV). The specimen which is believed to be an upper premolar (TMM 937-923) has a very open parastyle and a bifurcate mesostyle. The protocone is elongated and very slightly convex on the lingual side. The post protoconal groove is relatively wider than in the teeth believed to be molars. A pli caballin is present but is small. The hypoconal groove is narrow and almost parallel sided. The posterior side of the anterior fossett and the anterior side of the posterior fossett are considerably folded. The pli protoconule is simple but deep and narrow. The pli protoloph is simple. The pli hypostyle is barely discernible.

The three upper teeth which appear to be premolars (TMM 937-738A, 191, 678A) differ little from the molar. The pli caballin of the molar is very small or absent and the fossettes have somewhat fewer crenulations.

The distal end of a metapodial is larger than that assigned E. conversidens (Table XLVI). The difference seems to be too great to be accounted for by normal variation and is assigned to E. niobrarensis on that basis. It is much smaller than another metatarsal which is assigned to E. scotti.

The anterior first phalanx is also too large to be assigned to E. conversidens and too small for E. scotti (Table XXXVI).

Discussion: This is the taxon called E. caballos laurentius by Quinn (1957). For reasons discussed above it is considered unlikely to find two subspecies of the same species in a quarry assemblage. Consequently it is recognized as a separate taxon.

These teeth show many similarities to those of Equus niobrarensis. The size is close. The measurements given by Hay (1913A) for the type are slightly smaller than the Blackwater Draw material but the difference is slight (see Table XLV). The post protoconal groove is relatively wide and is directed so as to pass along the lingual border of the anterior fossette. The borders of the fossettes show the same degree of complication. The major differences are a somewhat better development of the pli caballin and a greater tendency of the hypocone to be set off by a small groove coming from the post protoconal groove in E. niobrarensis.

The Blackwater Draw teeth differ from those of E. laurentius in the same characters that the type of E. niobrarensis does (wide post protoconal groove, more complicated fossettes, better developed pli caballin, larger size, better developed hypoconal groove, protocones flattened on the labial side). The assignment of these teeth to E. niobrarensis extends the geologic range of this species to late Wisconsin.

Equus scotti Gidley

Material: Left P^3-M^2 probably from one individual (TMM 937-170-173), figured by Quinn (1957); two upper premolars (TMM 937-678, 253); two upper molars (TMM 937-760, 738); seven lower molars and premolars (TMM 937-169, 251, 250, 678, 738, 760, 678); one left M_3 (TMM 937-859); one left tibia (TMM 937-829); two left astragali (TMM 937-174, 746); one left metatarsal (TMM 937-733) (Fig. 126a, b, c).

Description: The upper premolars are large with broad parastyles and mesostyles which may be slightly bifurcated. The protocones are relatively short and have a well developed lingual groove. The pli caballin is very long with the length two to two-and-one-half times the width. The preprotoconal groove is short and V-shaped. The post protoconal groove is wide relative to its length and is expanded at the anterior end. The fossettes are relatively narrow. The pli protoloph is deep but narrow and is oriented antero-posteriorly.

TABLE XLV

TOOTH MEASUREMENTS OF EQUIDS (mm.)

				Equus conversidens			Equus niobrarensis	
Measurement	M^1	TMM 937-261 M^2	M^3	TMM 937-194 Molar	TMM 937-195 Molar	TMM 937-191 Molar	TMM 937-678A Molar
Length of ectoloph	22.7	23.0	25.7	23.5	23.7	26.1	27.5?
Width normal to parastyle-metastyle	24.9	----	21.9	20.7	23.6	26.4	----
Length protocone	13.6	14.7	14.8	13.3	14.2	13.7	13.4

			Equus scotti			
	TMM 937-170 P^3	TMM 937-171 P^4	TMM 937-172 M^1	TMM 937-173 M^2	TMM 937-738 molar	TMM 937-678 premolar
Length of ectoloph	32.3	30.8	32.6	29.9	32.0	34.6
Width normal to parastyle-metastyle	28.1	28.8	26.7	25.2	28.4	31.1
Length of protocone	14.0	14.9	14.2	14.8	15.8	13.3

TABLE XLVI

MEASUREMENTS OF METAPODIALS OF EQUIDS (mm.)

	E. conversidens (metacarpal)	E. scotti (metatarsal)	E. niobrarensis	E. scotti* Topotype
	TMM 937-917	TMM 937-733	TMM 937-876	
Length	219	290	---	244
Proximal width	43.8	55	---	57.3
Distal width	---	53	41.1	57.7
Antero-post. diam. distal end	26.1	36	32.3	42.7
Width at mid-shaft	31.6	40	---	41.0

*Data from Troxell (1915, p. 620).

The pli protoconule is deep and oriented 45° to the long axis of the tooth. The posterior side of the anterior fossette and the anterior side of the posterior fosette have two to three deep plications. A pli hypostyle is present. The hypoconal groove is wide. The hypocone tends to be isolated by the hypoconal groove and a shallow groove from the post protoconal groove.

The molars differ from the premolars in having para- and metastyles narrower, fewer plications on the fossettes, smaller pli caballin, and a narrower post protoconal groove.

The lower teeth that are assigned to this species are assigned only on the basis of size.

Only the largest of the teeth have been assigned to avoid mistaking the lower premolars of E. niobrarensis with the lower molars of E. scotti. The metaconids and metastylids are compressed to rounded with a wide U-shaped valley between them. The metaconids are tied to the metastylids by a narrow isthmus. The entoconid is rounded and is joined to the entoconulid by a narrow channel rather than a broad one as in E. conversidens. The anterior lobe of the entoflexid tends to be enlarged and rounded and may have small plications. The median valley is usually shallow. A pli caballinid is present.

The tibia, two astragali, metatarsal, and phalanx are similar in form to those of a large

TABLE XLVII

MEASUREMENTS OF PHALANGES OF EQUIDS FROM BLACKWATER DRAW (mm.)

	E. conversidens			E. niobrarensis
Measurement	1st anterior TMM 937-228	1st posterior TMM 937-227	2nd posterior TMM 937-229	1st anterior TMM 937-876
Length	69.6	65.1	34.1	76.8
Anterior width	41.0	40.5	40.6	46.4
Posterior width	36.0	34.2	37.2	37.6
Width at mid-shaft	26.0	24.8	33.1	27.6

TABLE XLVIII

MEASUREMENTS OF ASTRAGALI OF EQUIDS (mm.)

Measurement	E. conversidens TMM 937-185	E. scotti TMM 937-746	E. scotti TMM 937-174
Length of longest diagonal	67.7	84.2	78.8
Width of distal articular facet	46.0	63.0	----

Recent horse. The tibia measures 358 mm. in length. The measurements of the astragali are given in Table XLVIII.

In general, the measurements of these bones are close to those of a large domestic horse. The astragalus is not quite as large as that of a draft horse, and the trochlear ridges are not as massive.

Discussion: The material described above was assigned by Quinn (1957) to E. caballos caballos and E. midlandensis. However, there is no reason to subdivide the sample of large horse teeth, and it is considered to represent one living population. Stock and Bode (1937) referred the larger horse teeth from Blackwater Draw to E. cf. excelsus.

The two upper teeth figured by Stock and Bode (1937, Fig. 4c, 4e) from the gravel pit cannot be readily compared with the Texas Memorial Museum material because one of them is an M^3 which is not represented in the Texas Memorial Museum collection, and the other is not sufficiently worn to completely expose the pattern. They do not appear to be separable from the Texas Memorial Museum sample.

The Blackwater Draw material has been compared with a figure of a topotype of E. scotti. The following similarities are seen: size, degree of complexity of the fossettes, relative size and shape of the protocones, tendency of the hypocone to be isolated by the hypoconal groove and a shallow groove from the post protoconal groove, wide post protoconal and hypoconal grooves and the narrow isthmus joining the protocone to the remainder of the tooth. The major differences are the lesser bifurcation of the parastyles and metastyles of the premolars and greater development of the pli caballin in the Blackwater Draw specimens. These characters show some vari-

ation within the Blackwater Draw sample and are not considered to be significant.

No measurements are available in the literature for the metatarsals of E. scotti from the type locality. Troxell (1915) gives measurements for a metacarpal. They are approximately what would be expected for a metacarpal from the same species as the metatarsal from Blackwater Draw. It is on the basis of the similarities in the dentition and the post cranial skeleton that the large horse remains are referred to E. scotti.

The assignment of these teeth to E. scotti extends the range of that species into the late Pleistocene and gives the species a total known geologic range from Kansan to late Wisconsin. Slaughter et al. (1962) noted that some horse material from the Hill-Shuler faunas (Sangamon) is similar to E. scotti but referred them to E. midlandensis on the basis of their considerably younger age. It appears that E. scotti and E. midlandensis cannot be reliably differentiated, and they are here considered to be synonyms.

Order PROBOSCIDIA

Mammuthus sp.

Material: Three partial, semiarticulated skeletons; scattered skeletal elements of at least one other, all left in place at the north end of the Sam Sanders Pit; miscellaneous fragments of bones and teeth (Figs. 74, 75).

Remarks: Mammoth remains are most abundant at the north end of the pit where at least four, and possibly five, individuals were found.

The difficulties of specific identification of mammoths from teeth alone have been discussed by Lance (1959) and others. Only one specimen had teeth sufficiently well preserved to give dependable measurements. The measurements of the two lower teeth, probably M_3's are given in Table XLIX. The preservation is such that the width measurement is not reliable, but the teeth do not appear to be wide. No cement sheath is present, but the poor preservation makes this an unreliable character as well.

TABLE XLIX

MEASUREMENTS OF LOWER MOLARS OF <u>MAMMUTHUS</u> SP.
(MAMMOTH NO. 3, EL LLANO DIG 1)

	Length (mm.)	No. Plates	No. Plates 100 mm.
Right	238	12	5
Left	254	14	5 1/4

The tooth measurements are not typical for <u>M</u>. <u>columbi</u>, but they fall within the range given for this species by Osborn (1942). The apparent narrowness of the M3's and the lack of a cement sheath indicate that it is probably not <u>M</u>. <u>imperator</u>. The three semi-articulated skeletons are associated with numerous artifacts and bones of other animals, the prey of human hunters. The mammoths have been numbered one through five, although four and five may represent the same individual.

A. Mammoth No. 1: This is the skeleton of a young individual as the epiphyses of the distal long bones are unfused. The large size of the long bones and the fact that the epiphyses of most of the rest of the skeleton are fused indicates that this individual had almost completed its growth.

The skull is smashed and appears to be lying on its side. The mandibles are next to the skull but are not articulated with it. The cervical and anterior dorsal vertebrae and ribs are articulated. The ribs are spread out with the dorsal side down. The posterior vertebrae are disarticulated and somewhat scattered, but they tend to be concentrated between the rib cage and the pelvis. The two halves of the pelvis are disarticulated but are lying together. In general, the limb bones are not articulated, but they are not badly scattered. The foot bones are widely scattered, and all could not be accounted for.

B. Mammoth No. 2: In this large adult the skull is badly smashed and rotten. The mandibles are next to the skull with the teeth up. They are joined at the symphysis. The right mandible appears to have two teeth, a small anterior one and a larger posterior one, but the preservation is too poor to be certain. One tusk is present and is completely separated from the skull. It is somewhat distorted and has a knot approximately one foot from the distal end. This knot has the appearance of a

pathological condition. It could also be caused by plastic deformation around a hard object. The vertebrae and ribs are disarticulated and somewhat scattered, but they are located between the remnants of the skull and the pelvis.

The forelimbs have been somewhat disarranged. The scapulae are close to the remnants of the skull, the right one with the outside up, the left with the inside up. Both humeri are present and are side by side with a radius at right angles to them.

The pelvis is badly broken. Both femora are articulated with the pelvis. The left femur is, in addition, articulated with the tibia. The foot bones are missing.

C. Mammoth No. 3: The skull of this adult individual is crushed, and both tusks are present. They are massive, but apparently they were not particularly long. Remnants of the sheaths are present, and the pulp cavities have filled with dentine at the proximal end. Their orientation suggests that the skull is upside down, and the tusks have been broken away from the skull by being pulled outward.

The mandibles are separated and badly broken. One apparently has two teeth.

The skeleton bones are piled in a heap and in general are poorly preserved. This is particularly true of the ends of the limb bones, which makes identification difficult.

TABLE L

MEASUREMENTS OF MAMMOTH SKELETONS
(EL LLANO DIG 1) (cm.)

	Mammoth #1	Mammoth #2	Mammoth #3	Mammoth #4	Mammoth #5
Length scapula	85			94	
Length humerus	109	117			114
Length radius	75				
Length ulna (from articular to articular surface)	80				
Length pubis (from acetabulum)	25.4				
Length ischium (from acetabulum)	45.7				
Length of chord of iliac crest	89				
Length femur	113	137			
Length tibia	78.5	78.5			
Length fibula					
Length of tusk along outside curve	103	190			
Diameter of tusk at sheath	17.8		22.8		

D. Mammoth No. 4: This consists of a left scapula measuring 94 cm. along the spine to the coracoid process. The upper and lower ends show considerable erosion.

E. Mammoth No. 5: This consists of a humerus, scapula, and sacrum, all widely scattered. The ends are rotten and eroded.

Conditions of Accumulation

Evans and Sellards (Evans, 1951; Sellards, 1952; Sellards and Evans, 1960) proposed a springhead origin for the Gray Sand. This was confirmed by Haynes and Agogino (1966) with the exposure of spring-feeder conduits. The Gray Sand appears to have been deposited in a spring fed pond.

Most of the bones from the Gray Sand in The University of Texas collection are much the same in their preservation. There are a few fragmentary specimens in which the degree of mineralization and the color are different. These are believed to have been reworked from an older deposit. The fragment of a large thick turtle carapace mentioned previously is an example.

Green (personal communication in Warnica, 1966) has come to the same conclusion regarding other material from the Gray Sand. He recognizes two other types of preservation. One he interprets as being derived from the "Bedrock Gravels" (termed "Red Gravel" elsewhere in this volume). The other he interprets as being derived from a basin fill which is younger than the "Bedrock Gravels" but older than the Gray Sand. All the material which is used here in the ecological interpretation shows the same preservation and is believed to be contemporaneous.

The degree of articulation and association of the mammoth skeletal elements are in marked contrast to those of all the other species represented in the Gray Sand. None of the other species show any significant articulation or association. This difference is understandable as it is most likely that most of the bones are of animals killed by man. Mammoths were very large, heavy animals, difficult to move after being killed. Lance (1953 and 1959), Haury (1953), and Antevs (1953) have suggested that these animals were butchered by stripping the flesh from the skeleton. This method would leave at least the major skeletal elements together. The widely scattered foot bones are

relatively small and could be easily moved. Whether they were removed from the carcasses by man or carnivores is not known. None show any signs of having been burned.

The smashed skulls are similar to the situation at the Naco and Lehner sites reported by Haury (1953), Antevs (1953), and Lance (1953 and 1959). They suggest that the skulls were opened to obtain the brains. The skulls of many animals found in archaeological sites are broken, suggesting that the brains were commonly eaten. The thick, though spongy, bone of the mammoth skull would not be much of an obstacle to a determined man.

The preservation of the mammoth material is not uniform. Of the four or five skeletons, one or two (Nos. 4 and 5) are badly scattered, and three (Nos. 1, 2 and 3) are semiarticulated. This suggests that the mammoths represent at least two different kills, the scattered skeletons representing the earlier kill. The three semiarticulated skeletons are not equally well preserved. Mammoth No. 1 is better preserved than numbers 2 and 3. This is contrary to expectation, as number 1 is an immature individual in which some epiphyses were still open. These bones should have deteriorated faster than those of an adult. This indicates either a difference in the length of exposure to surface conditions, or a difference in the burial or pre-burial environment. The fact that the best preserved skeleton is located nearest the shore and would be more accessible to scavengers and to trampling by other animals indicates that it was exposed for a shorter time than the other specimens. The skeletal remains thus represent a series of kills over a period of time.

The three semiarticulated skeletons must have been buried in a body of water to be protected from the activity of scavengers. The two large carnivores in the faunal assemblage, Aenocyon dirus and Canis lupus, would have been attracted to such kills and would have scattered the bones.

Lance (1959) has suggested that the local physiography at the Lehner site was significant in having a steep bluff on one side of the stream which was a barrier to rapid escape and thus aided the hunters in containing their prey until they could be killed. A similar situation existed at the Clovis site. The deposits containing the bones and artifacts are located in a depression in caliche cemented sands. The north side of this depression was fairly steep walled (up to 20° according to Hester, personal communication) and would probably have slowed down the escape of animals in that direction. There is little doubt that the Gray Sand is primarily a water laid deposit. It is possible that the mammoths were attacked while they were in the water, and the depth of the water and the softness of the bottom sediments were sufficient to slow their movements and make them more vulnerable.

Age and Environmental Conditions

The faunal assemblage from the Gray Sand is clearly late Pleistocene in age. The presence of such forms as Smilodon, Platygonus, and Aenocyon indicate an age in excess of 8,000 years (Hester, 1960). Haynes (1964) has reported a radiocarbon date of 11,170 B.P. $\pm$ 360 years on carbonaceous material from a clay lens in and around the skull of a mammoth. This is believed to be equivalent in age to the Brown Sand Wedge. Haynes (ibid) also states that the Gray Sand is probably considerably older than this (perhaps more than 16,000 years) and that at least some of the bones have been intruded into the Gray Sand.

The fauna of the Gray Sand indicates environmental conditions quite different from the present ones. Many of the species are extinct and had wide ranging distributions. Consequently, they are poor ecologic indicators. However, the presence of Terrapene canaliculata and Ondatra zibethica gives some hint of past conditions.

Ondatra requires the presence of permanent water in either streams or ponds, as their present distribution is apparently limited by this factor. This probably means a higher rainfall more evenly distributed throughout the year.

The ecological significance of Terrapene canaliculata is less easy to interpret. Its closest living relative, T. carolina, is widely distributed through the forested areas of the southeastern United States. The presence of T. canaliculata in the Gray Sand may well indicate wooded conditions, probably along stream courses or lake borders. This is supported by the association of T. canaliculata with other south-eastern forest species in late Pleistocene cave deposits in Central Texas (Lundelius, 1960).

SUMMARY AND CONCLUSIONS

The prehistoric pond termed Blackwater Locality No. 1 functioned as one of the more permanent water holes on the Llano Estacado during the time interval from approximately 15,000 to 6,000 years before the present. This fact was due to unique geological features at the site. One of the consequences of the existence of this pond was that it was visited periodically by Paleo-Indian hunters in search of game. The net result of these factors was the accumulation of geological and archaeological data to the extent that this site has become one of the "type sites," documenting Late Pleistocene events in North America. In this section we will review the unique aspects of this site and their importance to Late Pleistocene studies.

Life History of the Pond

The formation of the pond appears to be due to gravel beds deposited in a former channel of the Brazos River (since beheaded by the Pecos drainage). These gravel beds, of probable Pleistocene age, functioned as an acquifer carrying subsurface waters down the former river channel. At Blackwater Locality No. 1, these beds reach the low escarpment of the modern Blackwater Draw. At this point water from the gravel beds could escape from beneath the caliche cap through spring conduits to form a pond. All of the evidence at hand suggests that the pond was never very deep and was also intermittent in nature as attested by the frequent erosional unconformities. During periods of good water supply, the pond overflowed to the south and drained into Blackwater Draw. Arroyos draining into the depression were present at its northwest and northeast margins.

The earliest unit of pond sediments is the Gray Sand which is a homogenous medium sand with almost no associated clastic materials. Haynes (in Wendorf and Hester, n.d.) regards this unit to be full Pluvial in age (between 13,000 and 25,000 years old). Haynes further states that much of Pleistocene time is represented by the eolian sands and pedogenic caliches of units A_6-A_{13}. Immediately below the Gray Sand are pink and yellow sand units of the riverine deposits. At present, there is no adequate geologic explanation as to why the pond formed at this specific time.

The Gray Sand averages about three feet in thickness. The clean homogenous nature of the deposit suggests this was a time of ample and steady water supply. Late Pleistocene vertebrates including horse, camel, bison, mammoth, dire wolf, sabertooth, coyote, fox, and muskrat and a large terrapin are found throughout the unit as are implements of the Clovis culture. However, Haynes (personal communication) has emphasized the possibility that the artifacts and bones may have been distributed throughout the unit by gravity and the roiling action of feeder springs.

During the deposition of the Gray Sand the spring conduits were open as attested by six conduits found along the northwest edge of the pond (Haynes and Agogino, 1966, Fig. 4). Although the presence of the spring conduits were not verified until the 1963-64 researches of Vance Haynes, such a conduit was also reported from the northeast wall of the pit by Oscar Shay in 1955 (correspondence to Sellards). The polished artifacts within the ENMU spring conduit suggest that it was also such a feature.

The Gray Sand is separated from overlying sediments by an erosional unconformity which is more pronounced in the center of the pond than at the pond margins. The reasons for this phenomena are due to the nature of the next overlying unit, the Brown Sand Wedge. This unit consists of massive and laminated brown sands and silts laid down by the springs adjacent to the pond margins. These deposits have been identified around most of the perimeter of the pond. During the deposition of this unit the spring flow appears to have been somewhat intermittent as the beds are frequently laminated. They also include considerable detritus washed into the depression from the adjacent caliche bedrock.

Haynes and Agogino (1966) using evidence from the North Bank, El Llano Dig 1, have divided the Brown Sand Wedge deposits into four units (C_0, C_1, D_{1a}, D_{1b}). Units C_0 and C_1 are facies and contained the butchered mammoths of Clovis age dated 11,040 B.P. $\pm$ 500 years to 11,630 B.P. $\pm$ 400 years. It is assumed here that the Brown Sand Wedge unit identified by Sellards and Evans along the eastern margin of the pond may be correlated with C_0 and C_1 as their "Brown Sand Wedge" was overlain by diagnostic portions of the Diatomite. Haynes and Agogino (1966) regard the variations within these beds as indicating turbulence near the spring conduits and quieter waters away from the conduits. Units C_0 and C_1 are separated from overlying units by a slight unconformity suggesting that the pond dried up temporarily. In the center of the pond this unconformity is much more pronounced.

Units D_{1a} and D_{1b}, also termed Brown Sand Wedge, are shoreward facies of the Diatomite. These beds represent alluvial dumping of sands, caliche nodules, bones, and other detritus around the pond margin (only documented along the west and northwest margins of the pond). Where identified these beds occur within the limits of the arroyo channels draining into the pond. The included fossils and artifacts are of Folsom age.

In the center of the pond the finer grained sediments (D_2) were accumulating with the remains of a diatom flora to form a dark colored, organic stained diatomaceous silty clay with numerous naturally carbonized plant fragments dated between 10,170 B.P. $\pm$ 260 years and 10,490 B.P. $\pm$ 200 years. This is the classic Diatomite which in the center of the pond contained numerous bison kills of Folsom Age.

The brown sand facies (D_{1a} D_{1b}) and the Diatomite (D_2) are for the most part contemporaneous.

A reconstruction of the nature of the pond during this interval is as follows: The springs were reactivated and the shoreward facies began to be deposited. Simultaneously, rains swept detritus into the pond. The runoff col-

lected in the center of the depression and a shallow somewhat stagnant pond was formed. According to detailed studies of the diatoms (reported in Wendorf and Hester, n.d.) the pond fluctuated considerably in salinity during the deposition of the Diatomite. The presence of bison leg bones in upright positions in the Diatomite suggests that at this time the pond had a rather firm but muddy bottom. The Diatomite is separated from overlying units by a strong unconformity suggesting that following deposition of the unit the pond temporarily dried up and was subjected to wind erosion.

The next succeeding unit, the Carbonaceous Silt (unit E) indicates similar conditions of deposition as those represented by the classic Diatomite. Again there was present a shallow stagnant pond or marsh with presumably slow or intermittent drainage into Blackwater Draw. The diatom flora was not as prevalent as in the preceding period. During this interval most of the spring conduits were closed. The water table probably lay at about the same elevation as the bottom of the pond, and the pond level was probably dependent on rainfall runoff. During this interval the pond sediments, for the first time, lapped over the edge of the caliche bedrock surrounding the depression. This additional surface area contributed to additional evaporation resulting in a marsh rather than a pond. According to Haynes and Agogino (1966, p. 820) the unit contained . . ."subrounded and frosted quartz grains and well-developed soil structure in some exposures which suggest aeolian deposition in wet meadow or morass in conjunction with declining spring activity. This drying trend culminated in complete dessiccation of the morass, development of a calcareous soil, and finally deflation. By the time unit E was deposited only one spring conduit (No. 5) containing an Archaic type of projectile point may have been active at the northwall location. If so, the velocity of discharge was insufficient to carry sand out of the conduit as there was no associated wedge of sediment."

Subsequent to this deposition the Carbonaceous Silt was severely eroded by the wind which in some places in the center of the pond completely removed the unit and cut into the underlying and more resistant Diatomite. It was during this arid interval that the hand-dug wells were excavated by Archaic peoples. The drop in the water table at this time, as indicated by the depth of the wells, was between 5 and 8 feet. The wells were located in the center of the depression, in arroyos tributary to the depression, and near the site of former springs. The depression probably held runoff after rains as evidence of bison kills by Archaic peoples on this surface has been preserved by their being enveloped in sands of the next overlying unit the Jointed Sand.

The Jointed Sand (unit F) is a massive quartz sand with a coarse prismatic structure. The unit is an oxidized reddish brown and represents a time of erosion which has been correlated with the Altithermal. The included artifacts are of the Archaic culture with the exception of a few reworked Folsom implements. Fossils and artifacts are not common but one bison kill, toward the base of the unit, has been dated at 4950 B.P. $\pm$ 150 years.

Separated by another unconformity, the next overlying unit is another sand dune deposit, the Tan Aeolean Sand (unit G). It contains Recent Indian artifacts and is still being deposited and reworked by the wind.

Observations on Occurrences of Artifacts

A tally of all artifacts recovered in the excavations reported in this volume and believed to have valid provenience is presented in Table LI. This total of 1,375 artifacts includes 1,085 which have provenience assigned to a specific stratigraphic unit, the remainder were either collected from the surface or the gravel pit dumps. The provenience by bed of the artifacts assignable to a specific unit is as follows: Red Gravel--4(0.3%), Gray Sand--289(27.4%), Brown Sand Wedge--512(47.2%), Diatomite--28(2.5%), Carbonaceous Silt--67(6.1%), and Jointed Sand--176(16.2%). Interpretations based on this distribution of artifacts are:(1) The artifacts in the Red Gravel are of Clovis Age and are probably the result of churning of the fluidized sediments of the pond bottom by animals, especially elephants. (2) The high number of artifacts in the Brown Sand Wedge (primarily of Folsom Age) indicates that this was the period of maximum occupation of the site by Paleo-Indian peoples. It is interesting to note that this concentration of artifacts in the Brown Sand Wedge was not noted by Sellards during the 1949-50 excavations. As a consequence he described the Diatomite as being the Folsom age deposit (Sellards, 1952). The evidence presented in this volume suggests that both statements are correct as portions of the Brown Sand Wedge are facies of the Diatomite and thus contemporaraneous. (3) The Clovis period represents the second most frequent use of the pond. (4) Archaic peoples utilized the site next most frequently. (5) The most limited use of the pond by Paleo-Indian peoples was during the deposition of the

TABLE LI

SUMMARY OF ARTIFACTS RECOVERED BY STRATIGRAPHIC UNIT

Excavation	Blue Sands	Hole in Bedrock	RG	GS	BSW	D	CS	JS	Surface	NIP	Dump	Unknown
University Museum Phila. Acad. 1932-1937	8			11	3	1			2	9		
TMM 1949-50			4	5	13	29	5		10			
TMM April-May 1954				4	7	11	1	6	5			1
Warnica & Shay, July-Aug. 1954		1						129				
TMM Clovis Bison Dig, 1955				12					1		20	1
Warnica & Brown Peccary Dig, 1955		1										
TMM Oct-Nov. 1955			7					1			1	3
Shay Mammoth Dig 1956					3?							
Dittert & Wendorf May 1956			4				1	35				
Wendorf & Green 1958					1	1						
Locality 2 1961									1			
Locality 3 1961				3								
Locality 4 1962				15	179							
Locality 5 1962					11							
ENMU spring conduit 1962				45	244							
Locality 6 1962				3	17		11			4		
Green 1962				17?								
El Llano Dig 1 1962-63				113	17		23	1		11		
El Llano Dig 1, 1963, El Llano Society *				60								
Warnica collection				1						141		
Locality 20 (Warnica collection)									31			
Brown collection										4		
Collins collection										7		
Krieble collection										6		
Murray collection										24		
Collins collection Locality 15H				31								
Agate Basin Locality 1962				9								
Totals	8	1	4	298	512	28	67	176	32	214	30	
											Contact	

? Provenience not certain

* Described in Warnica (1966)

The above tally does not include approximately 40 artifacts from the base of the BSW at Locality 4 reported to have been collected by F.E. Green in 1962 nor artifacts from the North Wall spring conduits reported by Haynes and Agogino (1966).

Carbonaceous Silt, the time of the Parallel Flaked Horizon.

Subsequent to the preparation of the main text of this manuscript numerous artifact finds were made in the conduits of springs adjacent to the north wall of the El Llano Dig. While these artifacts were not available for typological analysis, their presence yields information about the prehistoric occupations at the pond.

According to Haynes and Agogino (1966, pp. 817-18), the following artifacts were present in the specific conduits: Conduit 2--600 flakes and artifacts including 3 Clovis, 6 Folsom, 1 Midland, and 11 Agate Basin points. Conduit 3--174 flakes and artifacts including 3 Folsom and 3 Midland points. Conduit 4--contained no diagnostic artifacts but 9 Agate Basin points were found nearby. Conduit 5--contained an aberrant side notched point. Conduit 6--several Folsom points were found in the immediate vicinity.

According to the type of the included artifacts and geological character of the sediments contributed by the conduits Haynes and Agogino (1966, p. 818) date the functioning of the conduits as follows: Conduits 2 and 7 were open during Clovis times and contributed sediments to units C_0 and C_1. Conduits 2, 3, 4, and 6 were open during the deposition of unit D_1 and were contemporaneous with the Folsom and Agate Basin occupations. Conduit 5 may have been active as late as Archaic times. The high number of flakes and artifacts which occur in relatively pure assemblages within the respective conduits lead Haynes and Agogino to infer the following: (1) The springs were visited infrequently--hence the low incidence of cultural mixture; and (2) Flakes and artifacts were thrown into the springs either as a means of conveniently discarding them or possibly as offerings.

Campsites

Three campsite areas have been recorded (Fig. 127). Occupational debris was recovered from the west margin of the old pond at Locality 4 and the nearby ENMU spring conduit. These remains included a limited quantity of Clovis materials and the largest Folsom collection from the site. A second major occupation site was the northwest margin of the pond in the vicinity of spring conduits along the north bank of El Llano Dig 1. The campsite debris was found throughout the El Llano excavation, but it is believed this occurrence was the result of alluvial deposition. The area thought to have been occupied was the Caliche Caprock rimming the pond immediately to the north and west of the pond margin at the El Llano dig. This area represents the most heavily occupied camping area during the Clovis Period and also featured a fairly sizable Folsom occupation. Excavation on the Caliche Caprock failed to reveal any artifacts. It is thus assumed that the Caliche had been swept clean of occupational debris by rainfall runoff which dumped the cultural materials into the pond. A third campsite area features Archaic age materials present at the Carbonaceous Silt--Jointed Sand contact along the northeast margin of the pond. The Station B excavations of Warnica and Shay and Trench A of Dittert and Wendorf revealed these Archaic materials. Also noted from the Archaic occupation are numerous hand dug wells at the site, indicative of camping activity. No deposit of campsite debris was located in the Carbonaceous Silt unit.

Killsites

The number of identified killsites within the pond may also be described by type and period (Fig. 128). Bison kills are the most numerous and are recorded from the Gray Sand, Brown Sand Wedge, Diatomite, Carbonaceous Silt, and Jointed Sand. Although these killsites are common at the site it should be kept in mind that they cover a time interval of some 6,000 years and, therefore, actually record infrequent events. A summary of these kills is presented in Table LII.

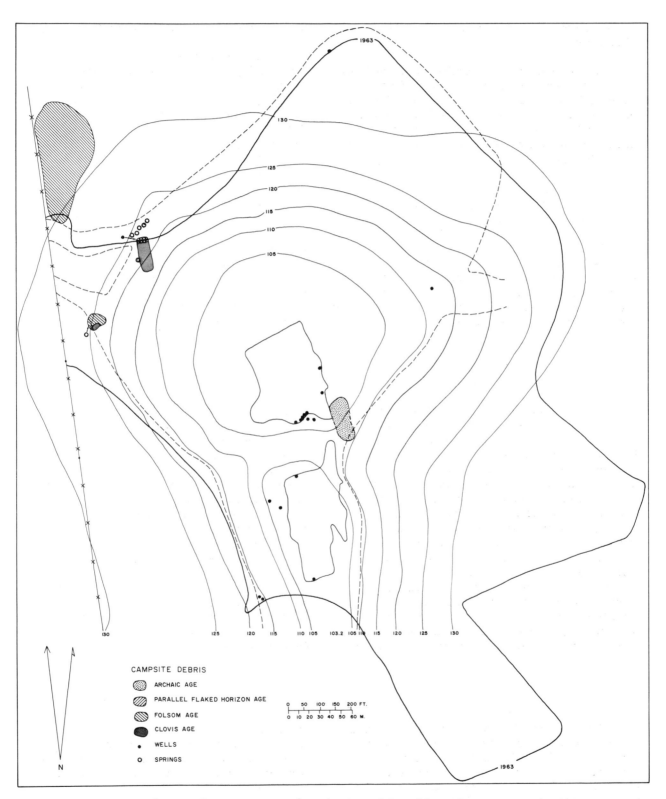

Fig. 127. Location of campsite areas around perimeter of the old pond.

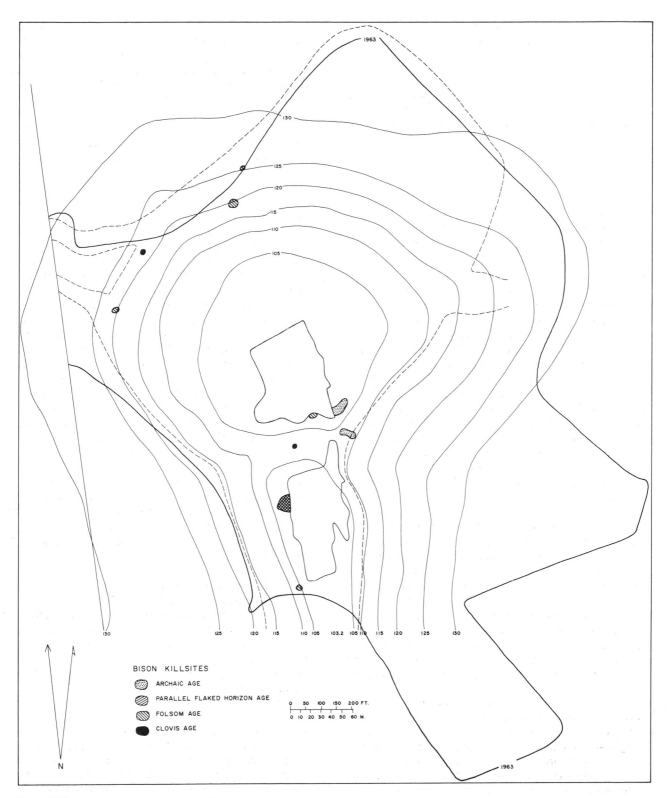

Fig. 128. Location of bison killsite areas.

TABLE LII

SUMMARY OF DATA ON BISON KILLS

Bison Kills

Area	Bed	Culture	Excavation
E. Side N. Pit	JS	Archaic	Station B, Warnica & Shay 1954, Dittert & Wendorf Trench A 1956
S. Side N. Pit	CS	Parallel Flaked	TMM 1949-50, Station A
W. Side S. Pit	CS	Parallel Flaked	TMM 1949-50, Station E
W. Side S. Pit	D	Folsom	TMM 1949-50, Station E
S. Side S. Pit	D	Folsom	Cotter 1937
N.W. Side N. Pit	BSW	Folsom	Locality 3, Hester 1961
N.W. Side N. Pit	BSW	Folsom	Green & Wendorf 1958
W. Side N. Pit	BSW	Folsom	Locality 5, Hester 1961
N.W. Side N. Pit	BSW	Folsom	El Llano Dig 1, 1962-63
S. Side N. Pit	GS	Clovis	TMM 1955

Exact information is not available on all the above kills as to the number of animals represented. The average number of bison in these kills appears to have been five or six. Seven are noted by Sellards in his 1955 excavation, five are recorded by Cotter (1938), five were present at Locality 3, two or three at Locality 5, one reported by Green and Wendorf, and one was found at El Llano Dig 1. There is no evidence to my knowledge of any massive kills on the order of those at Plainview or Olsen Chubbuck. On the contrary the evidence suggests that the kills at Blackwater Locality No. 1 consisted of the surprising of a few bison at a time.

The distribution of these kills through time--ten documented kills, distributed over five to six thousand years--leads us to infer a relatively infrequent use of the pond. There are, of course, a large number of isolated bones scattered throughout the deposits indicating an additional undeterminable number of kills. However, even if these bones represent an equal number of kills we are presented with evidence of intermittent use of the pond on the order of one bison kill every 200 or 300 years.

The mammoth kills are also not particularly common. Documented kills, with associated Clovis artifacts, were present at El Llano Dig 1--4 mammoths; the Cotter excavation of 1936-37--2 mammoths; excavations at Station A--1 mammoth; and Shay's 1956 excavation--1 mammoth. An additional seven mammoths (complete or partial), all found separately, are known

from the pit, but none had artifacts associated with them. Scattered finds occurring at other localities represent several additional mammoths (Fig. 129). Sam Sanders, the gravel pit owner, reports that several more mammoths were removed by the bulldozers without any scientific recording. In any event the evidence at hand provides us with no more than about one mammoth kill per hundred years and twice that often if we accept all mammoth remains as indicating human initiated kills.

The evidence from these killsites and campsites could all be the remains of very small bands of people, about 20 in number, who visited the site at infrequent intervals. Our best evidence is from the Locality 5 killsite with the associated campsite debris from Locality 4, the ENMU spring conduit, and Locality 6. These artifacts totaling nearly 400 include only slightly more than 100 shaped implements of which 30 are Folsom points. It is conceivable that this evidence, the most abundant at the site, represents a camp of approximately 20 people, who killed the two or three bison at Locality 5 and then camped on the margin of the pond adjacent to the spring conduit. They butchered the bison and remained in the area while the women processed the hides and the meat was consumed. It is possible the men went out on daily hunts bringing additional small game back to the camp. They also repaired their broken spears making new points and discarding their old broken ones. After the men succeeded in making a new kill of big game at another site the group moved there after having spent two or three weeks at the Blackwater site.

The mammoth remains within the pit occur in several definite clusters. Groups of mammoth were killed at three locations: (1) the northwest side of the pit near the spring conduits at the El Llano dig site, (2) near the eastern margin of the pond at Station A, and (3) the southwest corner of the pit near the outlet channel. These occurrences all suggest that favored watering spots occurred at these localities and furthermore access to the edge of the pond was available. Access to the northwest corner of the pond was afforded by two arroyos while the outlet channel permitted easy access from the south. We may assume a similar easy access was available on the east side of the pond although evidence of an arroyo or other route

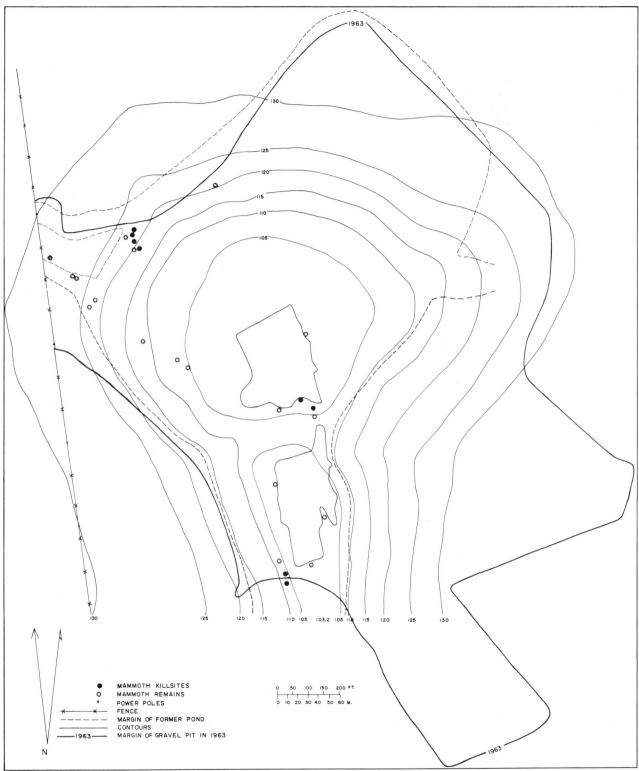

Fig. 129. Location of mammoth kills and areas with mammoth remains not known to have had associated artifacts. The mammoth shown at the southern end of the South Pit was excavated by Portales amateurs Clifton McGehee and Ben Donathan in 1935 and was reported to Cotter the following year.

was not located near Station A.

A fourth occurrence of mammoth remains is a group of specimens or isolated bones aligned in a NW-SE trending line leading up the channel of one of the arroyos on the northwest side of the pond. These occurrences indicate a much used access route and also document the post depositional scattering of bones by water transported in this arroyo. The absence of artifacts suggests that most of these remains pertain to naturally occurring deaths. The remains farther out in the pond are most complete, thus indicating less scattering through water activity.

Observations on Vertebrate Remains

Cultural inferences based on the presence or absence of specific animal bones are limited by the quality of the data. We have available the bones listed in the Texas Museum accession record for excavations between 1949 and 1956. Unfortunately, these bones were identified in the field and, therefore, are subject to some probable inaccuracies. In many cases these finds were not identified as to species and, therefore, cannot be of service to our study. A tabulation of the specimens from these excavations with both a specific identification and assignment to a specific stratum is presented in Table LIII.

Museum are compared with two additional Folsom Age bison kills at Locality 3 and Locality 5 (Table LIV). Remains of all other animals found in the Gray Sand occur in such limited quantity as to suggest that their presence may be due to natural causes rather than to human action.

TABLE LIII

VERTEBRATE SPECIMENS COLLECTED BY THE TEXAS MEMORIAL MUSEUM 1949-56, TALLIED BY SPECIES AND STRATUM

	Terrapene caniculata	Smilodon californicus	Ondatra zibethica	Platygonus sp.	Equus conversidens	Equus niobrarensis	Equus scotti	Equus sp.	Camelops sp.	Bison antiquus	Bison sp.	Mammuthus sp.	Turtle	Muskrat	Carnivore	Wolf	Peccary	Deer	Camel	Elephant	Sloth?	Bird	Unidentified
Gray Sand	3		1	2	1	8	4	16	41	4	1	43	4	9		1	1	1	1	5	8	1	1 55
Brown Sand Wedge									14				8										6
Diatomite									134	1	1								1				5
Carbonaceous Silt									14														7
Jointed Sand									10														79
Other proveniences (contacts, wells, etc.)					3				15	2									2				5
Unknown provenience					2				12									1	2				8

Only the Gray Sand possesses a reasonably complete fauna of which bison, horse, turtle, and elephant may have been utilized for food by man. We have conclusive evidence that bison and elephants were killed and butchered. The turtles may have been eaten, but there is no conclusive evidence of butchering and, to my knowledge, none of the bones are charred. The turtles presumably inhabited the pond. Horse remains are numerous in the Gray Sand. The frequency of individual bones of horse and bison remains from the Gray Sand and Diatomite collected by the Texas Memorial

TABLE LIV

FREQUENCY OF BISON AND HORSE REMAINS BY INDIVIDUAL BONE

	Astragali	Phalanges	Calcaneus	Metapodials	Other foot bone	Teeth	Skulls	Horn-cores	Jaws	Scapulae	Femur	Tibiae	Ulnae	Leg bones	Radii	Ribs	Humeri	Pelves	Vertebrae	Unidentified
TMM ALL DIGS 1949-1956 Horse Gray Sand	2	2		1		60								1		1				2
TMM ALL DIGS 1949-1956 Bison Gray Sand	5	4	1	4		4	4	1	6	3		1		2		1				4 3
TMM ALL DIGS 1949-1956 Bison Diatomite	10	34	3	22	53	2			3	1				3		1		1		
Locality 3 Bison Kill	2	3		9	2	3	3		1	1	1	2	1	2		16	2	1	1	14
Locality 5 Bison Kill			5	1						1		1				2	3	2	2	8 16

These comparisons reveal that the bison remains include high percentages of lower limb and foot bones with most other bones present but rare. The horse remains are almost exclusively individual teeth although a few foot bones are also present. To me, this distribution suggests that since only the more resistant bones of horse have been preserved, these specimens, for the most part, may have been redeposited and, therefore, they antedate human occupation of the site.

The bison remains do not occur in an expectable frequency based on the number of specific bones in a bison skeleton. This fact has been documented in Table LV which compares the actual bones found in one of the bet-

TABLE LV

COMPARISON OF BISON REMAINS WITH EXPECTABLE FREQUENCY
OF THESE REMAINS

Locality 3 Bison Kill	Astragali	Phalanges	Other Foot Bones	Metapodials	Teeth	Skulls
Actual	2	3	2	9	3	3
Potential	6	36	24	12	-	3
Missing	4	34	22	4	-	0

Locality 3	Jaws	Scapulae	Femora	Tibiae	Ulni	Leg Bones	Ribs	Humeri	Pelves
Actual	1	1	1	2	1	2	16	2	1
Potential	6	6	6	6	6	24	78	6	6
Missing	5	5	5	4	5	17	65	4	5

Locality 3	Vertebrae	Unidentified
Actual	1	14
Potential	78	-
Missing	77	-

ter documented bison kills (Locality 3) with the number of bones potentially present at such a kill.

The difference between these two figures is the number of bones missing which may have been carried away by the hunters. In the present case the evidence suggests the major portions of the animal were cut up and carried away with the bones enclosed. These sections included the upper legs, ribcage, backbone, and pelvic area. The tail was presumably also removed with the skin as caudal vertebrae have not been identified. This pattern of butchering of bison was not universally the case, as some scapulae, upper leg bones, and pelves are present. However, the butchering pattern described seems to have been the most common. Data from other levels, the Diatomite, Carbonaceous Silt, and Jointed Sand, are comparable, although it is believed our data are only reliable in a general sense. Therefore, percentile calculations on the specific occurrences would be fallacious. There is considerable variation in recording of the finds from the different excavations. For example, unidentified bones were rarely recorded by the Texas Memorial Museum. In addition, Sellards specifically requested that Warnica and Shay collect astragali for weight studies of the type described in the Milnesand site report (Sellards, 1955). The missing foot bones may be due to their small size, simply not being preserved, or possibly being overlooked by the excavators.

In summary, we have evidence of human ambush and butchering of elephants and bison with use of all other species not clearly demonstrated. The elephants were butchered pri-

marily by cutting meat from the bones, which were then left at the killsite. The meatier portions of the bison killed were carried elsewhere for consumption with the bones enclosed. The evidence available suggests that this pattern of bison butchering was utilized throughout the Paleo-Indian occupation of the site.

The evidence for the fauna present in each bed is also limited by differential study and reporting. Another limiting factor seems to be that bone preservation was much better in the sandy units deposited in an aqueous environment (Gray Sand and Brown Sand Wedge) than it was in the overlying silty units representing an alternately wet and dry marsh environment. Notwithstanding these problems it is possible to summarize the known faunas by bed (Table LVI).

TABLE LVI

SUMMARY OF VERTEBRATE SPECIES PRESENT BY BED

Species	RG	GS	BSW	D	CS	JS
Terrapene canaliculata		X				
Turtle		X		X		
Aenocyon dirus (Leidy)		X		X		
Canis lupus		X				
Wolf			X			
Canis latrans		X				
Vulpes velox		X				
Smilodon californicus		X				
Microtus pennsylvanicus			X			
Lepus alleni			X			
Ondatra zibetheca		X				
Muskrat				X		
Platygonus sp.		X				
Camelops sp.		X				
Tanupolama macrocephala		X				
Antilocaprid		X				
Bison antiquus		X				
Bison sp.		X	X	X	X	X
Equus conversidens		X				
E. niobrarensis		X				
E. scotti		X				
Mammuthus sp.		X	X			

The fauna reported by Stock and Bode (1937) has provenience assigned to undifferentiated "Blue Sands" and, therefore, is not included here. The fauna they report includes two species not present in the list above; Cynomys near ludovicianus (Ord) and Cervus sp. A third species, Terrapene ornata agassiz, is reported from Anderson Basin which is another site nearby. The above list does not include specimens collected from the Brown Sand Wedge by Slaughter. He washed and screened material from that unit and obtained a fauna of 12 to 14 species which is described in another publication (Wendorf and Hester, n.d.). With the exception of Bison remains, vertebrate specimens in the Diatomite, Carbonaceous Silt, and Jointed Sand were rare.

Radiocarbon Dating

Although fifteen radiocarbon dates have been obtained on samples from the gravel pit, the site is still inadequately dated in some respects. A schematic diagram, Figure 130, and a map, Figure 131, illustrate the position of these dates with respect to the stratigraphic units and their associated cultural material.

The Clovis horizon is represented by three dates between 11,040 B.P. $\pm$ 500 years and 11,630 B.P. $\pm$ 400 years. While these samples would appear to date the Clovis artifacts associated with the mammoths in El Llano Dig 1, they do not cover the full thickness of the Gray Sand unit as it existed in the center of the pond. Sample A-536 although obtained on a mammoth rib yielded an age of 6370 $\pm$ 160 which is interpreted as being too young and thus contaminated with younger organic matter (Haynes, et al., 1967).

The Folsom horizon is represented by four dates ranging from 10,170 B.P. $\pm$ 250 years to 10,490 B.P. $\pm$ 900 years. These dates appear to bracket the Folsom occupation rather well, and it may be considered the best dated culture and enclosing stratigraphic unit (the Diatomite) at the site.

The Carbonaceous Silt and associated artifacts are not well dated even though four

dates are available for the unit. All these dates are on samples collected from the top of the unit, thus leaving the age of the beginning of the deposition of the Carbonaceous Silt a matter of speculation. In addition, these dates show a range from 8,890 B.P. $\pm$ 290 years, to 6,230 B.P. $\pm$ 150 years, a range of more than 2,500 years. It seems reasonable to assume that some of these dates are not reliable. If an error exists it seems probable that the dates on bone of 6,230 B.P. $\pm$ 150 years and 6,300 B.P. $\pm$ 150 years are too young. Numerous samples of charred bone were collected by Sellards, and it might be possible to have some of these dated. In any event, the age of the Carbonaceous Silt is still in doubt.

The Jointed Sand with its Archaic culture is represented by one date of 4,950 B.P. $\pm$ 150 years. More samples from this horizon should be dated.

Dates on contacts are available for the Diatomite (D1-D2 contact, Haynes, 1965) 10,170 $\pm$ 250 and 10,490 $\pm$ 200; and for the Jointed Sand-Carbonaceous Silt (E-F contact, Haynes, 1965) 8470 $\pm$ 350. A list of radiocarbon samples collected with information as to their disposition is presented below.

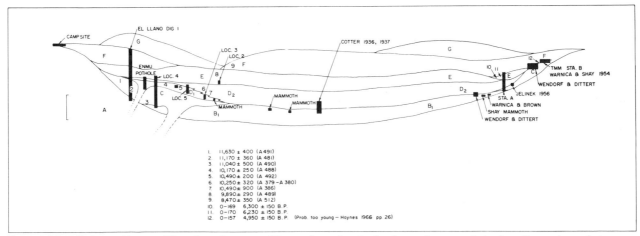

Fig. 130. Schematic profile showing position of geologic beds and associated radiocarbon dates.

TABLE LVII

RADIOCARBON SAMPLES COLLECTED AND PROCESSED

Cat. No.	Type of Sample	Location	Bed	Collected By	Laboratory Receiving Sample	Result of Test	Date	Remarks
937-303	Burned bone	Station A	JS	Witte 5/54				
937-330	"Carbon"	Warnica & Shay Dig 1954 Fig. 15 Loc. 6	JS	Shay 6/10/54				
937-411	Unknown	Warnica & Shay Dig 1954 Fig. 15 Loc. 6	JS	Shay 7/1/54	Chicago			
937-449	Bones	Station C Fig. 15 Loc. 4	JS	Sellards 4/23/54				
937-450	Bones	Station C Fig. 15 Loc. 4	DS	Sellards 4/23/54				
937-451	Elephant bones	Station C Fig. 15 Loc. 4	GS	Sellards 4/23/54				
937-452	Elephant bones	Station C Fig. 15 Loc. 4	GS	Sellards 4/23/54				
937-453	Bison bones	Station C Fig. 15 Loc. 4	DS	Sellards 4/23/54				
937-444	Elephant tusk	Unknown	GS	Shay 4/23/54	Chicago			
937-445	Elephant tusk	Station A	Un-known	Shay 4/26/54	Chicago, Lamont 7/23/55	Returned to Sellards		
937-446	Bison bones	Unknown	GS	Shay 5/54				
937-454	Bison bones (11 packages)	Warnica & Shay Dig 1954 Fig. 15 Loc. 6	Base of JS	Shay & Warnica 8/54	3 packages Lamont 6/29/55			Could be top of CS
937-462	Burned bone	Warnica & Shay Dig 1954 Fig. 15 Loc. 6	JS	Shay & Warnica 8/54				
937-463	Burned bone	Warnica & Shay Dig 1954 Fig. 15 Loc. 6	Base of JS	Shay & Warnica 8/54				Could be top of CS
937-464	Burned bone (20 packages)	Warnica & Shay Dig 1954 Fig. 15 Loc. 6	JS	Shay & Warnica 8/54	Chicago 9/54 2 packages Lamont 7/30/55 4 packages			
937-502	Charred bone	Warnica & Shay Dig 1954 Fig. 15 Loc. 6	Base of JS	Probably Shay	Humble 8/1/55 2 packages plated		4,950 ± 130	Brannon, et al. (1957)
937-503	Bones	N. Side W. Pit	GS	Probably Shay				
937-506	Charred bone	E. of Station B	Un-known	Shay				
937-509	Charred bone	E. of Station B	JS	Shay				
937-545	Unknown	E. of Station B	CS					
937-590	Bones	Pit 2 Fig. 15 Loc. 7C	GS	Sellards	Lamont 6/23/55			
937-592	Bones	Clovis Bison Kill Fig. 15 Loc. 7A	GS		Humble			
937-624	Bones	Unknown	D	Unknown	Lamont 6/30/55			
937-625	Bones	Clovis Bison Kill Fig. 15 Loc. 7A	GS	Shay				
937-693	Bones	Unknown	GS	Unknown				
937-694	Skull	Unknown	Un-known	J. Warnica				
937-695	Skull	Unknown	GS	Unknown				
937-720	Bones	Unknown	Un-known	Unknown	Humble 8/1/55			
937-720-A	Charred bones	Sellards Oct.-Nov. 1955 Dig Fig. 15 Loc. 7	CS	Sellards & Schoen 10/55	Humble 12/8/55		6,230 ± 150	Brannon, et al. (1957)
937-799-B	Uncharred bones	Sellards Oct.-Nov. 1955 Dig Fig. 15 Loc. 7	CS	Sellards & Schoen 10/55	Humble 12/8/55		6,300 ± 150	Brannon, et al. (1957)
937-793	Charred earth	Sellards Oct.-Nov. 1955 Dig Fig. 15 Loc. 7	CS	Sellards & Schoen 10/55				Same Location as 937-779
937-855	Bones	Unknown	Base of CS	Warnica & Brown 1955				
937-858	Bone	Pit 2 Fig. 15 Loc. 7C	CS	Sellards 5/56				
937-860	Charred bone	Pit 2 Fig. 15 Loc. 7C	Un-known	Schoen & Warnica 5/56				From Dark Brown Sand, could be JS
3324-1	Burned bone	Fig. 15, Loc. 10, Trench A, Sec. 1.5	JS	Dittert & Wendorf 5/56				
3324-2	Burned bone	Fig. 15, Loc. 10, Trench A, Sec. 5	JS	Dittert & Wendorf 5/56				
3324-3	Burned bone	Fig. 15, Loc. 10, Trench A, Sec. 6	JS	Dittert & Wendorf 5/56				

Cat. No.	Type of Sample	Location	Bed	Collected By	Laboratory Receiving Sample	Result of Test	Date	Remarks
3324-4	Burned bone	Fig. 15, Loc. 10, Trench A, Sec. 5	JS	Dittert & Wendorf 5/56				
3324-5	Burned bone	Fig. 15, Loc. 10, Trench A, Sec. 6	JS	Dittert & Wendorf 5/56				
3324-6	Burned bone	Fig. 15, Loc. 10, 6'W of Trench A	CS	Dittert & Wendorf				
3324-7	Burned bone	Fig. 15, Trench A, Sec. 5	JS CS	Dittert & Wendorf 5/56				
3324-8	Burned bone	Fig. 15, 6'W of Trench A	CS	Dittert & Wendorf 5/56				
3324-9	Burned bone	Fig. 15, Trench A, Sec. 6	JS CS	Dittert & Wendorf 5/56				
A-379	Carbonized plants	Fig. 15, Loc. 15C	D	Harbour, Hester, Haynes 2/62	Arizona	Dated	9,900 ± 320	Damon, et al. 1964
A-380	Carbonized plants	Fig. 15, Loc. 15C	D	Harbour, Hester, Haynes 2/62	Arizona	Dated	10,600 ± 320	Humic acids fraction
							10,250 ± 320	Average of A-379 & A-380
A-386	Carbonized plants	Fig. 15, Loc. 15C	D	Harbour, Hester, Haynes 2/62	Arizona	Dated	10,490 ± 900	Damon, et al. 1964
A-345	Snail shells	Locality 1 Fig. 15, Loc. 12A	D?	Hester, Harbour 9/61	Texas	Returned to Museum of N.M.		Not processed
Unknown	Snail shells	Locality 1 Fig. 15, Loc. 12A	D?	Hester, Harbour 9/61	Arizona			Same sample as A-345
Unknown	Elephant tusk	Fig. 15, Loc. 5D	BSW	Hester 8/62	Arizona	no carbon		**Brown Sand** facies of D
Unknown	Elephant tusk	Locality 4 Fig. 15, Loc. 15E	BSW	Hester 9/62	Arizona			Brown Sand facies of D
Unknown	Burned bone	El Llano Dig 1	BSW	Hester 9/62	Arizona	Dated		Brown Sand facies of D
A-481		El Llano Dig 1	BSW	Haynes 63	Arizona	Dated	11,170 ± 360	Damon, et al. 1964
A-488	Carbonized plants	El Llano Dig 1 Fig. 15, Loc. 18	D	Haynes 63	Arizona	Dated	10,170 ± 250	Haynes, et al. 1966
A-489	Carbonized plants	El Llano Dig 1 Fig. 15, Loc. 18	C	Haynes 63	Arizona	Dated	9,890 ± 290	Haynes, et al. 1966
A-490	Carbonized plants	El Llano Dig 1 Fig. 15, Loc. 18	BSW	Haynes 63	Arizona	Dated	11,040 ± 500	Haynes, et al. 1966
A-491	Carbonized plants	El Llano Dig 1 Fig. 15, Loc. 18	BSW	Haynes 63	Arizona	Dated	11,630 ± 400	Haynes, et al. 1966
A-492	Carbonized plants	El Llano Dig 1 Fig. 15, Loc. 18	D	Haynes 63	Arizona	Dated	10,490 ± 200	Haynes, et al. 1966
A-512	Charred bone	El Llano Dig 1 Fig. 15, Loc. 18	CS JS	Haynes 63	Arizona	Dated	8,470 ± 350	Haynes, et al. 1966
							8,560 ± 350	corrected Haynes, et al. 1967
A-536	Mammoth rib	not given		Haynes 63	Arizona	Dated	6370 ± 160	Haynes, et al. 1967 contaminated

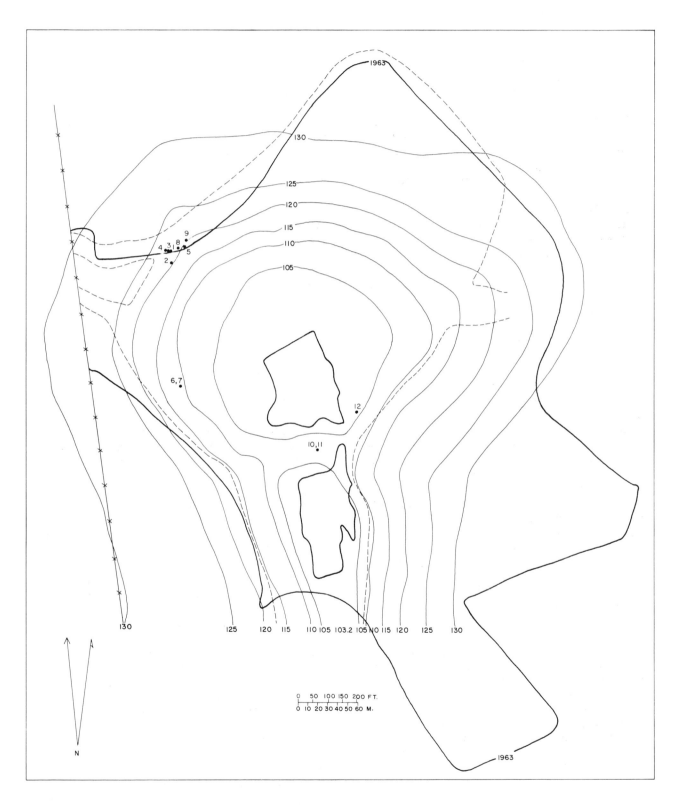

Fig. 131. Map showing location of radiocarbon samples dated.

Paleo Indian Uses of the Pond

Through time the pond functioned primarily as a favored hunting site of the Paleo-Indian occupants of the Llano Estacado. For the Clovis period there is abundant evidence that mammoths were ambushed, killed, and butchered as they stood in the shallow water at the edge of the pond. The major portion of the evidence suggests that these animals were killed individually rather than in small family groups. The mammoths were butchered where they fell with a minimum of disarticulation of the bones, which suggests the meat was cut from the bones and carried elsewhere to be consumed. The skulls were frequently smashed which may mean that brains were collected and eaten. The foot bones and tail vertebrae were missing suggesting that they were also carried away for cultural purposes. As the carcasses were left to rot near the springs it is assumed the hunting band soon moved on after a kill.

The only Clovis campsite areas located were situated on the caliche cap on the west and northwest edges of the pond adjacent to the spring conduits. As these areas were subsequently cleaned of cultural debris by sheetwash, we have been able to learn little about the campsites. It is presumed that these areas were where the meat from the kills was consumed and some tools were manufactured. At one locality within the pond several bison were killed and butchered by Clovis peoples, but little information is available as to the exact butchering techniques utilized. Numerous other vertebrate remains have been recovered from the Clovis level, but there is no conclusive evidence that these species were consumed by men.

The mixed nature of the artifactual stone, all of which was imported from quarries up to 100 miles away, suggests that this particular pond was only one of many visited on an irregular basis as the band hunted over the area. The favorite stone was Alibates chert quarried near the Canadian river approximately 100 miles northeast of the site. A grinding stone suggests that, even at this early date, gathering of plant foods supplemented the diet.

The succeeding Folsom hunters utilized the pond in almost the same fashion as the Clovis peoples. The hunting techniques were similar, and the same areas were utilized for camping. There was much more frequent use, however, than in the preceding period, which could be due to several causes.

The Folsom peoples relied heavily on bison for their food, the mammoth having become extinct after Clovis time. The nature of the pond had also altered to a muddy bottom rather than a sandy one which may have helped the hunters by miring the bison. Butchering techniques included the grouping of skulls with mandibles removed which suggests some differentiation of the work by worker. Also a metapodial was used to break the mandible loose from the skull in order to remove the tongue. The lower limb bones were usually left in place where the animal fell.

The springs were also known and used as attested by the inclusion of numerous artifacts and bones within them. Haynes and Agogino (1966) have even suggested the springs were given artifacts as offerings by the Paleo-Indian peoples. There was a shift in preference in stone types to Edwards chert. Presumably, this also records an associated shift in the territory hunted as the Edwards chert quarry lies approximately 150 miles to the southeast of the site.

Circular shallow firepits are reported from the Brown Sand Wedge along the eastern pond margin. These pits, 36 inches in diameter and 8 inches deep, may also be associated with the Folsom occupation.

The use of the pond by the peoples of the Parallel Flaked Horizon followed a pattern similar to that of the Folsom peoples. The site was again extensively hunted with small herds of bison being surprised at the edges of the pond where they were killed and butchered. The lower limb bones were usually left in place as were the scapulae, ribs, and lower jaws. The upper leg bones and pelves were rare and tail bones were absent. This suggests the animals were skinned and the better portions of meat with included bones were transferred elsewhere to be eaten. Some of the tools used in butchering were manufactured on the spot. No concentration of campsite debris was located although it is assumed the people camped nearby. One shell artifact indicated fresh water mussels were known and utilized but it is not known if they were eaten. Again the absence of cooking pits restricts our knowledge of the prehistoric diet.

The Archaic peoples practised similar bison hunts around the pond margin. However, these were soon terminated by increasing aridity. The Archaic use of the site included the digging of wells to reach the water table.

About 20 of these wells are known, situated for the most part in the center of the depression. The wells included steps cut into the side to facilitate reaching the water table. One campsite was located on the eastern side of the pit.

The Recent Indians do not seem to have utilized the pond depression to any degree which suggests that after the Altithermal the depression did not collect sufficient surface runoff to be a more reliable source of surface water than hundreds of similar depressions in the area.

Typological Considerations

The Paleo-Indian artifactural collections studied herein represent some of the largest reported to date. The Clovis collection is the largest (223) known from any Clovis site in the Western United States. The Folsom collection (534) is larger than any reported except that from Lindenmeier. The more recent materials are important but are not present in large quantity. The decision implemented in this report has been to describe by attribute the artifacts present in such a way that they may be compared both collectively and individually with artifacts from other sites. It has also been my intent to describe in detail all of the artifacts, not just varieties of projectile points. The net result of this methodology has been the compilation of a sizable body of data on these industries which is not matched by most of the Paleo-Indian materials in print to date. The latter feature detailed descriptions of projectile point types found in killsites, rather than descriptions of industries. As a result of this situation I have chosen not to make detailed comparisons with other site collections at this time, as I believe most are not comparable in a statistically valid sense. However, to facilitate future such comparative studies a cumulative graph (based on the data in Table LVIII) of all the industries present at Blackwater Locality No. 1 is presented in Figure 132.

I have in another publication (Hester, 1966) expressed the point of view that the Clovis industry is a continent-wide complex. Sellards definition of the Llano complex seems to me to be too narrowly restricted in a geo-

graphic sense as the same cultural manifestations occur from Nova Scotia to Arizona. Therefore, for purposes of standardization of terminology, I believe the older, more widely used term "Clovis" should be retained for this complex. In this report I have also suggested that the term "Portales Complex" be dropped from the literature, as, in my opinion, it is not based on a true cultural assemblage but is in fact an

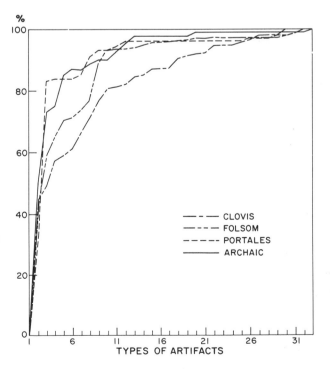

Fig. 132. Cumulative graph of all tools by culture.

assemblage accumulated through geologic activity.

The decision not to make detailed typological comparisons postpones this important research to a later date. However, I have made this decision with the knowledge that studies of major Paleo-Indian collections are now underway by a number of researchers, including Henry Irwin, Edwin Wilmsen, Joe Ben Wheat, Hans Müeller Beck, Marie Wormington, and others. When their efforts are completed, we will have available for comparison large well-described site collections including those from Lindenmeier, Hell-Gap, Frazier, and Van Horn. At that time it would seem appropriate to consider a large scale comparative study of Paleo-Indian industries with the aid of a computer.

TABLE LVIII*

ARTIFACT PERCENTAGES BY CULTURE AND TYPE
SUMMARIZED FROM APPENDIX I

Type	Clovis	Folsom	Portales	Archaic
1 Flakes	44.3	44.1	33	50.0
2 Points	5.1	14.8	50	23.7
3 Side Scrapers	7.9	6.6	1	1.2
4 End Scrapers	1.7	5.2		10.0
5 Gravers	2.2	1.0		2.4
6 Unifacial Knives	5.1	2.3	1	
7 Bifacial Knives	5.1	2.5	6	1.2
8 Flake Scrapers	5.6	12.6	2	1.2
9 Flake Knives	3.2	4.2		
10 Scraper-Gravers	0.4	0.5	1	2.4
11 Scrapers	0.4	0.8	2	3.6
12 Hammerstones	2.2	0.3		2.4
13 Channel Flakes	0.4	1.1		
14 Hollow Edge Scrapers	1.7	0.5		
15 Nodules		0.1		
16 Unidentified Point Frags.		0.3		
17 End and Side Scrapers	2.7	0.1		
18 Choppers	0.4	0.1		1.2
19 Cores	0.4	0.5		
20 Flake Graver		0.1		
21 Pebbles	2.2	0.1		
22 Abrader		0.1		
23 Flake Knife and Graver	0.8			
24 Burin and Scraper	0.4			
25 Flake Scraper-Knife	1.7		1	
26 Chips	0.4			
27 Pebble Scraper	0.4		1	
28 Grinding Stone	0.4			
29 Bone Artifacts	6.2	0.5	1	
30 Shell Artifacts			1	
31 Burins	0.4			
32 Paint Stones				1.2
Total	101.6	98.4	100	100.5

*These data are graphed in Figure 83.

APPENDIX I

Cat. No.	Type	Locus	Culture	Date Found	Found By	Material	Core Tool	Secondary Flake	Prepared Core	Primary Flake	Bulb Trimmed	Billet Technique	Percussion Flaked	Pressure Chipped	Unifacially Retouched	Bifacially Retouched	Upper Face Retouched
937-1	Scraper	NIP	Unknown	1949-50	Witte	Ed. Chert			P	x					x	x	x
937-2	Point, Archaic	NIP	Unknown	1949-50	Witte	Chal.								x		x	
937-3	Point frag. Folsom variant	NIP	Folsom	1949-50	Witte	Chert								x		x	
937-4	Scraper	4E,D	Folsom	1949	Witte	Ed. Chert			P	x				x	x	x	x
937-5	Point	4E,D	Portales	1949	Witte	Ed. Chert								x		x	
937-6	Knife	4E,CS	Portales	1949	Witte	Quartzite								x	x	x	
397-7	Flake	4E,CS	Portales	1949	Witte	Basalt		x									
397-8	Flake scraper	4E,CS	Portales	1949-50	Witte	Chert		x				x					
937-9	Nodule	4E,D	Folsom	1949-50	Witte	Jasper											
937-10	Point fragment	NIP	Unknown	1949-50	Witte	D. Quart.								x		x	
937-11	Point frag. Folsom	NIP	Folsom	1949-50	Witte	Ed. Chert								x		x	
937-12	Point frag. Folsom	4E,D	Folsom	1949	Witte	Chert								x		x	
937-13	Milnesand point	4E,CS	Portales	1949-50	Witte	Ed. Chert								x		x	
937-14	Knife scraper	4E,CS	Portales	1949-50	Witte	Alibates		x	x					x	x		x
937-15	Knife unifacial	NIP	Unknown	1949-50	Witte	Chal.			x					x	x		x
937-16	Point fragment	4E,CS	Portales	1949-50	Witte	Chert								x		x	
937-18	Point frag. Folsom	4E,D	Folsom	1949-50	Witte	Ed. Chert								x		x	
937-19	Knife frag.	4E,CS	Portales	1949-50	Witte	Alibates								x		x	
937-20	Knife frag.	4E,CS	Portales	1949-50	Witte	Alibates								x		x	
937-21	Point, Scottsbluff	4E,CS	Portales	1949-50	Witte	T. Jasper								x		x	
937-22	Point, Milnesand	4E,CS	Portales	1949-50	Witte	Ed. Chert								x		x	
937-23	Point fragment	4E,CS	Portales	1949-50	Witte	Obsid.								x		x	
937-24	Point, Scottsbluff	4E,CS	Portales	1949-50	Witte	Alibates								x		x	
937-25	Flake	4E,CS	Portales	1949-50	Witte	Chert		x					x	x			
937-25(a)	Flake	4E,CS	Portales	1949-50	Witte	T. Jasper			x								
937-25(a2)	Flake	4E,CS	Portales	1949-50	Witte	Alibates		x	x	x							
937-26	Point (Eden)	4E,CS	Portales	1949-50	Witte	Ed. Chert								x		x	
937-27	Point, Folsom	4A,D	Folsom	1949-50	Witte	Chert								x		x	
937-28	Point frag. Folsom	4I,D	Folsom	1949-50	Witte	Ed. Chert								x		x	
937-29	Core	NIP	Unknown	1949-50	Witte	Quartzite	x							x		x	
937-30	Scraper	4G,D	Folsom	1949-50	Witte	Ed. Chert			P	x				x	x	x	x
937-31	Point frag. Eden	4E,CS	Portales	1949-50	Witte	Alibates								x		x	
937-32	Point, Milnesand	4E,CS	Portales	1949-50	Witte	Ed. Chert								x		x	
937-33	Point fragment	4E,CS	Portales	1949-50	Witte	Obsid.								x		x	
937-33(a)	Point, frag. Scottsbluff	4E,CS	Portales	1949-50	Witte	D. Quart.								x		x	
937-51	Scraper	4A,D	Clovis	1949-50	Witte	Red Jasper		x	x					x	x		x
937-53	Scraper	4A,JS	Portales	1949-50	Witte	Ed. Chert		P	x	x			x	x	x		
937-54	Scraper frag.	4A,D	Folsom	1949-50	Witte	Alibates		x	x					x	x		x
937-55	Scraper	4A,JS	Archaic	1949-50	Witte	Ed. Chert		P	x					x	x		x
937-56	Scraper frag.	4A,JS	Unknown	1949-50	Witte	Chert		x	x					x	x		x
937-58	Point	4G,JS	Archaic	1949-50	Vick	Chert								x		x	
937-59	Point, Folsom	4A,D	Folsom	1949-50	Witte	T. Jasper								x		x	
937-60	Knife frag. bifacial	4J,JS	Archaic	1949-50	Meade	Jasper		x	x				x			x	
937-61	Bone tool	4A,GS	Clovis	1949-50	Sellards	Bone											
937-62	Point frag. Scottsbluff	4E,CS	Portales	1949-50	Witte	Ed. Chert								x		x	
937-63	Point, Angostura	4E,CS	Portales	1949-50	Witte	Ed. Chert								x	x	x	
937-64	Knife frag.	4E,CS	Portales	1949-50	Meade	T. Jasper		x	x					x		x	
937-65	Point frag.	4E,CS	Portales	1949-50	Meade	Ed. Chert								x		x	
937-66	End scraper	4E,D	Folsom	1949-50	Witte	Ed. Chert		x	x					x	x		x
937-67	Point base, Eden	4E,CS	Portales	1949-50	Witte	Chert								x		x	
937-68	Point, Scottsbluff	4E,CS	Portales	1949-50	Witte	Ed. Chert								x		x	
937-69	Flake	NIP	Unknown	1949-50	Mear	Chert		x	x					x		x	
937-70	Scraper-Graver	4E,CS	Portales	1949-50	Mear	Ed. Chert		x	x					x	x		x
937-71	Flake	4E,D	Folsom	1949-50	Witte	Ed. Chert			x			x					
937-72	Point, Clovis	4A,GS	Clovis	1949-50	Witte	Alibates								x		x	

Cat. No.	Nether Face Retouched	Modified by use	Transverse X Sec.	Anterior-Posterior X Sec.	Edge Angles	Expanding Stem	Shoulder Stem	Contracting Stem	Side Notches	Straight Base	Convex Base	Concave Base	Fluted	Parallel Flaking	Length of Grinding on Sides	Base Ground	Base Thinning	Blade Form	Tip Reworked	Portion of Edge Worked	Points on Perimeter	Median Ridge on Blade	Serrated Edge	Length	Width	Thickness	Length of Flute
937-1			ST	ST	45°																			2.4	1.7	0.5	
937-2			LEN	LEN		x						x	0	x	0.7		x	leaf						2.2	0.7	0.25	
937-3			LEN	LEN									2		0.3			leaf						1.7	0.75	0.15	0.3
937-4			PLCX	BCCX																7/8				1.9	1.6	0.5	
937-5			LEN	LEN						x					0.5	x	x	tri.						1.0	0.6	0.2	
937-6			LEN							x							x							2.6	1.3	0.3	
937-7			PLCX	LEN																				1.2	0.6	0.15	
937-8	x		PLCX	BCCX																				1.4	0.9	0.1	
937-9																								3.3	2.8	1.5	
937-10			LEN	LEN									x											0.5	0.9	0.3	
937-11			LEN										2	x				leaf						1.5	0.8	0.15	
937-12			BCCX									x	2		0.9	x	x	leaf						0.9	0.8	0.15	
937-13	x		LEN	LEN								x			1.4	x	x	leaf						2.8	1.0	0.25	
937-14	x		ST	TRAP	45°																			2.1	1.0	0.2	
937-15			PLCX	PLCX																				1.7	0.8	0.15	
937-16			LEN	LEN								x		x	1.0	x	x	leaf						3.2	0.9	0.2	
937-18			BCCX									x	2		1.3	x	x	elong						1.6	0.7	0.1	1.7
937-19			LEN															leaf						1.1	1.0	0.25	
937-20			LEN															leaf						0.8	1.3	0.25	
937-21			LEN									x		x			x	leaf						2.2	1.0	0.25	
937-22			LEN								x	x					x	leaf						3.0	0.8	0.3	0.8
937-23			LEN									x					x	leaf						1.5	0.9	0.2	
937-24			LEN								x	x			0.6		x	leaf						2.2	1.0	0.3	
937-25																								1.0	0.8	0.1	
937-25(a)	x		PLCX	BCCX																				1.0	1.1	0.2	
937-25(a2)	x	x	PLCX	BCCX																				1.1	1.2	0.15	
937-26		x	DIA						x			x			0.7	x	x	strt						4.3	0.7	0.3	
937-27			LEN									x	1		0.7									1.4	0.7	0.15	1.0
937-28			CC									x	1		0.7	x	x					x		1.0	0.7	0.15	0.9
937-29			PLCX	PLCX																				1.9	1.2	0.9	
937-30			PLCX	BCCX	60°																			3.5	2.7	0.3	
937-31			DIA										x					leaf						0.9	0.7	0.2	
937-32			DIA									x	x		1.8	x	x	leaf						3.7	1.0	0.3	
937-33			LEN										x					leaf						0.9	0.8	0.25	
937-33(a)			LEN			1						x	x	x				strt						2.1	0.8	0.2	
937-51		x	PLCX	RT	50°																			1.2	0.9	0.1	
937-53			ST	PLCX	60°																			2.4	1.3	0.7	
937-54			ST	RECT	40°-60°															1/2				1.0	1.8	0.25	
937-55		x	ST	BCCX	40°-60°																			5.0	1.9	0.5	
937-56			ST	ST	70°															1/3				1.5	0.7	0.2	
937-58			LEN	LEN								x		x	0.4		x	leaf						1.3	0.6	0.2	
937-59			LEN	LEN								x			0.7		x			2/3				1.2	0.7	0.15	
937-60			TRAP	TRAP														strt						2.2	1.7	0.35	
937-61			RECT	BCCX																				9.8	0.8	0.5	
937-62			DIA																					2.7	0.9	0.3	
937-63			LEN								x				0.9		x	leaf						1.8	0.8	0.2	
937-64			PLCX	TRAP																				1.6	1.3	0.3	
937-65			DIA																					1.4	0.8	0.25	
937-66			ST	RECT	40°-70°															1/1				1.4	1.0	1.5	
937-67	x		DIA										x	x	0.6		x							1.8	0.7	0.2	
937-68			LEN			x						x		x	0.5	x	x							1.7	0.8	0.2	
937-69	x		ST	BCCX																				1.5	1.4	0.2	
937-70			TRAP	TRAP	70°																			1.3	0.8	0.25	
937-71			LEN	PLCX																				1.7	1.2	0.15	
937-72			LEN									x	2					leaf						1.3	0.6	0.2	0.4/0.5

Cat. No.	Type	Locus	Culture	Date Found	Found By	Material	Core Tool	Secondary Flake	Prepared Core	Primary Flake	Bulb Trimmed	Billet Technique	Percussion Flaked	Pressure Chipped	Unifacially Retouched	Bifacially Retouched	Upper Face Retouched
937-73	Point, Folsom	NIP	Folsom	1949-50	Meade	Ed. Chert								x		x	
937-74	Knife frag.	4E,CS	Portales	1949-50	Mear	Chert							x	x		x	
937-75	Point, Plainview	4B,CS	Portales	1949-50	Witte	T. Jasper								x		x	
937-76	Scraper frag.	4B,GS	Clovis	1949-50	Mear	D. Quart.		x	x					x	x		x
937-77	Hammerstone	4G,GS	Clovis	1949-50	Meade	D. Quart.											
937-78	Point frag.	NIP	Unknown	1949-50	Meade	Chert								x		x	
937-84	Bone tool	4A,GR	Clovis	1949-50	Evans	bone											
937-88	Bone tool	4E,GS	Clovis	1949-50	Witte	Bone											
937-89	Cut bone	4E,GR	Clovis	1949-50	Sellards	Bone											
937-94	Bone tool	4H,GR	Clovis	1949-50	Mear & Witte	Bone											
937-95	Bone tool	4H,GR	Clovis	1949-50	Mear & Witte	Bone											
937-281	Point frag. Eden	5,NIP	Portales	1954	Shay	Chert		x	x					x		x	
937-289	Point frag. Angostura	5,NIP	Portales	1954	Shay	Ed. Chert		x	x					x		x	
937-293	Flake	5(4C)BSW	Folsom	1954	Schoen	Quart.		no	x								
937-297	Side scraper	5(4A)GS	Clovis	1954	Witte	Alibates		x	x	x				x		x	x
937-298	Point base, Eden	C5(4C)JS		1954	Sellards	D.Quart.		x	x				x			x	
937-300	Burin Bec de Flute	5,JS	Portales	1954	Warnica	Ed. Chert	x						x			x	
937-302	Point frag. Eden &Angost.	5,JS	Portales	1954	Sellards	Ed. Chert		x	x				x	x		x	
937-305	Flake scraper	C5(4C)JS	Portales	1954	Sellards	Quart.		P	x			x		x	x		x
937-306	Scraper frag.	5(4C)JS	Portales	1954	Sellards	Ed. Chert		x	x					x	x		x
937-326	Point frag. paral. flaked	5 JS	Archaic	1954	Marshall	Ed. Chert		x	x				x	x		x	
937-327	Point frag. paral. flaked	5 JS	Archaic	1954	Marshall	Ed. Chert		x	x				x	x		x	
937-328	Point frag. paral. flaked	5 JS	Archaic	1954	Marshall	Ed. Chert		x	x				x	x		x	
937-329	Point frag. paral. flaked	5 JS	Archaic	1954	Marshall	Quart.		x	x				x	x		x	
937-425	Base point, stem., ind.	6 JS	Archaic	1954	Shay & Warnica	Quart.		x	x					x		x	
937-426	Notched point	6 JS	Archaic	1954	Shay & Warnica	Jasper		x	x					x		x	
937-428	Stemmed point base	6 JS	Archaic	1954	Shay & Warnica	Quart.		x	x					x		x	
937-427	Stemmed point	6 JS	Archaic	1954	Shay & Warnica	Chert		x	x					x		x	
937-429	Stemmed point frag.	6 JS	Archaic	1954	Shay & Warnica	D. Quart.		x	x					x		x	
937-430	Scraper	6 JS	Archaic	1954	Shay & Warnica	Chert		x	x					x	x		x
937-431	Side scraper	6 JS	Archaic	1954	Shay & Warnica	Chert		x	x				x	x		x	x
937-432	End scraper	6 JS	Archaic	1954	Shay & Warnica	Jasper		x	x					x	x		x
937-436(1)	Scraper-Graver	6 JS	Archaic	1954	Shay & Warnica	Ed. Chert		x	x					x	x		x
937-436(2)	Flake	6 JS	Archaic	1954	Shay & Warnica	Ed. Chert		P	x								
937-436(3)	End scraper frag.	6 JS	Archaic	1954	Shay & Warnica	Alibates		x	x					x	x		x
937-436(4)	Scraper frag.	6 JS	Archaic	1954	Shay & Warnica	Chert		x	x					x	x		x
937-436(5)	End scraper	6 JS	Archaic	1954	Shay & Warnica	Ed. Chert		x	x	x				x	x		x
937-436(6)	End scraper frag.	6 JS	Archaic	1954	Shay & Warnica	Alibates		x	x					x	x		x
937-436(7)	End scraper	6 JS	Archaic	1954	Shay & Warnica	Ed. Chert		x	x	x				x	x		x
937-436(8)	Flake scraper	6 JS	Archaic	1954	Shay & Warnica	Ed. Chert		x	x	x				x	x		x
937-436(9)	Graver	6 JS	Archaic	1954	Shay & Warnica	Ed. Chert		x	x			x		x	x		x
937-436(10)	Flake	6 JS	Archaic	1954	Shay & Warnica	Chert		x	x	x				x	x		'
937-436(11)	Point frag.	6 JS	Archaic	1954	Shay & Warnica	Ed. Chert		x	x					x		x	
937-436(12)	End scraper	6 JS	Archaic	1954	Shay & Warnica	Ed. Chert		x	x	x				x	x		x
937-436(13)	End scraper	6 JS	Archaic	1954	Shay & Warnica	Ed. Chert		x	x					x	x		x
937-436(14)	Point frag.	6 JS	Archaic	1954	Shay & Warnica	Ed. Chert		x	x					x	x	x	
937-436(15)	End scraper	6 JS	Archaic	1954	Shay & Warnica	Chert		x	x					x	x		x
937-436(16)	Scraper-Graver	6 JS	Archaic	1954	Shay & Warnica	Ed. Chert		x	x					x	x		x
937-440	Paintstone	6 JS	Archaic	1954	Shay & Warnica	Hematite											
937-441	Hammerstone	6 JS	Archaic	1954	Shay & Warnica	Chert											
937-688	Bone tool	8 GS	Clovis	1955	Brown	Bone											
937-684	Stemmed point	NIP	Archaic	1955		Ed. Chert											
937-602	Side scraper	8 GS	Clovis	1955		Alibates											
937-605	Angostura point	NIP	Portales	1955	Shay	Chert		x	x					x		x	
937-680	Bone bead	7A,GS	Clovis	1955	Sellards	Bone											

Cat. No.	Nether Face Retouched	Modified by use	Transverse X Sec.	Anterior-Posterior X Sec.	Edge Angles	Expanding Stem	Shoulder Stem	Contracting Stem	Side Notches	Straight Base	Convex Base	Concave Base	Fluted	Parallel Flaking	Length of Grinding on Sides	Base Ground	Base Thinning	Blade Form	Tip Reworked	Portion of Edge Worked	Points on Perimeter	Median Ridge on Blade	Serrated Edge	Length	Width	Thickness	Length of Flute
937-73													x	2	0.8	x	x	leaf						1.7	0.7	0.1	1.5/1.1
937-74			LEN															leaf						1.5	1.4	0.2	
937-75			LEN				x						x		0.6	x	x	leaf						2.0	0.8	0.2	
937-76			PLCX	ST	30°-40°								x											1.8	1.6	0.35	
937-77																								3.6	3.2	1.8	
937-78			CC											1				leaf						1.0	0.8	0.1	0.5
937-84																								6.7	1.5	0.4	
937-88																								3.2	0.5	0.8	
937-89																								1.3	0.7	0.5	
937-94																								8.0	1.9	0.9	
937-95																								6.1	1.5	0.9	
937-281			LEN	LEN										x				tri.		all			x	1.8	0.7	0.25	
937-289			LEN	LEN					x	x				x	1.2		x	leaf		all				2.4	0.9	0.2	
937-293	x		ST	PLCV																				2.3	1.1	0.4	
937-297			ST	PLCV	40°-50°															1/2				2.9	1.4	0.4	
937-298			LEN	LEN					x	x				x	x			leaf		all				1.0	0.75	0.4	
937-300			ST	TRAP																				1.1	0.8	0.5	
937-302			DIA	LEN										x				leaf		all			x	2.0	0.8	0.25	
937-305			ET	PLCV																1/2				1.7	0.8	0.4	
937-306			PLCV	PLCV	60°-70°															?				0.7	0.4	0.2	
937-326			LEN	LEN			x							x			x	leaf		all				3.4	0.9	0.25	
937-327			LEN	LEN			x							x				tri.		all				2.5	0.8	0.2	
937-328			LEN	LEN										x				leaf		all				1.5	0.9	0.2	
937-329			LEN	LEN		x								x				leaf		all				2.1	1.0	0.2	
937-425			LEN	LEN			x					x						tri.		all				1.6	0.8	0.2	
937-426			LEN	LEN			x		x	x								tri.		all				1.4	1.1	0.1	
937-428			LEN	LEN		x												tri.		all				1.7	0.9	0.3	
937-427			LEN	LEN		x				x								tri.		all				1.6	0.7	0.2	
937-429			LEN	LEN			x					x						leaf		all				1.7	1.4	0.35	
937-430			PLCV	BICX																2/3				1.5	0.9	0.2	
937-431	x		PLCV	BICX																all				2.7	1.5	0.6	
937-432			ST	TRAP	30°& 80°															2/3				2.0	1.0	0.4	
937-436(1)			IT	ST	60°															2/3	1			1.1	0.8	0.2	
937-436(2)			TRI	PA																				1.2	1.1	0.4	
937-436(3)			PLCV	TRAP	40°-70°															all	1			0.7	1.0	0.25	
937-436(4)			BICV	PLCV	70°															3/4				1.0	1.0	0.2	
937-436(5)			ET	ST	50°-70°															all	2			1.0	0.9	0.2	
937-436(6)			PLCV	BCC	60°															all				0.8	0.9	0.3	
937-436(7)			ST	PA	60°-80°															7/8				1.0	1.0	0.3	
937-436(8)			PLCV	CC	80°															2/3				1.2	0.6	0.1	
937-436(9)			PLCV	R																1/4	1			1.2	0.8	0.2	
937-436(10)	x		PLCV	PLCV																				1.1	0.8	0.2	
937-436(11)			LEN	LEN											?					all				1.0	0.7	0.15	
937-436(12)			TRAP	PA	60°-80°															2/3				0.9	1.0	0.3	
937-436(13)			TRAP	PLCV	70°															1/3	3			0.9	0.7	0.3	
937-436(14)			ST	PLCV																1/3	1			1.2	1.0	0.3	
937-436(15)			PLCV	PLCV	60°-70°															2/3	1			1.9	1.3	0.3	
937-436(16)			PLCV	PLCV	50°-70°															1/2	2			0.9	0.7	0.2	
937-440			R	R														tri.		all				1.0	0.7	0.3	
937-441			Oval	Oval																1/8				3.9	1.8	1.0	
937-688																					1			6.3	2.0	1.6	
937-684			LEN	LEN					x									tri.		all				1.6	1.0	0.3	
937-602			TRAP	TRAP	40°-60°															1/3				2.6	1.5	0.3	
937-605			LEN	LEN					x	x							x	leaf	x	all				2.7	0.8	0.3	
937-680			OVAL	OVAL																				0.5	0.3	0.2	

Cat. No.	Type	Locus	Culture	Date Found	Found By	Material	Core Tool	Secondary Flake	Prepared Core	Primary Flake	Bulb Trimmed	Billet Technique	Percussion Flaked	Pressure Chipped	Unifacially Retouched	Bifacially Retouched	Upper Face Retouched
2-1	Point frag. Folsom	17,BSW	Folsom	1962	King	Ed. Chert								x	x		
2-2	Point frag. Folsom	17,BSW	Folsom	1962	King	T. Jasper								x	x		
2-3	Point frag. Folsom	17,BSW	Folsom	1962	King	Chert								x	x		
2-4	Point frag. Folsom	17,BSW	Folsom	1962	King	Ed. Chert								x	x		
2-5	Point frag. Folsom	17,BSW	Folsom	1962	King	Chert								x	x		
2-6	Point frag. Folsom	17,BSW	Folsom	1962	King	Ed. Chert								x	x		
2-7	Point frag. Folsom	17,BSW	Folsom	1962	King	Ed. Chert		x	x					x	x		
2-8	Point frag. Folsom	17,BSW	Folsom	1962	King	Ed. Chert								x	x		
2-9	Point frag. Folsom	17,BSW	Folsom	1962	King	Ed. Chert									x	x	
2-10	Point frag. Folsom	17,BSW	Folsom	1962	King	Ed. Chert								x		x	
2-11	End scraper	17,BSW	Folsom	1962	King	Ed. Chert		x	x	x				x	x	x	x
2-12	End scraper	17,BSW	Folsom	1962	King	Ed. Chert		x	x	x			x	x	x	x	x
2-13	End scraper	17,BSW	Folsom	1962	King	Quart.		x	x	x	x	x	x	x	x		x
2-14	End scraper	17,BSW	Folsom	1962	King	Ed. Chert		x	x	x	x	x	x	x		x	
2-15	End scraper frag.	17,BSW	Folsom	1962	King	T. Jasper		x	x				x	x	x		x
2-16	Side scraper frag.	17,BSW	Folsom	1962	King	Ed. Chert		x	x	x				x	x		x
2-17	Side scraper frag.	17,BSW	Folsom	1962	King	Alibates		x	x	x				x	x		x
2-18	Side scraper frag.	17,BSW	Folsom	1962	King	Ed. Chert		x	x	x	x	x	x	x	x		x
2-19	Side scraper	17,BSW	Folsom	1962	King	Quart.		x	x	x			x	x		x	
2-20	Side scraper	17,BSW	Folsom	1962	King	Ed. Chert	P	x						x	x		x
2-21	Side scraper frag.	17,BSW	Folsom	1962	King	Ed. Chert	P	x						x	x		x
2-22	Side scraper	17,BSW	Folsom	1962	King	Ed. Chert	P	x						x	x		x
2-23	Side scraper	17,BSW	Folsom	1962	King	Ed. Chert		x	x	x	x			x	x		x
2-23(a)	Knife, bifacial	17,BSW	Folsom	1962	King	Ed. Chert		x	x					x	x	x	
2-24	Knife, bifacial	17,BSW	Folsom	1962	King	Ed. Chert		x	x					x	x	x	
2-24(a)	Side scraper	17,BSW	Folsom	1962	King	Chert		x	x						x	x	x
2-25	Flake	17,BSW	Folsom	1962	King	Quart.		No	x								
2-26	Abrader	17,BSW	Folsom	1962	King	Sandstone											
2-27	Flake	17,BSW	Folsom	1962	King	Chert		x	x								
2-28	Flake scraper	17,BSW	Folsom	1962	King	Chert		x	x	x					x		x
2-29	Flake knife	17,BSW	Folsom	1962	King	Ed. Chert		x	x	x						x	
2-30	Flake knife	17,BSW	Folsom	1962	King	Chert		x	x	x						x	
2-31	Flake scraper	17,BSW	Folsom	1962	King	Jasper		x	x	x					x		
2-32	Graver	17,BSW	Folsom	1962	King	Chert		x	x				x	x	x		
2-33	End scraper	17,BSW	Folsom	1962	King	Chert		x	x	x					x		x
2-34	Flake scraper	17,BSW	Folsom	1962	King	Ed. Chert		x	x						x	x	x
2-35	Flake scraper	17,BSW	Folsom	1962	King	Ed. Chert		x	x	x					x		
2-36	Flake scraper	17,BSW	Folsom	1962	King	T. Jasper		x	x	x					x		x
2-37	Flake	17,BSW	Folsom	1962	King	Ed. Chert		x	x	x							
2-38	Flake	17,BSW	Folsom	1962	King	Ed. Chert	x	x	x	x							
2-39	Flake knife	17,BSW	Folsom	1962	King	Ed. Chert		x	x	x						x	
2-40	Flake scraper frag.	17,BSW	Folsom	1962	King	Ed. Chert		x	x							x	
2-41	Flake scraper	17,BSW	Folsom	1962	King	Ed. Chert		x	x	x						x	x
2-42	Flake	17,BSW	Folsom	1962	King	Chert	P	x	x	x	x						
2-43	Side scraper	17,BSW	Folsom	1962	King	T. Jasper	P	x						x	x		x
2-44	Flake scraper	17,BSW	Folsom	1962	King	Chert		x	x						x	x	x
2-45	Flake knife	17,BSW	Folsom	1962	King	Chert		x	x								
2-46	Flake knife	17,BSW	Folsom	1962	King	Ed. Chert		x	x								
2-47	Flake	17,BSW	Folsom	1962	King	Chert		x	x	x							
2-48	Flake	17,BSW	Folsom	1962	King	Ed. Chert	x										
2-49	Flake frag.	17,BSW	Folsom	1962	King	Ed. Chert		x	x	x							
2-50	Flake knife	17,BSW	Folsom	1962	King	Ed. Chert		x	x	x	x						
2-51	Flake scraper	17,BSW	Folsom	1962	King	Ed. Chert		x	x							x	x
2-52	Flake	17,BSW	Folsom	1962	King	T. Jasper		x	x	x							
2-53	Flake graver	17,BSW	Folsom	1962	King	Ed. Chert		x	x							x	

Cat. No.	Nether Face Retouched	Modified by use	Transverse X Sec.	Anterior-Posterior X Sec.	Edge Angles	Expanding Stem	Shoulder Stem	Contracting Stem	Side Notches	Straight Base	Convex Base	Concave Base	Fluted	Parallel Flaking	Length of Grinding on Sides	Base Ground	Base Thinning	Blade Form	Tip Reworked	Portion of Edge Worked	Points on Perimeter	Median Ridge on Blade	Serrated Edge	Length	Width	Thickness	Length of Flute
2-1			BICC	BICC	45°								2	x				leaf		1/3				1.0	0.7	0.1	
2-2			LEN	LEN								x	0		0.6		x	leaf						1.0	0.8	0.2	
2-3			LEN	LEN									0	x				leaf						1.5	0.9	0.1	
2-4			LEN	LEN								x	1		0.8	x	x	leaf						0.8	0.7	0.1	
2-5			LEN	LEN									0	x			x	leaf						1.4	0.7	0.1	
2-6			CC	LEN								x	1	x		x	x	leaf						0.7	0.9	0.1	
2-7			LEN	LEN								x	0					leaf						1.2	0.9	0.1	
2-8			BIC	BICC								x	2	x		x	x	ind.						0.8	0.8	0.1	
2-9			ST	ST								x	1	x				ind.						0.4	0.5	0.1	
2-10			IND	IND								x	x	x			x	ind.						0.6	0.2	0.1	
2-11			ST	R	30°-80°															A	1			1.1	1.0	0.2	
2-12			PLCX	PLCX	45°-60°															A	2			1.2	1.0	0.3	
2-13			IT	P	35°-70°															A	1			2.0	1.1	0.4	
2-14			ST	PLCX	30°-50°															A				1.6	1.3	0.2	
2-15			ST	PLCX	30°-50°															A				0.9	1.3	0.3	
2-16			CC	R	30°																			1.3	1.3	0.2	
2-17			ST	R	40°																			1.1	0.8	0.2	
2-18			TR	BICV	40°																			2.1	2.0	0.2	
2-19			ST	PLCX	20°-60°															A				1.6	1.4	0.3	
2-20			IT	BICV	60°															2/3				2.0	0.9	0.4	
2-21			IT	BICV	50°															1/2				2.5	1.1	0.5	
2-22			TR	R	20°															1/2				1.5	0.7	0.2	
2-23			ST	BICV	30°															1/2				1.8	1.2	0.2	
2-23(a)			PLCX	PLCX	30°																			2.4	0.8	0.2	
2-24			LEN	PLCX	20°															2/3				1.3	1.2	0.2	
2-24(a)			ST	ST	20°															1/3				1.2	0.9	0.1	
2-25			PLCX	ST																				1.9	1.5	0.8	
2-26																								3.7	2.9	0.6	
2-27			IT	ST	10°																			1.5	0.8	0.2	
2-28		x	IT	R	15°															A				1.3	0.8	0.1	
2-29		x	PLCX	BICV	10°															3/4				2.0	1.0	0.2	
2-30		x	TR	BICV	30°-40°															2/3				1.3	0.7	0.2	
2-31		x	PLCX	BICV	10°															A				1.4	0.9	0.1	
2-32			LEN	ST	30°															3/4				1.1	1.4	0.4	
2-33			TR	BICV	30°-60°															7/8	2			1.3	1.4	0.2	
2-34		x	ST	TR	60°-80°															A				1.4	0.8	0.6	
2-35		x	PLCX	BICV	10°															2/3				1.1	1.5	0.2	
2-36	x	x	ST	BICV	10°-20°															1/2				1.7	0.9	0.2	
2-37			ST	BICV	10°-80°																			0.7	0.7	0.1	
2-38			ST	ST	10°																			0.7	0.8	0.1	
2-39		x	ST	BICV	20°															7/8				1.5	0.6	0.1	
2-40		x	ST	R	20°																			0.5	0.5	0.1	
2-41		x	LEN	PLCX	10°															7/8				2.0	1.3	0.2	
2-42		x	PLCX	BICV	20°																			1.3	1.8	0.2	
2-43			ST	ET	40°															1/2				1.5	2.4	0.7	
2-44			ST	BICV	50°-60°															2/3	1			1.4	0.7	0.1	
2-45		x	ST	ST	50°															2/3				1.1	1.1	0.1	
2-46		x	PLCX	BICV	10°-20°															2/3				1.5	1.1	0.1	
2-47			PLCX	BICV	10°-20°																			1.6	1.0	0.2	
2-48			PLCX	TR	10°&90°																			1.0	0.8	0.1	
2-49			PLCX	TR	10°&90°																			0.8	0.7	0.1	
2-50		x	ST	ST	10°-40°																			1.4	1.3	0.4	
2-51		x	IT	CC	10°-30°															7/8	1			1.3	0.8	0.2	
2-52			T-CV	ST	20°																			1.1	0.8	0.2	
2-53	x	x	ST	CC	10°															1/2	1			1.1	0.7	0.1	

Cat. No.	Type	Locus	Culture	Date Found	Found By	Material	Core Tool	Secondary Flake	Prepared Core	Primary Flake	Bulb Trimmed	Billet Technique	Percussion Flaked	Pressure Chipped	Unifacially Retouched	Bifacially Retouched	Upper Face Retouched
2-54	Flake scraper	17, BSW	Folsom	1962	King	Chert		x	x					x	x		x
2-55	Flake knife frag.	17, BSW	Folsom	1962	King	Chert		x	x								
2-56	Flake	17, BSW	Folsom	1962	King	Chert		x	x	x							
2-57	Flake knife	17, BSW	Folsom	1962	King	Ed. Chert		x	x	x							
2-58	Flake	17, BSW	Folsom	1962	King	Chert		x	x	x							
2-59	Flake	17, BSW	Folsom	1962	King	Ed. Chert		x	x	x							
2-60	Flake	17, BSW	Folsom	1962	King	T. Jasper		x	x								
2-61	Flake frag.	17, BSW	Folsom	1962	King	Ed. Chert		x	x								
2-62	Flake knife	17, BSW	Folsom	1962	King	Ed. Chert		x	x			x					
2-63	Flake frag.	17, BSW	Folsom	1962	King	Ed. Chert		x	x								
2-64	Flake scraper	17, BSW	Folsom	1962	King	Ed. Chert		x	x	x	x					x	x
2-65	Flake scraper	17, BSW	Folsom	1962	King	Ed. Chert		P	x	x						x	x
2-66	Flake scraper frag.	17, BSW	Folsom	1962	King	Ed. Chert		P	x					x	x	x	
2-67	Flake scraper	17, BSW	Folsom	1962	King	Jasper		x	x						x	x	x
2-68	Flake scraper	17, BSW	Folsom	1962	King	Chert		x	x	x					x	x	x
2-69	Flake	17, BSW	Folsom	1962	King	Quart.		x	x	x							
2-70	Flake scraper	17, BSW	Folsom	1962	King	Ed. Chert		x	x	x					x		x
2-71	Flake knife frag.	17, BSW	Folsom	1962	King	Chert		x	x	x							
2-72	Flake knife	17, BSW	Folsom	1962	King	Chert		x	x	x							
2-73	Flake	17, BSW	Folsom	1962	King	Quart.		x	x								
2-74	Flake	17, BSW	Folsom	1962	King	Ed. Chert		x	x		x						
2-75	Flake scraper frag.	17, BSW	Folsom	1962	King	Ed. Chert		x	x						x	x	
2-76	Flake knife	17, BSW	Folsom	1962	King	Chert		x	x	x							
2-77	Flake knife	17, BSW	Folsom	1962	King	Ed. Chert		x	x	x	x						
2-78	Flake	17, BSW	Folsom	1962	King	Chert		x	x								
2-79	Flake frag.	17, BSW	Folsom	1962	King	Ed. Chert		x	x								
2-80	Flake	17, BSW	Folsom	1962	King	Ed. Chert		x	x	x	x						
2-81	Flake knife	17, BSW	Folsom	1962	King	Chert		x	x	x							
2-82	Flake frag.	17, BSW	Folsom	1962	King	Ed. Chert	x										
2-83	Flake	17, BSW	Folsom	1962	King	Ed. Chert		x	x								
2-84	Flake	17, BSW	Folsom	1962	King	Ed. Chert		x	x	x							
2-85	Flake knife frag.	17, BSW	Folsom	1962	King	Chert		x	x								
2-86	Flake knife	17, BSW	Folsom	1962	King	Chert		x	x								
2-87	Flake	17, BSW	Folsom	1962	King	Ed. Chert	x										
2-88	Pebble	17, BSW	Folsom	1962	King	Quart.											
2-89	Flake	17, BSW	Folsom	1962	King	Chert		x	x	x	x						
2-90	Flake knife	17, BSW	Folsom	1962	King	Ed. Chert		x	x	x							
2-91	Flake frag.	17, BSW	Folsom	1962	King	Ed. Chert		x	x	x							
2-92	Flake	17, BSW	Folsom	1962	King	Chert	x										
2-93	Flake frag.	17, BSW	Folsom	1962	King	Ed. Chert				x							
2-94	Flake scraper frag.	17, BSW	Folsom	1962	King	Chert		x	x						x	x	x
2-95	Flake	17, BSW	Folsom	1962	King	Ed. Chert		x	x	x							
2-96	Channel flake	17, BSW	Folsom	1962	King	Ed. Chert	x								x	x	x
2-97	Flake	17, BSW	Folsom	1962	King	Alibates	x										
2-98	Scraper frag.	17, BSW	Folsom	1962	King	Ed. Chert		x	x						x	x	x
2-99	Flake	17, BSW	Folsom	1962	King	Quart.		x	x								
2-100	Flake	17, BSW	Folsom	1962	King	Ed. Chert		x	x	x							
2-101	Point frag. Folsom	17, BSW	Folsom	1962	King	Ed. Chert									x	x	
2-102	Channel flake frag.	17, BSW	Folsom	1962	King	Ed. Chert	x								x	x	x
2-103	Flake	17, BSW	Folsom	1962	King	Ed. Chert	x										
2-104	Flake frag.	17, BSW	Folsom	1962	King	Ed. Chert						x					
2-105	Flake graver	17, BSW	Folsom	1962	King	Ed. Chert	x	No									
2-106	Channel flake frag.	17, BSW	Folsom	1962	King	Ed. Chert	x								x	x	x
2-107	Flake	17, BSW	Folsom	1962	King	Ed. Chert	x										
2-108	Flake frag.	17, BSW	Folsom	1962	King	T. Jasper		x	x	x						x	
2-109	Flake	17, BSW	Folsom	1962	King	T. Jasper	x										

Cat. No.	Nether Face Retouched	Modified by use	Transverse X Sec.	Anterior-Posterior X Sec.	Edge Angles	Expanding Stem	Shoulder Stem	Contracting Stem	Side Notches	Straight Base	Convex Base	Concave Base	Fluted	Parallel Flaking	Length of Grinding on Sides	Base Ground	Base Thinning	Blade Form	Tip Reworked	Portion of Edge Worked	Points on Perimeter	Median Ridge on Blade	Serrated Edge	Length	Width	Thickness	Length of Flute
2-54		x	IT	ST	10°-20°															1/2				1.3	0.7	0.1	
2-55		x	ST	R	10°															1/3				0.5	1.0	0.1	
2-56			ST	ST	10°-30°																			0.8	0.6	0.1	
2-57		x	ST	CC	10°															1/2				0.9	0.5	0.1	
2-58		x	ST	ST	10°															2/3				1.3	0.6	0.1	
2-59		x	PLCX	R	10°&90°															1/3				1.0	1.0	0.1	
2-60			PLCX	ST	10°,30°,90°																			0.9	0.9	0.1	
2-61			ST	TR	30°&90°																			0.7	0.7	0.2	
2-62		x	IT	CC	10°															1/2				0.9	0.6	0.1	
2-63		x	PLCX	R	10°															1/2				1.0	0.7	0.1	
2-64		x	ST	TR	20°-30°															2/3				1.3	1.1	0.4	
2-65		x	ST	BICV	20°-60°															1/3				1.7	1.3	0.2	
2-66	x		IT	TR	30°															1/3				1.0	1.5	0.5	
2-67			PA	TR	30°															1/2				1.1	0.7	0.2	
2-68		x	ST	CC	20°-40°															3/4				1.5	0.8	0.2	
2-69		x	PLCX	TR	10°&80°																			1.1	1.1	0.2	
2-70		x	PLCX	CC	20°															1/3				1.2	0.6	0.1	
2-71		x	ST	R	5°															2/3				0.8	0.8	0.1	
2-72		x	ST	CC	5° & 90°															1/3				1.0	0.7	0.1	
2-73			ST	TR	20°-40°															1/2				1.0	1.4	0.2	
2-74			ST	ST	10°																			1.4	0.8	0.1	
2-75			BICV	ST	20°															1/3				0.6	0.9	0.1	
2-76		x	ST	R	10°-20°															2/3				1.1	0.5	0.1	
2-77		x	IT	ST	5°															7/8				1.2	0.8	0.1	
2-78			TR	CC	20°-30°																			0.8	0.6	0.1	
2-79		x	ST	R	10°																			0.4	0.8	0.1	
2-80			ST	ST	10°-20°																			0.8	0.8	0.2	
2-81		x	IT	R	20°															2/3				1.1	0.6	0.2	
2-82		x	PLCX	R	5°															1/3				0.6	0.6	0.1	
2-83		x	IT	ST	5°															7/8				1.2	0.5	0.1	
2-84		x	CC	CC	10°,20°,90°															1/2				0.9	0.9	0.2	
2-85		x	BICV	RT	20°															2/3				0.5	1.0	0.1	
2-86		x	IT	R	20°															2/3				1.0	0.6	0.1	
2-87		x	ST	CC	10°-20°																			0.8	0.7	0.1	
2-88			R	R																				3.5	2.5	0.7	
2-89			TR	TR	30°																			0.6	0.6	0.1	
2-90		x	St	R	10°-30°															2/3				0.8	0.6	0.1	
2-91			LEN	ST	10°&80°																			0.5	0.8	0.2	
2-92			ST	R	40°-60°																			0.6	0.3	0.2	
2-93			R	ST	10° & 90°															1/4				0.3	0.7	0.1	
2-94			ST	R	10°																			0.3	0.7	0.1	
2-95			ST	CC	5°-20°																			0.8	0.5	0.1	
2-96		x	PLCX	ST	10°																			0.9	0.5	0.1	
2-97			CC	PLCX	10°-20°																			0.6	0.5	0.1	
2-98			TRAP	R	40°																			0.6	0.5	0.1	
2-99		x	IT	TRAP	20°															1/4				0.7	0.6	0.1	
2-100			ST	TRAP	10°-20°																			0.6	0.7	0.1	
2-101			BICV	R	40°								2	x										0.6	0.4	0.1	
2-102		x	LEN	R	5°															1/2				0.4	0.5	0.1	
2-103			LEN	ST	5°																			0.5	0.3	0.1	
2-104			ST	ST	10°																			0.6	0.4	0.1	
2-105		x	PA	TRAP	10°																1			0.6	0.3	0.2	
2-106		x	PLCX	R	5°															1/2				0.6	0.4	0.1	
2-107			PLCX	TRAP	10°																			0.5	0.2	0.1	
2-108		x	ST CX	PA	10°															1/2				0.6	0.6	0.1	
2-109			PLCX	CC	5°																			0.4	0.3	0.05	

Cat. No.	Type	Locus	Culture	Date Found	Found By	Material	Core Tool	Secondary Flake	Prepared Core	Primary Flake	Bulb Trimmed	Billet Technique	Percussion Flaked	Pressure Chipped	Unifacially Retouched	Bifacially Retouched	Upper Face Retouched
2-110	Flake	17, BSW	Folsom	1962	King	Quart.		x	x								
2-111	Flake	17, BSW	Folsom	1962	King	Quart.	x	x	x				x			x	
2-112	Hammerstone frag.	17, BSW	Folsom	1962	King	Quart.	x						x			x	
2-113	Flake	17, BSW	Folsom	1962	King	P. Wood		No	x								
2-114	Flake knife frag.	17, BSW	Folsom	1962	King	Ed. Chert		x	x								
2-115	Chopper	17, BSW	Folsom	1962	King	Quart.	x						x			x	
2-116	Hammerstone	17, BSW	Folsom	1962	King	Quart.	x		No				x				
2-117	Core	17, BSW	Folsom	1962	King	Quart.	x		No				x				
W-4	Point frag. Folsom	NIP	Folsom	1962	Warnica	Ed. Chert									x	x	
W-6	Folsom point	NIP	Folsom	1962	Brown	Ed. Chert									x	x	
W-7	Folsom point	NIP	Folsom	1962	Brown	Ed. Chert									x	x	
W-8	Folsom point	NIP	Folsom	1962	Brown	Ed. Chert									x	x	
W-44	Folsom point frag.	NIP	Folsom	1962	Warnica	Chert									x	x	
W-45	Folsom point frag.	NIP	Folsom	1962	Warnica	Ed. Chert									x	x	
W-48	Folsom point frag.	NIP	Folsom	1962	Warnica	Chert									x	x	
W-65	Folsom point frag.	NIP	Folsom	1962	Warnica	Ed. Chert									x	x	
W-94	Folsom point frag.	NIP	Folsom	1962	Warnica	Ed. Chert									x	x	
W-97	Folsom point frag.	NIP	Folsom	1962	Warnica	Ed. Chert									x	x	
W-100	Folsom point	NIP	Folsom	1962	Warnica	Ed. Chert									x	x	
W-106	Folsom point frag.	NIP	Folsom	1962	Warnica	Ed. Chert									x	x	
W-121	Folsom point	NIP	Folsom	1962	Warnica	Ed. Chert									x	x	
W-129	Folsom point	NIP	Folsom	1962	Warnica	Ed. Chert									x	x	
W-122	Folsom point	NIP	Folsom	1962	Warnica	Ed. Chert									x	x	
W-9	Folsom point frag.	NIP	Folsom	1962	Brown	Ed. Chert									x	x	
W-77	Folsom point base	NIP	Folsom	1962	Warnica	Ed. Chert									x	x	
W-109	Folsom point	NIP	Folsom	1962	Warnica	Chert									x	x	
W-148	Flake frag.	15E, BSW	Clovis	1962	Warnica	Chert		x	x	x							
W-149	Flake frag.	15E, BSW	Clovis	1962	Warnica	Chert		x	x	x							
W-150	Flake	15E, BSW	Clovis	1962	Warnica	Alibates		x	x								
W-151	Flake	15E, BSW	Clovis	1962	Warnica	Ed. Chert		x	x	x							
W-152	Flake	15E, BSW	Clovis	1962	Warnica	Ed. Chert		x	x	x							
W-153	Flake frag.	15E, BSW	Clovis	1962	Warnica	Alibates		x	x								
W-155	Flake frag.	15E, BSW	Clovis	1962	Warnica	Alibates		x	x	x							
W-156	Flake	15E, BSW	Clovis	1962	Warnica	Alibates		x	x	x							
W-157	Flake	15E, BSW	Clovis	1962	Warnica	Ed. Chert		x	x	x							
W-415	Flake	17, BSW	Clovis	1962	Warnica	Ed. Chert		x	x								
S-1	End scraper	21, BSW	Folsom	1962	Slaughter	Alibates		x	x					x	x	x	x
3324-4	Flake	15G, GS	Clovis	1962	ENMU Students	Alibates		x	x	x							
3324-2a	Flake	15G, NIP	Clovis	1962	ENMU Students	Alibates		x	x	x							
3324-2b	Flake frag.	15G, NIP	Clovis	1962	ENMU Students	Ed. Chert		x	x								
3324-2c	Flake frag.	15G, NIP	Clovis	1962	ENMU Students	Alibates		x	x								
3324-2d	Flake frag.	15G, NIP	Clovis	1962	ENMU Students	Alibates		x	x								
31961/11a	Folsom point base	11A, D	Folsom	1958	Green & Wendorf	Alibates									x	x	x
2-140	Folsom point base	15G, BSW	Folsom	1962	ENMU Students	Ed. Chert									x	x	x
2-136	Flake	15G, CSE	Portales	1962	ENMU Students	Alibates		x	x								
2-137	Flake frag.	15G, CSE	Portales	1962	ENMU Students	T. Jasper		x	x								
2-138	Flake frag.	15G, CSE	Portales	1962	ENMU Students	Chert		x	x	x							
2-141	Flake	15G, CSE	Portales	1962	ENMU Students	Quart.		x	x								
2-142	Flake	15G, CSE	Portales	1962	ENMU Students	T. Jasper		x	x	x							
2-143	Flake frag.	15G, CSE	Portales	1962	ENMU Students	T. Jasper		x	x								
2-144	Flake frag	15G, CSE	Portales	1962	ENMU Students	T. Jasper		x	x								
2-145	Flake	15G, CSE	Portales	1962	ENMU Students	T. Jasper	x			x							
2-147	Flake frag.	15G, CSE	Portales	1962	ENMU Students			x	x								
2-148	Flake frag.	15G, CSE	Portales	1962	ENMU Students	Quart.		x	x								
2-150	Flake	15G, CSE	Portales	1962	ENMU Students	Basalt	x			x							

Cat. No.	Nether Face Retouched	Modified by use	Transverse X Sec.	Anterior-Posterior X Sec.	Edge Angles	Expanding Stem	Shoulder Stem	Contracting Stem	Side Notches	Straight Base	Convex Base	Concave Base	Fluted	Parallel Flaking	Length of Grinding on Sides	Base Ground	Base Thinning	Blade Form	Tip Reworked	Portion of Edge Worked	Points on Perimeter	Median Ridge on Blade	Serrated Edge	Length	Width	Thickness	Length of Flute
2-110			ST	CC	20°-40°																			1.3	1.2	0.4	
2-111			TRAP	ST	20°&90°																			0.9	1.3	0.3	
2-112		x	PLCX	ET	70°															1/3				2.5	1.5	1.1	
2-113			R	PA	70°																			2.2	1.1	0.5	
2-114		x	IT	R	10°															2/3				0.7	0.6	0.1	
2-115		x	TRAP	R	70°															1/3				3.4	2.3	1.2	
2-116		x	TRAP	PLCX																1/8				3.5	2.0	1.4	
2-117			PA	R	70°-80°															A				3.5	2.7	1.8	
W-4			BICV	LEN	45°		x					x	2		0.6	x		leaf		A				1.5	0.8	0.15	1.5,1.3
W-6			BICV	LEN	30°	x						x	2		0.8	x	x	leaf	x	A				1.2	0.6	0.1	0.8,0.9
W-7			BICV	LEN	35°		x					x	2		0.6	x		leaf	x	A				0.9	0.6	0.1	0.7,0.8
W-8			BICV	Len	35°		x					x	2		0.9	x	x	leaf		A				2.0+	0.8	0.15	2.+,2.+
W-44			CC	CC	35°								1					leaf		A				0.5	0.8	0.15	0.5+
W-45			CC	PLCX	30°								1	x					x	A				0.8	0.9	0.1	0.6+
W-48			CC	CC	40°								1							A				0.7	0.8	0.2	0.5+
W-65			LEN	LEN	25°		x					x	2		0.9	x	x	leaf	x	A				1.5	0.7	0.15	0.5
W-94			BICV	LEN	25°								2	x				leaf	x	A				0.7	0.5	0.1	.3+,.6+
W-97			BICV	LEN	35°	x						x	2		0.8	x	x	leaf		A				0.9	0.7	0.1	0.8+
W-100			BICV	LEN	35°		x					x	2		1.1	x	x	leaf		A				1.6	0.8	0.15	1.3
W-106			BICV	LEN	30°		x					x	2		0.8+	x	x	leaf		A				0.8	0.8	0.2	0.8+
W-121			LEN	LEN	20°		x					x	1		0.9	x	x	leaf	x	A				1.3	0.7	0.1	0.6
W-129			BICV	BICV	30°		x					x	2		1.0	x	x	leaf	x	A				1.6	0.8	0.15	1.2,1.1
W-122			BICV	LEN	20°		x					x	2		0.9	x	x	leaf		A				1.5	0.7	0.1	0.7
W-9			BICV	LEN	35°		x					x	2	x		x				A				0.6	0.4	0.15	
W-77			LEN	LEN	10°-20°		x					x	2		0.9	x	x	leaf		A				0.9	0.8	0.1	0.4
W-109			LEN	LEN	25°		x					x	0		0.7	x	x	leaf		A				1.2	0.8	0.1	
W-148			LEN	ST	10°																			0.7	1.2	0.2	
W-149			PLCV	CC	30°-60°																			1.6	1.0	0.2	
W-150			CC	ST	10°																			0.6	0.8	0.2	
W-151		x	LEN	CC	10°																			1.0	0.4	0.1	
W-152			LEN	ST	10°																			1.2	0.8	0.1	
W-153		x	ST	CC	20°															1/2				1.9	0.7	0.2	
W-155		x	ST	ST	10°-20°															1/4				0.7	0.6	0.1	
W-156		x	ST	CC	10°-20°															3/4				0.8	0.3	0.1	
W-157			ST	CC	10°-40°																			1.3	1.0	0.2	
W-415		x	ST	PLCV	20°															1/2				0.8	0.5	0.1	
S-1			TRAP	TRAP	20°,60°-80°															3/4				2.0	1.1	0.3	
3324-1			CC	TRAP	20°-30°																			0.6	0.9	0.3	
3324-2a		x	LEN	ST	10°-20°															1/2				1.5	1.3	0.4	
3324-2b		x	LEN	ST	10°-20°															1/4				0.9	1.2	0.2	
3324-2c		x	ST	ST	10°															1/2				1.5	0.7	0.2	
3324-2d			PLCV	ST	10°																			0.5	0.5	0.1	
31961/11a			LEN	LEN	20°			x				x	1		0.7	x	x	leaf	x	all				1.2	0.8	0.2	0.8
2-140			LEN	LEN	20°			x				x	0	x	1.0	x	x	leaf		all				1.0	0.8	0.15	
2-136			PLCV	ST	20°																			0.5	1.0	0.2	
2-137			ST	CC	10°																			0.4	0.4	0.1	
2-138		x	CC	LEN	10°,60°															1/4				0.6	0.8	0.2	
2-141			TRAP	ST	30°																			0.9	0.9	0.2	
2-142		x	TRAP	ST	10°-70°															3/4				1.3	0.4	0.1	
2-143			TRAP	ST	10°-90°																			1.2	0.8	0.1	
2-144			ST	ST	10°-80°																			0.7	0.8	0.1	
2-145			PLCV	CC	10°																			0.7	0.5	0.1	
2-147			TRAP	ST	70°-90°																			0.7	0.5	0.2	
2-148			ST	ST	10°-90°																			0.3	0.4	0.1	
2-150			ST	ST	10°-20°																			0.7	0.4	0.1	

Cat. No.	Type	Locus	Culture	Date Found	Found By	Material	Core Tool	Secondary Flake	Prepared Core	Primary Flake	Bulb Trimmed	Billet Technique	Percussion Flaked	Pressure Chipped	Unifacially Retouched	Bifacially Retouched	Upper Face Retouched
2-177	Point frag.	17,BSW	Folsom	1962	ENMU Students	Ed. Chert								x		x	
2-167	Blade frag. bifacial	17,BSW	Folsom	1962	ENMU Students	Ed. Chert		x	x				x			x	
2-169	Blade base, bifacial	17,BSW	Folsom	1962	ENMU Students	Ed. Chert		x	x				x			x	
2-153	Unifacial knife	17,BSW	Folsom	1962	ENMU Students	Alibates		x	x		x				x	x	x
2-166	Unifacial knife frag.	17,BSW	Folsom	1962	ENMU Students	Ed. Chert		x	x						x		x
2-168	Side scraper	17,BSW	Folsom	1962	ENMU Students	Ed. Chert		x	x	x	x		x	x	x		x
2-174	End scraper	17,BSW	Folsom	1962	ENMU Students	Ed. Chert		x	x		x			x	x		x
2-151	Flake scraper	17,BSW	Folsom	1962	ENMU Students	Ed. Chert		x	x		x			x	x		
2-154	Flake scraper	17,BSW	Folsom	1962	ENMU Students	Ed. Chert		P	x						x		
2-157	Flake scraper frag.	17,BSW	Folsom	1962	ENMU Students	Ed. Chert		x	x						x		x
2-160	Flake scraper	17,BSW	Folsom	1962	ENMU Students	Ed. Chert		x	x	x	x				x		x
2-171	Flake scraper	17,BSW	Folsom	1962	ENMU Students	Ed. Chert		x	x						x		x
2-172	Flake scraper	17,BSW	Folsom	1962	ENMU Students	Chert		x	x		x				x		x
2-152	Flake frag.	17,BSW	Folsom	1962	ENMU Students	Ed. Chert		x	x	x	x				x		
2-155	Flake frag.	17,BSW	Folsom	1962	ENMU Students	Ed. Chert		x	x						x		
2-156	Flake	17,BSW	Folsom	1962	ENMU Students	Ed. Chert		x	x						x		x
2-162	Flake frag.	17,BSW	Folsom	1962	ENMU Students	Ed. Chert		P	x						x		
2-163	Flake frag.	17,BSW	Folsom	1962	ENMU Students	Ed. Chert		x	x						x		
2-159	Flake frag.	17,BSW	Folsom	1962	ENMU Students	Ed. Chert		x	x		x				x		x
2-161	Flake frag.	17,BSW	Folsom	1962	ENMU Students	Ed. Chert		x	x		x				x		
2-165	Flake frag.	17,BSW	Folsom	1962	ENMU Students	Ed. Chert		x	x						x		x
2-164	Flake frag.	17,BSW	Folsom	1962	ENMU Students	T. Jasper	x										
2-170	Flake	17,BSW	Folsom	1962	ENMU Students	Ed. Chert		P	x	x	x				x		x
2-173	Flake	17,BSW	Folsom	1962	ENMU Students	Ed. Chert		x	x	x					x		x
2-175	Flake frag.	17,BSW	Folsom	1962	ENMU Students	Ed. Chert		x	x		x				x		
2-176	Flake frag.	17,BSW	Folsom	1962	ENMU Students	Ed. Chert		x	x						x		x
2-178	Flake frag.	17,BSW	Folsom	1962	ENMU Students	Quart.		x	x								
2-180	Flake frag.	17,BSW	Folsom	1962	ENMU Students	Ed. Chert		x	x								
2-181	Flake	17,BSW	Folsom	1962	ENMU Students	Ed. Chert	x										
2-182	Flake frag.	17,BSW	Folsom	1962	ENMU Students	Ed. Chert		x	x						x		x
2-214	Clovis point, Type I	17,GS	Clovis	1962	ENMU Students	Basalt							x	x		x	
2-221	Clovis point frag. Type I	17,GS	Clovis	1962	ENMU Students	Alibates							x	x	x	x	
2-197	Channel flake	17,GS	Clovis	1962	ENMU Students	Alibates	x				x						
2-205	Bifacial knife frag.	17,GS	Clovis	1962	ENMU Students	Quart.		x	x	x			x			x	
2-199	Bifacial knife frag.	17,GS	Clovis	1962	ENMU Students	Quart.		x	x	x			x			x	
2-204	End scraper	17,GS	Clovis	1962	ENMU Students	Alibates		P	x	x			x	x	x		x
2-187	Flake scraper	17,GS	Clovis	1962	ENMU Students	Ed. Chert		x	x			x		x	x		x
2-202	Flake scraper	17,GS	Clovis	1962	ENMU Students	Alibates		x	x					x	x		x
2-192	Side scraper frag.	17,GS	Clovis	1962	ENMU Students	Ed. Chert		P	x					x	x		x
2-196	Side scraper frag.	17,GS	Clovis	1962	ENMU Students	Alibates		x	x					x	x		x
2-203	Side scraper	17,GS	Clovis	1962	ENMU Students	Ed. Chert		x	x				x	x		x	
2-206	Side scraper	17,GS	Clovis	1962	ENMU Students	Alibates		x	x					x	x		x
2-215	Side scraper	17,GS	Clovis	1962	ENMU Students	Alibates		x	x	x				x	x		x
2-217	Side scraper	17,GS	Clovis	1962	ENMU Students	Quart.		x	x			x		x	x		x
2-183	Unifacial knife frag.	17,GS	Clovis	1962	ENMU Students	Alibates		x	x					x	x		x
2-190	Unifacial knife frag.	17,GS	Clovis	1962	ENMU Students	Alibates		x	x		x			x	x		
2-198	Unifacial knife	17,GS	Clovis	1962	ENMU Students	Alibates		x	x		x			x	x		x
2-191	Core	17,GS	Clovis	1962	ENMU Students	Ed. Chert	x	No					x				
2-184	Flake	17,GS	Clovis	1962	ENMU Students	Ed. Chert		x	x		x						
2-185	Flake	17,GS	Clovis	1962	ENMU Students	Alibates	x				x						
2-186	Flake	17,GS	Clovis	1962	ENMU Students	Ed. Chert		x	x		x						
2-189	Flake frag.	17,GS	Clovis	1962	ENMU Students	Ed. Chert		x	x								
2-193	Flake frag.	17,GS	Clovis	1962	ENMU Students	Ed. Chert		x	x								
2-194	Side scraper frag.	17,GS	Clovis	1962	ENMU Students	Ed. Chert		x	x						x	x	x
2-195	Flake frag.	17,GS	Clovis	1962	ENMU Students	Quart.	x										

Cat. No.	Nether Face Retouched	Modified by use	Transverse X Sec.	Anterior-Posterior X Sec.	Edge Angles	Expanding Stem	Shoulder Stem	Contracting Stem	Side Notches	Straight Base	Convex Base	Concave Base	Fluted	Parallel Flaking	Length of Grinding on Sides	Base Ground	Base Thinning	Blade Form	Tip Reworked	Portion of Edge Worked	Points on Perimeter	Median Ridge on Blade	Serrated Edge	Length	Width	Thickness	Length of Flute
2-177			LEN	LEN	20°																			0.8	0.4	0.1	
2-167			ST	TRAP	25°															1/4				1.0	0.9	0.1	
2-169			LEN	LEN	25°															all				1.2	1.0	0.2	
2-153			PLCV	ST	30°-40°															2/3				1.9	1.2	0.2	
2-166			PLCV	ST	40°															2/3				1.2	1.1	0.1	
2-168		x	TRAP	TRAP	20°-70°															all				1.5	1.2	0.4	
2-174		x	ST	CC	30°-70°															2/3	2			1.4	0.9	0.2	
2-151	x	x	LEN	TRAP	10°-40°															2/3				1.1	1.4	0.2	
2-154	x	x	ST	PLCV	30°-40°															2/3				1.0	0.6	0.2	
20157	x	x	ST	ST	30°-40°															3/4				1.8	1.2	0.2	
2-160	x	x	TRAP	CC	20°-40°															all				2.2	1.4	0.3	
2-171	x	x	ST	CC	30°															3/4				1.9	1.2	0.3	
2-172		x	TRAP	TRAP	20°-60°															2/3				1.7	0.9	0.3	
2-152	x	x	LEN	CC	10°															2/3				1.0	1.2	0.1	
2-155	x	x	PLCV	TRAP	10°-40°															1/4				0.7	0.9	0.1	
2-156		x	ST	TRAP	30°															1/4				0.9	0.2	0.1	
2-162		x	TRAP	TRAP	60°															1/2				0.5	0.8	0.1	
2-163	x		ST	R	10°															1/2				1.7	0.8	0.1	
2-159		x	ST	TRAP	30°-40°															2/3				0.7	0.8	0.2	
2-161		x	PLCV	R	10°															2/3				0.8	0.7	0.1	
2-165		x	CC	ST	10°															1/2				0.6	0.8	0.1	
2-164			PLCV	TRAP	20°-40°																			0.4	0.6	0.1	
2-170		x	CC	ST	10°															1/4				0.8	1.3	0.2	
2-173		x	PLCV	ST	10°															1/2				1.7	1.4	0.2	
2-175	x	x	ST	ST	10°															1/2				1.5	0.8	0.2	
2-176		x	ST	ST	10°															1/4				0.8	0.8	0.1	
2-178			TRAP	TRAP	20°																			0.4	0.6	0.1	
2-180			LEN	R	10°																			0.4	0.9	0.1	
2-181			ST	R	20°																			0.4	0.4	0.1	
2-182		x	LEN	ST	10°															1/3				0.6	0.3	0.1	
2-214			LEN	LEN	40°		x		x	2					1.0	x	x	leaf	x	all				2.9	1.1	0.3	0.5
2-221			LEN	ST	25°		x		x	2					6.0+	x	x			all				0.6	1.5	0.2	0.6+
2-197		x	PLCV	R	10°															1/2				1.2	0.5	0.1	
2-205			LEN	LEN	40°													leaf		all				1.8	1.1	0.3	
2-199			LEN	ST	30°													leaf		2/3				1.2	1.2	0.3	
2-204		x	PLCV	PLCV	70°															7/8	1			1.2	1.0	0.4	
2-187		x	ST	LEN	50°-60°															1/2				1.5	1.1	0.4	
2-202	x	x	PLCV	R	20°-40°															1/2				1.1	1.0	0.2	
2-192			ST	PLCV	30°															1/2				1.0	0.6	0.3	
2-196		x	TRAP	TRAP	30°-60°															2/3				1.5	1.0	0.2	
2-203			PLCV	TRAP	40°-60°															all	1			1.3	1.2	0.4	
2-206	x		ST	TRAP	25°-50°															2/3				1.3	1.0	0.3	
2-215		x	TRAP	TRAP	20°-60°															all	2			1.6	1.2	0.3	
2-217	x		LEN	ST	50°															1/3				1.5	2.3	0.4	
2-183	x		ST	TRAP	20°															1/3				1.0	1.3	0.1	
2-190	x		LEN	TRAP	30°															1/4				0.8	0.8	0.2	
2-198		x	ST	PLCV	20°															7/8				1.9	0.7	0.2	
2-191		x	ST	ST	60°															1/4				1.4	1.3	0.7	
2-184			R	ST	10°-90°																			1.1	1.0	0.1	
2-185		x	LEN	CC	10°															3/4				1.3	1.3	0.1	
2-186		x	ST	CC	10°															1/2				1.1	0.8	0.1	
2-189			ST	TRAP	30°-60°																			0.4	0.3	0.1	
2-193			ST	ST	10°															1/2				0.8	0.9	0.1	
2-194			TRAP	PA	60°															1/8				0.5	1.1	0.2	
2-195			PLCV	ST	20°																			0.7	0.5	0.1	

Cat. No.	Type	Locus	Culture	Date Found	Found By	Material	Core Tool	Secondary Flake	Prepared Core	Primary Flake	Bulb Trimmed	Billet Technique	Percussion Flaked	Pressure Chipped	Unifacially Retouched	Bifacially Retouched	Upper Face Retouched
2-200	Flake frag.	17,GS	Clovis	1962	ENMU Students	Alibates	x								x		x
2-201	Flake frag.	17,GS	Clovis	1962	ENMU Students	Alibates		x	x						x		x
2-207	Flake	17,GS	Clovis	1962	ENMU Students	Quart.		x	x			x					
2-208	Flake frag.	17,GS	Clovis	1962	ENMU Students	Alibates		x	x								
2-211	Flake	17,GS	Clovis	1962	ENMU Students	Basalt		x	x								
2-212	Flake frag.	17,GS	Clovis	1962	ENMU Students	Alibates		x	x								
2-216	Flake	17,GS	Clovis	1962	ENMU Students	Alibates		x	x			x					
2-218	Flake	17,GS	Clovis	1962	ENMU Students	Alibates		x	x								
2-219	Flake	17,GS	Clovis	1962	ENMU Students	Alibates		x	x			x					
2-220	Flake frag.	17,GS	Clovis	1962	ENMU Students	T. Jasper		x	x								
2-222	Flake frag.	17,GS	Clovis	1962	ENMU Students	Ed. Chert		x	x			x			x		x
2-223	Flake frag.	17,GS	Clovis	1962	ENMU Students	Alibates		x	x								
2-129	Bifacial knife	17,GS	Clovis	1962	Durett	Alibates		x	x				x			x	
2-127	Graver	15E,GS	Clovis	1962	Durett	Alibates		x	x	x					x	x	x
2-119	Unifacial knife	15E,GS	Clovis	1962	Durett	Alibates		x	x	x	x				x	x	x
2-121	Unifacial knife frag.	17,GS	Clovis	1962	Durett	Alibates		x	x						x	x	x
2-118	Flake frag.	17,GS	Clovis	1962	Durett	Ed. Chert		x	x								
2-120	Flake	15E,GS	Clovis	1962	Durett	Basalt		x	x	x							
2-122	Flake	15E,GS	Clovis	1962	Durett	Alibates		x	x	x							
2-123	Bone tool	15E,GS	Clovis	1962	Durett	Alibates											
2-124	Flake	15E,GS	Clovis	1962	Durett	Quart.		x	x	x							
2-125	Flake frag.	15E,GS	Clovis	1962	Durett	Chert		x	x	x							
2-126	Flake	17,GS	Clovis	1962	Durett	Shale	No	x									
2-131	Flake	17,GS	Clovis	1962	Durett	Alibates		x	x								
2-132	Bifacial knife	17,GS	Clovis	1962	Durett	Chalcedony		x	x						x	x	
2-133	Flake frag.	15E,GS	Clovis	1962	Durett	Alibates		x	x							x	x
2-134	Flake	16,GS	Clovis	1962	Durett	Alibates		x	x	x							
2-135	Flake	16,GS	Clovis	1962	Durett	Alibates	x			x							
W-408	Flake	16,BSW	Folsom	1962	Warnica	T. Jasper	x										
W-409(8)	Unifacial knife	16,BSW	Folsom	1962	Warnica	Alibates		P	x	x					x	x	x
W-410(1)	Flake knife frag.	16,BSW	Folsom	1962	Warnica	Ed. Chert		x	x							x	
W-411(N)	Flake knife frag.	16,BSW	Folsom	1962	Warnica	Ed. Chert		x	x						x		
W-412(9)	Flake	16,BSW	Folsom	1962	Warnica	Alibates		x	x	x					x		
W-413(3)	Flake frag.	16,BSW	Folsom	1962	Warnica	Ed. Chert		x	x						x		x
W-414(12)	Flake frag.	16,BSW	Folsom	1962	Warnica	Ed. Chert		x	x								
W-170	Folsom point frag.	17,BSW	Folsom	1962	Warnica	Chert								x	x		x
W-199	Folsom point frag.	17,BSW	Folsom	1962	Warnica	Chert								x	x		x
W-235	Folsom point frag.	17,BSW	Folsom	1962	Warnica	Ed. Chert								x	x		x
W-251	Point tip	17,BSW	Folsom	1962	Warnica	Quart.								x	x		x
W-292	Folsom point frag.	17,BSW	Folsom	1962	Warnica	Ed. Chert								x	x		x
W-338	Folsom point frag.	17,BSW	Folsom	1962	Warnica	Alibates								x	x		x
W-384	Folsom point frag.	17,BSW	Folsom	1962	Warnica	Ed. Chert								x	x		x
W-221	Channel flake frag.	17,BSW	Folsom	1962	Warnica	Chert		x							x		
W-248	Channel flake frag.	17,BSW	Folsom	1962	Warnica	Ed. Chert		x							x		
W-282	Channel flake frag.	17,BSW	Folsom	1962	Warnica	Ed. Chert		x							x		
W-317	Channel flake frag.	17,BSW	Folsom	1962	Warnica	Ed. Chert		x							x		
W-177	End scraper	17,BSW	Folsom	1962	Warnica	Ed. Chert		P	x		x		x	x	x		x
W-178	End scraper	17,BSW	Folsom	1962	Warnica	Ed. Chert		No	x						x	x	x
W-193	End scraper frag.	17,BSW	Folsom	1962	Warnica	Ed. Chert		x	x						x	x	x
W-201	End scraper	17,BSW	Folsom	1962	Warnica	Ed. Chert		x	x	x					x	x	x
W-402	End scraper	17,BSW	Folsom	1962	Warnica	Ed. Chert		x	x	x					x		x
W-242	End scraper	17,BSW	Folsom	1962	Warnica	Ed. Chert		x	x					x	x	x	x
W-301	End scraper frag.	17,BSW	Folsom	1962	Warnica	Ed. Chert		x	x						x	x	x
W-240	Flake scraper frag.	17,BSW	Folsom	1962	Warnica	Ed. Chert		x	x						x	x	x
W-265	Flake scraper frag.	17,BSW	Folsom	1962	Warnica	Ed. Chert		x	x						x	x	x

Cat. No.	Nether Face Retouched	Modified by use	Transverse X Sec.	Anterior-Posterior X Sec.	Edge Angles	Expanding Stem	Shoulder Stem	Contracting Stem	Side Notches	Straight Base	Convex Base	Concave Base	Fluted	Parallel Flaking	Length of Grinding on Sides	Base Ground	Base Thinning	Blade Form	Tip Reworked	Portion of Edge Worked	Points on Perimeter	Median Ridge on Blade	Serrated Edge	Length	Width	Thickness	Length of Flute
2-200		x	ST	CC	10°															1/4				0.6	0.4	0.1	
2-201		x	DIA	TRAP	60°															1/10				0.6	1.3	0.5	
2-207		x	PLCV	CC	10°															1/2				1.1	0.7	0.1	
2-208			LEN	ST	10°																			1.1	0.9	0.1	
2-211			TRAP	ST	60°-70°																			1.2	0.9	0.5	
2-212			ST	ST	10°																			1.2	0.6	0.1	
2-216		x	PLCV	CC	10°															1/2				0.8	0.4	0.1	
2-219		x	ST	ST	10°-20°															1/2				1.0	1.0	0.2	
2-219		x	LEN	TRAP	10°															1/2				1.0	1.1	0.1	
2-220			PLCV	ST	10°-40°																			0.5	0.8	0.1	
2-222		x	PLCV	ST	10°-20°															2/3				0.8	0.8	0.1	
2-223		x	ST	TRAP	10°-20°															1/2				1.1	0.7	0.1	
2-129			LEN	LEN	30°								x					Tri.		all				1.6	0.8	0.3	
2-127			ST	TRAP	60°															1/4	3			1.1	0.7	0.2	
2-119			ST	CC	20°															1/2				2.9	0.9	0.3	
2-121			PLCV	CC	30°															1/2				1.2	0.9	0.1	
2-118		x	ST	TRAP	10°															1/4				0.8	1.0	0.1	
2-120			TRAP	DIA	20°-60°																			1.1	1.3	0.3	
2-122			ST	ST	10°-80°																			1.0	1.0	0.3	
2-123																								1.1	0.2	0.1	
2-124			ST	TRAP	20°-40°																			3.0	1.8	0.6	
2-125			TRAP	R	20°-90°																			1.0	0.8	0.1	
2-126		x	PLCV	ST	20°																			1.5	0.8	0.2	
2-131			ST	ST	10°																			0.4	0.6	0.1	
2-132			LEN	LEN	40°															all				1.0	0.7	0.3	
2-133		x	ST	TRAP	10°-20°															1/4				0.9	0.7	0.1	
2-134		x	LEN	ST	10°-30°															3/4				0.8	0.6	0.1	
2-135			CC	ST	10°																			0.2	0.4	0.1	
W-408			ST	CC	10°																			0.5	0.4	0.1	
W-409(8)			ST	CC	50°															all				2.9	0.8	0.3	
W-410(1)		x	PLCV	ST	20°															2/3				1.0	1.0	0.1	
W-411(N)	x	x	TRAP	R	20°															1/3				0.9	0.7	0.1	
W-412(9)	x	x	PLCV	LEN	20°															1/4				0.9	0.9	0.1	
W-413(3)		x	CC	R	20°															1/4				0.6	0.6	0.1	
W-414(12)			ST	R	20°																			1.2	0.6	0.1	
W-170			LEN	LEN	20°		x					x	0		0.9	x	x	leaf		all				1.0	0.7	0.1	
W-199			BICV	LEN	50°-60°		x					x	2		0.6	x	x			all				0.6	0.7	0.1	
W-235			LEN	LEN	25°		x					x	0		0.6	x	x	leaf		all				0.7	0.8	0.1	
W251			LEN	LEN	30°-50°								0					leaf		all				1.0	0.7	0.3	
W-292			BICV	LEN	30°								2		0.3	x	x			all				0.3	0.6	0.1	
W-338			BICV	LEN	30°								2							all				0.3	0.6	0.1	
W-384			PLCV	LEN	25°							x	1		0.7	x	x			all				0.7	0.4	0.1	
W-221			LEN	R	10°																			0.5	0.6	0.05	
W-248			LEN	ST	10°																			0.5	0.3	0.05	
W-282		x	LEN	R	10°															1/4				0.4	0.5	0.005	
W-317		x	LEN	R	10°															1/4				0.7	0.5	0.005	
W-177	x		TRAP	PA	70°															all	1			1.3	1.3	0.3	
W-178			TRAP	TRAP	40°-50°															all	2			1.5	1.3	0.3	
W-193			TRAP	PLCV	70°															all	1			0.6	1.0	0.3	
W-2-1			TRAP	PA	30°-70°															all	2			1.4	1.2	0.4	
W-402		x	ST	TRAP	30°-80°															all	2			1.2	1.0	0.3	
W-242			PLCV	PLCV	60°-80°															all	3			1.0	0.9	0.3	
W-301			PA	PLCV	50°															1/2				1.0	0.5	0.2	
W-240			ST	ST	50°															1/4				0.5	0.7	0.1	
W-265			ST	TRAP	60°-70°															1/2				0.5	0.8	0.2	

Cat. No.	Type	Locus	Culture	Date Found	Found By	Material	Core Tool	Secondary Flake	Prepared Core	Primary Flake	Bulb Trimmed	Billet Technique	Percussion Flaked	Pressure Chipped	Unifacially Retouched	Bifacially Retouched	Upper Face Retouched
W-311	Flake scraper frag.	17,BSW	Folsom	1962	Warnica	Ed. Chert		x	x					x	x		x
W-336	Flake scraper frag.	17,BSW	Folsom	1962	Warnica	Ed. Chert		x	x					x	x		x
W-392	Flake scraper frag.	17,BSW	Folsom	1962	Warnica	Ed. Chert		x	x					x	x		x
5A	Folsom point frag.	15E,BSW	Folsom	1962	Hester	Alibates		x	x				x	x		x	
1A	Folsom point frag.	15E,BSW	Folsom	1962	Hester	Ed. Chert		x	x					x		x	
8A	Folsom point frag.	15E,BSW	Folsom	1962	Hester	Ed. Chert		x	x					x		x	
30A	Folsom point frag.	15E,BSW	Folsom	1962	Hester	Ed. Chert		x	x					x		x	
51A	Folsom point frag.	15E,BSW	Folsom	1962	Hester	Ed. Chert		x	x					x		x	
W-142	Folsom point	NIP	Folsom	1962	Warnica	Ed. Chert		x	x					x		x	
W-144	Folsom point	NIP	Folsom	1962	Warnica	Ed. Chert		x	x					x		x	
W-143	Folsom point	NIP	Folsom	1962	Warnica	Ed. Chert		x	x					x		x	
W-145	Meserve point	NIP	Unk.	1962	Warnica	Chert		x	x					x		x	
47A	Flake	15E,BSW	Unk.	1962	Hester	Ed. Chert		x	x	x						x	x
38A	Flake	15E,BSW	Unk.	1962	Hester	Ed. Chert		x	x							x	
45A	Flake	15E,BSW	Unk.	1962	Hester	Chert		x	x	x						x	
52A	Flake	15E,BSW	Unk.	1962	Hester	Ed. Chert	x						x				
35A	Flake	15E,BSW	Unk.	1962	Hester	Ed. Chert		x	x				x				
2A	Flake	15E,BSW	Unk.	1962	Hester	Ed. Chert		x	x				x				
59A	Flake	15E,BSW	Unk.	1962	Hester	Ed. Chert	x						x			x	
37A	Flake	15E,BSW	Unk.	1962	Hester	Ed. Chert	x										
P	Flake	15F,BSW	Unk.	1962	Hester	Ed. Chert											
I	Flake	15E,BSW	Unk.	1962	Brown	Chert	x								x		
d-9	Flake	15E,BSW	Unk.	1962	Collins	Ed. Chert		x	x				x				
61A	Flake	15E,BSW	Unk.	1962	Hester	Chert	P		x						x		
50A	Flake	15E,BSW	Unk.	1962	Hester	Quart.		x	x								
4A	Flake	15E,BSW	Unk.	1962	Hester	Quart.	P		x								
21A	Flake	15E,BSW	Unk.	1962	Hester	Jasper	x										
22A	Flake	15E,BSW	Unk.	1962	Hester	Ed. Chert		x	x							x	x
58A	Flake	15E,BSW	Unk.	1962	Hester	Chert		x	x								
60A	Flake	15E,BSW	Unk.	1962	Hester	Quart.	No		x								
49A	Flake	15E,BSW	Unk.	1962	Hester	Quart.	P		x	x							
56A	Flake	15E,BSW	Unk.	1962	Hester	T. Jasper	x										
48A	Flake	15E,BSW	Unk.	1962	Hester	Quart.	No		x								
39A	Flake	15E,BSW	Unk.	1962	Hester	Chert		x	x								
8A	Flake	15E,BSW	Unk.	1962	Hester	Quart.		x	x								
13A	Flake	15E,BSW	Unk.	1962	Hester	Ed. Chert	x						x				
3A	Flake	15E,BSW	Unk.	1962	Hester	Chert	No		x								
K	Flake	15E,BSW	Unk.	1962	Brown	Ed. Chert	x										
d-5	Flake	15E,BSW	Unk.	1962	Brown	Ed. Chert		x	x								
d-6	Flake	15E,BSW	Unk.	1962	Greaves	Chalcedony		x	x								
d-13	Flake	15E,BSW	Unk.	1962	Collins	Ed. Chert	x										
d-12	Flake	15E,BSW	Unk.	1962	Collins	Ed. Chert		x	x								
L	Flake	15E,BSW	Unk.	1962	Brown	Quart.	x										
14	Flake	15E,BSW	Unk.	1962	Brown	Quart.		x	x								
1B	End scraper	15F,BSW	Folsom	1962	Hester	Chert		x	x	x				x	x	x	x
E	Side scraper	15E,BSW	Folsom	1962	Brown	Chert		x	x					x	x	x	x
23A	Side Scraper	15E,BSW	Folsom	1962	Hester	Quart.		x	x					x	x	x	x
d-4	End scraper	15E,BSW	Folsom	1962	Brown	Chert		x	x	x				x	x	x	x
27A	Flake scraper	15E,BSW	Folsom	1962	Hester	Chert	P		x		x						x
32A	Flake scraper	15E,BSW	Folsom	1962	Hester	Chert	P		x							x	x
34A	Flake scraper	15E,BSW	Folsom	1962	Hester	Ed. Chert	P		x							x	x
31A	Flake Scraper	15E,BSW	Folsom	1962	Hester	Ed. Chert		x	x	x						x	x
33A	Flake scraper	15E,BSW	Folsom	1962	Hester	Alibates		x	x						x	x	x
57A	Flake scraper	15E,BSW	Folsom	1962	Hester	Ed. Chert		x	x		x					x	x
43A	Flake scraper	15E,BSW	Folsom	1962	Hester	Chert	x				x					x	x

Cat. No.	Nether Face Retouched	Modified by use	Transverse X Sec.	Anterior-Posterior X Sec.	Edge Angles	Expanding Stem	Shoulder Stem	Contracting Stem	Side Notches	Straight Base	Convex Base	Concave Base	Fluted	Parallel Flaking	Length of Grinding on Sides	Base Ground	Base Thinning	Blade Form	Tip Reworked	Portion of Edge Worked	Points on Perimeter	Median Ridge on Blade	Serrated Edge	Length	Width	Thickness	Length of Flute
W-311			ST	PLCV	70°															1/2				1.0	0.3	0.1	
W-336			ST	ST	50°															1/3				1.1	0.6	0.2	
W-392			TRAP	TRAP	70°															1/3				0.4	0.5	0.1	
5A			PC	LEN	20°			x				x	0		1.3		x	leaf		A				1.4	0.8	0.2	
1A			LEN	LEN	20°								1		0.4+			leaf		A				0.9	0.8	0.1	0.7+
8A			LEN	LEN	15°-20°			x				x	0				x	leaf		A				1.0	0.9	0.1	
30A			BICV	LEN	30°			x				x	2		0.8		x	leaf	x	A				1.3	0.5	0.1	1.0+
51A			LEN	LEN	20°			x				x	0		0.7	x	x	leaf		A				1.0	0.7	0.1	
W-142			BICV	LEN	40°			x				x	2		1.0		x	leaf		A				1.9	0.8	0.1	1.1
W0144			LEN	LEN	15°			x				x	0		1.0		x	leaf		A				1.7	0.8	0.1	0.1
W-142			CC	LEN	25°			x				x	1		0.9		x	leaf		A				1.6	0.7	0.1	1.1
W-145			LEN	LEN	30°	x						x			0.5	x	x	tri.	x	A			x	1.3	0.7	0.2	
47A		x	ST	TRAP	20°-40°															1/2				0.8	0.5	0.2	
38A		x	ST	TRAP	30°															1/4				0.6	0.6	0.15	
45A	x	x	IT	PLCX	10°-15°															1/4				0.9	1.1	0.15	
52A		x	ST	TRAP	10°-20°															1/2				0.9	0.4	0.1	
35A		x	ST	TRAP	20°															1/4				0.6	0.7	0.1	
2A			LEN	TRAP	20°																			0.5	0.7	0.1	
59A	x	x	CC	CC	10°															1/4				0.7	0.5	0.1	
37A			ST	ST	5°																			0.3	0.2	0.05	
P		x	ST	TRAP	5°-10°															1/4				0.8	1.0	0.1	
I	x	x	TRAP	TRAP	20°-90°															1/3				0.7	0.7	0.2	
d-9		x	ST	TRAP	10°															3/4				1.2	0.9	0.2	
61A	x	x	TRAP	TRAP	70°															1/4				0.7	0.5	0.2	
50A			ST	TRAP	30°-70°																			1.4	2.3	0.6	
4A			ST	ST	30°																			1.0	0.9	0.3	
21A			R	R	90°																			0.6	0.2	0.1	
22A	x	x	ST	ST	10°															1/4	1			1.0	0.5	0.1	
58A			ST	LEN	10°																			1.2	1.0	0.1	
60A			PLCX	R	30°																			1.4	1.0	0.4	
49A			ST	TRAP	20°-40°																			2.0	1.3	0.4	
56A			TRAP	ST	30°-50°																			0.5	0.3	0.1	
48A			ST	R	20°																			0.8	0.6	0.3	
39A			ST	R	10°																			0.7	0.3	0.1	
8A			TRAP	ST	30°																			1.0	1.0	0.3	
13A			ST	TRAP	10°																			0.6	0.2	0.1	
3A			ST	TRAP	10°																			0.4	0.2	0.1	
K			TRAP	R	90°																			0.5	0.3	0.1	
d-5			TRAP	TRAP	90°																			0.8	0.8	0.1	
d-6			CC	TRAP	60°-90°																			1.0	1.0	0.3	
d013			PLCX	ST	10°																			0.3	0.3	0.1	
d-12			BICV	R	10°																			0.6	0.6	0.1	
L			IT	PA	20°-30°																			0.6	0.3	0.2	
14			TRAP	CC	20°																			0.9	0.8	0.2	
1B			PLCX	TRAP	30°-60°															3/4	1			1.8	1.5	0.4	
E			TRAP	PA	50°-70°															A	1			2.5	0.8	0.4	
23A			R	TRAP	50°															1/3				2.1	1.1	0.2	
d-4	x	x	IT	TRAP	30°-60°															A	2			1.2	1.0	0.4	
27A	x	x	ST	ST	40°															1/3				1.7	1.6	0.5	
32A		x	LEN	R	20°															2/3				1.5	1.4	0.2	
34A		x	ST	CC	20°															1/4				1.5	1.0	0.3	
31A		x	TRAP	R	30°-40°															2/3				1.4	1.2	0.3	
33A			LEN	ST	15°															1/3				1.2	1.5	0.3	
57A	x	x	LEN	LEN	20°															2/3				1.8	2.0	0.4	
43A		x	PLCX	CC	10°															2/3				1.2	0.7	0.1	

Cat. No.	Type	Locus	Culture	Date Found	Found By	Material	Core Tool	Secondary Flake	Prepared Core	Primary Flake	Bulb Trimmed	Billet Technique	Percussion Flaked	Pressure Chipped	Unifacially Retouched	Bifacially Retouched	Upper Face Retouched
11A	Flake scraper	15E, BSW	Folsom	1962	Hester	Ed. Chert		P	x				x		x		x
14A	Flake scraper	15E, BSW	Folsom	1962	Hester	Ed. Chert		x	x			x			x		
46A	Flake scraper	15E, BSW	Folsom	1962	Hester	Ed. Chert		x	x						x		
20A	Flake scraper	15E, BSW	Folsom	1962	Hester	T. Jasper		x	x					x		x	
16U	Flake scraper	BSW	Folsom	1962	Collins	Chert		x	x	x				x	x		x
B	Flake scraper frag.	15E, BSW	Folsom	1962	Brown	Ed. Chert		x	x					x	x		
C	Flake scraper	15E, BSW	Folsom	1962	Brown	Ed. Chert		x	x	x				x	x		x
d-3	Flake scraper	15E, BSW	Folsom	1962	Warnica	Chert		x	x	x					x		x
d-8	Flake scraper	15E, BSW	Folsom	1962	Collins	T. Jasper		x	x						x		
N	Flake scraper	15F, BSW	Folsom	1962	Collins	Ed. Chert		x	x							x	
4	Flake scraper	15E, BSW	Folsom	1962	Collins	Ed. Chert		x	x	x					x		
6	Flake scraper	15E, BSW	Folsom	1962	Collins	Ed. Chert		x	x						x		
H	Flake scraper	15E, BSW	Folsom	1962	Brown	Ed. Chert		x	x	x					x		x
3B	Flake scraper	15F, BSW	Folsom	1962	Warnica	Chert		P	x	x					x		x
J	Flake scraper frag.	15E, BSW	Folsom	1962	Brown	Ed. Chert		x	x						x		
25A	Flake scraper frag.	15E, BSW	Folsom	1962	Hester	Chert	x								x		x
53A	Hollow edge scraper	15E, BSW	Folsom	1962	Hester	Ed. Chert		x	x					x	x		x
4B	Hollow edge scraper	15F, BSW	Folsom	1962	Warnica	Alibates		x	x						x		
13	Scraper-Graver	NIP	Unk.	1962	Warnica	Ed. Chert		x	x	x					x		x
A	Scraper-Graver	15E, BSW	Unk.	1962	Brown	Ed. Chert		x	x				x	x	x	x	x
7	Scraper-Graver	15E, BSW	Unk.	1962	Brown	Ed. Chert		P	x	x	x		x		x		x
O	Scraper-Graver	15F, BSW	Unk.	1962	Collins	Chert		x	x		x		x		x		x
JC	Scraper-Graver	NIP	Unk.	1962	Collins	Chert		No	x						x		x
5	Flake scraper	15E, BSW	Unk.	1962	Collins	Ed. Chert		x	x				x	x	x		x
26A	Flake scraper	15E, BSW	Unk.	1962	Hester	Ed. Chert		x	x						x		x
d-2	Graver	15E, BSW	Folsom	1962	Brown	T. Jasper	x							x	x		x
d-11	Graver	15E, BSW	Folsom	1962	Collins	Chert	x			x					x		
29A	Flake knife	15E, BSW	Folsom	1962	Hester	Chert		x	x	x					x		x
M	Flake scraper	15E, BSW	Folsom	1962	Hester	Jasper		x	x	x			x		x		x
24A	Flake scraper	15E, BSW	Folsom	1962	Hester	Chert		x	x						x		
18A	Flake scraper	15E, BSW	Folsom	1962	Hester	Chert		x	x	x			x		x		x
d-1	Flake scraper	15E, BSW	Folsom	1962	Brown	Ed. Chert		x	x	x		x	x		x		x
11	Flake scraper	15E, BSW	Folsom	1962	Collins	Ed. Chert	x			x	x		x		x		x
G	Folsom point frag.	15E, BSW	Folsom	1962	Brown	Ed. Chert		x	x						x	x	
G(1)	Folsom point frag.	15E, BSW	Folsom	1962	Brown	Ed. Chert		x	x						x	x	
1-7	Projectile point frag.	15E, BSW	Unk.	1962	Brown	Alibates		x	x						x	x	
W-133	Flake	NIP	Unk.	1962	Warnica	Chert		x	x								
W-83	Flake	NIP	Unk.	1962	Warnica	Alibates		x	x								
W-31	Flake	NIP	Unk.	1962	Warnica	Ed. Chert		x	x	x							
W-81	Flake	NIP	Unk.	1962	Warnica	Ed. Chert		x	x	x							
W-22	Flake	NIP	Unk.	1962	Warnica	Chert		P	x								
W-113	Flake	NIP	Unk.	1962	Warnica	Quart.		x	x								
W-85	Flake	NIP	Unk.	1962	Warnica	Chert		x	x	x							
W-27	Flake	NIP	Unk.	1962	Warnica	Chert		x	x								
W-115	Flake	NIP	Unk.	1962	Warnica	Ed. Chert		x	x								
W-75	Flake	NIP	Unk.	1962	Warnica	Chert		x	x								
W-119	Flake	NIP	Unk.	1962	Warnica	Chert		x	x								
W-108	Flake	NIP	Unk.	1962	Warnica	Ed. Chert		P	x	x							
W-71	Flake scraper	NIP	Unk.	1962	Warnica	Chert		x	x	x						x	x
W-78	Flake frag.	NIP	Unk.	1962	Warnica	Ed. Chert		x	x	x							
W-49	Flake	NIP	Unk.	1962	Warnica	Ed. Chert		x	x							x	x
W-74	Flake	NIP	Unk.	1962	Warnica	Ed. Chert	x	x	x							x	x
W-99	Flake frag.	NIP	Unk.	1962	Warnica	Ed. Chert		P	x								
W-98	Flake frag.	NIP	Unk.	1962	Warnica	Ed. Chert		x	x								
W-101	Flake frag.	NIP	Unk.	1962	Warnica	Alibates		x	x	x							

Cat. No.	Nether Face Retouched	Modified by use	Transverse X Sec.	Anterior-Posterior X Sec.	Edge Angles	Expanding Stem	Shoulder Stem	Contracting Stem	Side Notches	Straight Base	Convex Base	Concave Base	Fluted	Parallel Flaking	Length of Grinding on Sides	Base Ground	Base Thinning	Blade Form	Tip Reworked	Portion of Edge Worked	Points on Perimeter	Median Ridge on Blade	Serrated Edge	Length	Width	Thickness	Length of Flute
11A		x	ST	TRAP	25°															2/3				1.7	1.0	0.4	
14A	x	x	PLCX	ST	5°-10°															1/3				1.5	1.0	0.2	
46A	x	x	ST	R	10°															1/4				1.4	0.6	0.1	
20A			TRAP	TRAP	40°-50°															1/3				1.0	0.6	0.2	
U	x	x	PLCX	CC	10°-20°															1/2				2.8	1.6	0.2	
B	x		ST	ST	20°-30°															2/3				1.1	1.4	0.2	
C			PLCX	CC	20°															1/3				1.5	1.1	0.2	
d-3	x	x	ST	CC	15°															1/2				1.1	1.1	0.1	
d-8	x	x	PLCV	CC	10°															1/4				0.9	0.8	0.1	
N		x	ST	TRAP	20°-50°															1/2				0.9	0.9	0.3	
4	x	x	ST	R	10°															1/2				1.0	0.7	0.1	
6	x	x	TRAP	ST	10°															1/2				0.9	0.9	0.1	
H		x	PLCV	CC	20°															1/3				1.0	0.7	0.1	
3B	x	x	ST	TRAP	60°-70°															2/3				1.2	0.5	0.3	
J	x	x	ST	TRAP	10°															1/3				0.7	0.3	0.1	
25A		x	ST	LEN	20°															1/3				0.9	0.5	0.1	
53A			TRAP	TRAP	70°															1/10				1.7	1.0	0.3	
4B	x	x	ST	LEN	20°															1/20				1.6	1.3	0.5	
13			TRAP	TRAP	60°															3/4	1			1.4	1.1	0.15	
A		x	TRAP	R	30°															2/3	2			1.4	1.1	0.2	
7		x	TRAP	TRAP	30°															1/2	2			1.0	1.5	0.2	
0	x	x	TRAP	R	20°-40°															1/3	3			1.7	1.5	0.2	
JC		x	R	PLCX	80°															1/8	1			1.7	1.1	0.2	
5		x	ST	CC	40°-50°															2/3				1.4	0.9	0.1	
26A		x	ST	ST	10°-20°															1/2				0.8	0.6	0.2	
d-2			TRAP	TRAP	20°															1/4	1			0.6	0.6	0.1	
d-11	x	x	CC	PLCX	10°															1/20	1			0.3	0.6	0.1	
29A		x	PLCX	PLCX	10°															3/4				1.4	0.8	0.1	
M			PLCX	CC	30°-40°															2/3				1.3	0.7	0.2	
24A		x	IT	TRAP	20°															3/4				1.7	0.8	0.2	
18A			PLCX	TRAP	20°															1/3				1.7	1.3	0.1	
d-1	x	x	IT	ST	30°															3/4				2.3	1.4	0.3	
1			PLCX	CC	60°-70°															A				1.7	0.9	0.1	
G			BICV	LEN	30°							2						leaf		A				0.1	0.7	0.1	0.8+
G(1)			BICV	LEN	35°	x			x			2			0.7	x	x	leaf		A				1.0	0.7	0.1	0.4+
I-7			LEN	LEN	20°	x	x						x		0.3+	x	x			A				0.3	0.7	0.1	
W-133		x	CC	CC	20°-70°																			1.5	1.0	0.15	
W-83		x	LEN	R	20°																			1.2	1.2	0.1	
W-31		x	CC	CC	20°																			1.2	0.8	0.2	
W-81		x	ST	CC	15°																			0.9	0.7	0.1	
W-22			TRAP	CC	80°																			2.9	1.3	0.3	
W-113			R	TRAP	30°																			1.3	0.4	0.2	
W-85			BICV	R	10°																			1.1	1.2	0.15	
W-27			PLCX	ST	5°																			1.9	1.1	0.2	
W-115			PLCX	CC	20°-30°																			1.1	0.9	0.2	
W-75			ST	ST	10°-20°																			1.0	1.4	0.3	
W-119			TRAP	TRAP	80°-90°																			1.1	1.1	0.2	
W-108			IT	PLCX	40°																			0.9	0.6	0.3	
W-71		x	IT	TRAP	10°-20°																			1.5	0.9	0.2	
W-78			BICV	TRAP	20°																			0.5	0.8	0.2	
W-49		x	ST	ST	10°-20°																			0.8	0.5	0.1	
W-74		x	PLCX	CC	30°																			0.4	0.6	0.1	
W-99			TRAP	TRAP	20°																			0.8	0.8	0.2	
W-98			TRAP	TRAP	30°-45°																			0.8	0.6	0.15	
W-101			ST	R	10°																			0.6	0.6	0.1	

Cat. No.	Type	Locus	Culture	Date Found	Found By	Material	Core Tool	Secondary Flake	Prepared Core	Primary Flake	Bulb Trimmed	Billet Technique	Percussion Flaked	Pressure Chipped	Unifacially Retouched	Bifacially Retouched	Upper Face Retouched
W-140	Flake	NIP	Unk.	1962	Warnica	Chert		x	x								
W-88	Flake frag.	NIP	Unk.	1962	Warnica	Chert		x									
W-70	Flake	NIP	Unk.	1962	Warnica	Quart.		x	x								
W-123	Bifacial knife frag.	NIP	Unk.	1962	Warnica	Chert								x	x	x	
W-184	Flake	NIP	Unk.	1962	Warnica	Alibates		x									
W-90	Flake	NIP	Unk.	1962	Warnica	Ed. Chert		x		x							
W-112	Flake	NIP	Unk.	1962	Warnica	T. Jasper		x		x							
W-89	Flake	NIP	Unk.	1962	Warnica	T. Jasper		x									
W-130	Flake frag.	NIP	Unk.	1962	Warnica	Chert		x	x								
W-40	Parallel point frag.	NIP	Portales	1962	Warnica	Obsidian										x	
10	Bone tool	15E, BSW	Folsom	1962	Brown	Bone									1		
R	Side scraper	15F, BSW	Folsom	1962	Collins	Ed. Chert		x	x	x				x	x		x
S	Bone tool	15F, BSW	Folsom	1962	Brown	Bone											
16A	Side scraper	15E, BSW	Folsom	1962	Hester	Chert		P	x					x	x		x
19A	Side scraper	15E, BSW	Folsom	1962	Hester	Alibates		x	x					x	x		x
36A	Side scraper	15E, BSW	Folsom	1962	Hester	Chert		x	x				x	x	x		x
2A	Side scraper	15E, BSW	Folsom	1962	Hester	Ed. Chert		No	x	x				x	x		x
28A	Side scraper	15E, BSW	Folsom	1962	Hester	T. Jasper		P	x				x	x	x		x
55A	Side scraper frag.	15E, BSW	Folsom	1962	Hester	Ed. Chert		x	x					x	x		x
25A	Side scraper	15E, BSW	Folsom	1962	Hester	Ed. Chert		x	x				x	x	x	x	x
17A	Side scraper frag.	15E, BSW	Folsom	1962	Hester	Ed. Chert		x	x					x	x		x
F	Side scraper frag.	15E, BSW	Folsom	1962	Brown	Ed. Chert		No	x					x	x		
16-T	Bifacial knife	BSW	Folsom	1962	Brown	Ed. Chert		x	x					x		x	
D	Side scraper	15E, BSW	Folsom	1962	Brown	Chert		x	x					x	x		x
d-10	Side scraper	15E, BSW	Folsom	1962	Brown	Quart.		x	x					x	x		x
9A	End scraper	15E, BSW	Folsom	1962	Hester	Ed. Chert		x	x	x				x	x		x
41A	End scraper	15E, BSW	Folsom	1962	Hester	Chert		x	x					x	x		x
42A	End scraper	15E, BSW	Folsom	1962	Hester	Chert		x	x	x				x	x		x
44A	End & side scraper	15E, BSW	Folsom	1962	Hester	Chert		x	x					x	x		x
W-57	Folsom point frag.	NIP	Folsom	1962	Warnica	Chert								x		x	
W-93	Folsom point frag.	NIP	Folsom	1962	Warnica	Ed. Chert								x		x	
W-84	Plainview point base	NIP	Unk.	1962	Warnica	Alibates								x		x	
W-38	Folsom point frag.	NIP	Folsom	1962	Warnica	Chert								x		x	
W-118	Point frag.	NIP	Unk.	1962	Warnica	Chert								x		x	
W-137	Folsom point base	NIP	Folsom	1962	Warnica	Chert								x		x	
W-124	Folsom point frag.	NIP	Folsom	1962	Warnica	Ed. Chert								x		x	
W-130	Plainview point base	NIP	Unk.	1962	Warnica	Ed. Chert								x		x	
W-127	Clovis point frag.	NIP	Clovis	1962	Warnica	Ed. Chert								x		x	
W-72	Folsom point frag.	NIP	Folsom	1962	Warnica	Ed. Chert								x		x	
W-34	Parallel flaked point	NIP	Portales	1962	Warnica	Chert								x		x	
W-10	Eden point frag.	NIP	Portales	1962	Warnica	Jasper								x		x	
W-33	Parallel flaked point frag.	NIP	Portales	1962	Warnica	Chert								x		x	
W-46	Parallel flaked point frag.	NIP	Portales	1962	Warnica	Chert								x		x	
W-52	Parallel flaked point frag.	NIP	Portales	1962	Warnica	Chert								x	x	x	
W-68	Parallel flaked point frag.	NIP	Portales	1962	Warnica	Alibates								x		x	
W-2	Portales point	NIP	Portales	1962	Warnica	Chert								x		x	
W-67	Scottsbluff point	NIP	Portales	1962	Warnica	Chert								x		x	
W-41	Parallel Flaked point frag.	NIP	Portales	1962	Warnica	Chert								x		x	
W-21	Parallel flaked point frag.	NIP	Portales	1962	Warnica	Chert								x		x	
W-47	Parallel flaked point frag.	NIP	Portales	1962	Warnica	Chert								x		x	
W-32	Parallel flaked point frag.	NIP	Portales	1962	Warnica	Chert								x		x	
W-102	Parallel flaked point	NIP	Portales	1962	Warnica	Chert								x		x	
W-116	Parallel flaked point frag.	NIP	Portales	1962	Warnica	Chert								x		x	
W-125	Parallel flaked point frag.	NIP	Portales	1962	Warnica	Ed. Chert								x		x	
W-73	Archaic point	NIP	Archaic	1962	Warnica	Chert								x		x	

Cat. No.	Nether Face Retouched	Modified by use	Transverse X Sec.	Anterior-Posterior X Sec.	Edge Angles	Expanding Stem	Shoulder Stem	Contracting Stem	Side Notches	Straight Base	Convex Base	Concave Base	Fluted	Parallel Flaking	Length of Grinding on Sides	Base Ground	Base Thinning	Blade Form	Tip Reworked	Portion of Edge Worked	Points on Perimeter	Median Ridge on Blade	Serrated Edge	Length	Width	Thickness	Length of Flute
W-140			ST	TRAP	10°																			0.6	0.5	0.1	
W-88			ST	CC	10°-30°																			0.8	0.6	0.1	
W-70			ST	ST	30°																			1.7	1.4	0.6	
W-123			LEN	LEN	35°																			0.9	0.8	0.2	
W-184			ST	ST	10°-20°																			0.6	0.3	0.1	
W-90			LEN	LEN	10°																			0.6	0.7	0.1	
W-112			LEN	LEN	10°																			0.5	0.5	0.1	
W-89			ST	ST	20°																			0.7	0.8	0.1	
W-130			TRAP	R	20°																			0.6	0.4	0.1	
W-40			LEN	LEN	25°									x	x									0.4	0.5	0.2	
10																								10.0	1.1	0.5	
R	x		TRAP	ST	20°															2/3				1.7	1.7	0.2	
S																								4.8	1.4	0.4	
16A			ST	ST	40°-80°															2/3				1.5	1.5	0.3	
19A			PLCX	PLCX	40°															3/4				2.1	1.1	0.4	
36A			PLCX	R	60°-70°															2/3				1.8	1.5	0.3	
2A			TRAP	TRAP	60°															1/3				1.8	1.5	0.4	
28A			PLCX	PLCX	70°															1/2				2.2	1.5	0.5	
55A			ST	TRAP	70°															1/8				1.3	0.8	0.2	
25A	x		PLCX	PLCX	50°-70°															2/3				1.4	1.2	0.3	
17A			R	ST	45°															1/3				1.2	0.5	0.15	
F			TRAP	TRAP	60°-70°															1/3				0.8	0.9	0.2	
T			PLCX	PLCX	30°													leaf		7/8				2.1	0.9	0.2	
D			TRAP	TRAP	30°-60°															2/3				1.6	1.5	0.5	
d-10			ST	TRAP	30°															2/3				1.5	0.8	0.4	
9A			ST	PA	30°-70°															7/8	2			1.4	1.5	0.4	
41A			PLCX	PLCX	30°-70°															A	1			1.2	1.1	0.3	
42A			PLCX	PLCX	20°-70°															2/3	2			1.3	1.3	0.2	
44A			PLCX	CC	20°-70°															A				2.8	1.3	0.4	
W-57			CC	CC	30°								1					leaf		A				0.6	0.7	0.1	0.2+
W-93			LEN	LEN	20°								1					leaf		A				0.4	0.6	0.1	0.4+
W-84			LEN	LEN	20°		x		x						0.8	x	x	leaf	x	A				0.8	0.9	0.2	
W-38			LEN	LEN	20°								0		x			leaf	x	A				1.0	0.6	0.1	
W-118			CC	PLCX	35°					x							x			A				0.6	0.6	0.1	
W-137			BICV	LEN	35°					x			2		x	x	x			A				0.5	0.8	0.1	0.5+
W-124			LEN	LEN	25°								0		x			leaf		A				0.8	0.6	0.1	
W-130			LEN	LEN	35°				x						x	x	x			A				0.5	0.9	0.2	
W-127			BICV	LEN	35°								2	x	x					A				0.4	0.8	0.2	
W-72			LEN	LEN	20°								0					leaf		A				0.9	0.7	0.1	
W-34			LEN	R	35°									x	x			leaf				x		1.1	0.7	0.2	
W-10			DIA	LEN	40°									x				leaf		A		x		1.7	0.6	0.3	
W-33			LEN	LEN	30°									x				leaf		A		x		0.5	0.5	0.2	
W-46			LEN	LEN	35°									x	1.0+			leaf		A				1.0	1.1	0.3	
W-52			LEN	LEN	35°									x				leaf		A				1.3	0.9	0.2	
W-68			LEN	LEN	30°		x			x				x	0.6			tri.		A				1.6	0.9	0.2	
W-2			LEN	LEN	40°						x			x	0.7	x	x	leaf		A				1.3	0.8	0.2	
W-67			LEN	LEN	30°		x		x					x	0.5		x	leaf		A				1.6	0.8	0.2	
W-41			LEN	LEN	20°									x				leaf		A				1.0	0.9	0.15	
W-21			LEN	LEN	25°									x				leaf		A		x		1.6	0.8	0.2	
W-47			LEN	LEN	35°									x				leaf		A				1.3	0.7	0.2	
W-32			LEN	LEN	25°	x					x			x	0.6	x	x	tri.		A				1.1	0.5	0.15	
W-102			LEN	LEN	25°	x			x					x			x	tri.		A				1.7	0.5	0.3	
W-116			LEN	LEN	20°									x				leaf		A				0.8	0.6	0.15	
W-125			LEN	LEN	35°									x				leaf		A		x		0.6	0.4	0.2	
W-73			LEN	LEN	35°	x	x							x	0.6	x	x			A				0.7	0.8	0.2	

Cat. No.	Type	Locus	Culture	Date Found	Found By	Material	Core Tool	Secondary Flake	Prepared Core	Primary Flake	Bulb Trimmed	Billet Technique	Percussion Flaked	Pressure Chipped	Unifacially Retouched	Bifacially Retouched	Upper Face Retouched
W-135	Clovis point, Type 2	NIP	Clovis	1962	Warnica	Alibates									x	x	
W-79	Archaic point	NIP	Archaic	1962	Warnica	Quart.									x	x	
W-39	Archaic point	NIP	Archaic	1962	Warnica	Obsidian									x	x	
W-80	Knife, bifacial	NIP	Unk.	1962	Warnica	Ed. Chert									x	x	
W-54	Knife, bifacial	NIP	Unk.	1962	Warnica	Ed. Chert									x	x	
W-53	Knife, bifacial	NIP	Unk.	1962	Warnica	Chert									x	x	
W-60	Knife, bifacial	NIP	Unk.	1962	Warnica	Ed. Chert									x	x	
W-120	Graver	NIP	Unk.	1962	Warnica	Chert		x	x						x	x	x
W-138	Graver frag.	NIP	Unk.	1962	Warnica	Chert		x	x						x	x	x
W-11	Graver	NIP	Unk.	1962	Warnica	Ed. Chert		x	x						x	x	x
W-124	Side scraper	NIP	Unk.	1962	Warnica	Chert		x	x						x	x	x
W-35	Side scraper	NIP	Unk.	1962	Warnica	Chert		x	x						x	x	x
W-62	Side scraper	NIP	Unk.	1962	Warnica	Alibates		x	x					x	x	x	x
W-23	Side scraper	NIP	Unk.	1962	Warnica	Chalcedony		x	x	x					x	x	x
W-17	Side scraper	NIP	Unk.	1962	Warnica	Chert		x	x					x	x	x	x
W-26	Side scraper	NIP	Unk.	1962	Warnica	Chert		x	x						x	x	x
W-1	Side scraper	NIP	Unk.	1962	Warnica	Alibates	P	x		x						x	x
W-25	Side scraper	NIP	Unk.	1962	Warnica	Ed. Chert		x	x					x	x	x	
W-16	Side scraper	NIP	Unk.	1962	Warnica	Ed. Chert		x	x						x	x	
W-42	Side scraper	NIP	Unk.	1962	Warnica	Quart.	No	x							x	x	
W-117	Side scraper frag.	NIP	Unk.	1962	Warnica	Ed. Chert		x	x						x	x	x
W-58	Side scraper frag.	NIP	Unk.	1962	Warnica	Chert		x	x						x	x	x
W-63	End scraper	NIP	Unk.	1962	Warnica	T. Jasper		x	x						x	x	x
W-56	End scraper	NIP	Unk.	1962	Warnica	Alibates		x	x						x	x	x
W-104	End scraper	NIP	Unk.	1962	Warnica	Chert		x	x						x	x	x
W-100	End scraper	NIP	Unk.	1962	Warnica	Chert		x	x						x	x	x
W-12	End scraper	NIP	Unk.	1962	Warnica	Chert		x	x						x	x	x
W-141	End scraper	NIP	Unk.	1962	Warnica	Chert		x	x						x	x	x
W-111	End scraper	NIP	Unk.	1962	Warnica	Ed. Chert		x	x						x	x	x
W-15	End scraper frag.	NIP	Unk.	1962	Warnica	Chert		x	x						x	x	x
W-69	End scraper	NIP	Unk.	1962	Warnica	Ed. Chert		x	x						x	x	x
W-14	End scraper	NIP	Unk.	1962	Warnica	T. Jasper		x	x						x	x	x
W-82	End scraper	NIP	Unk.	1962	Warnica	Chert		x	x						x	x	x
W-66	End scraper	NIP	Unk.	1962	Warnica	Chert		x	x						x	x	x
W-37	End scraper	NIP	Unk.	1962	Warnica	Chert		x	x				x		x	x	x
W-92	End scraper	NIP	Unk.	1962	Warnica	Chert	No	x							x	x	x
W-43	End scraper	NIP	Unk.	1962	Warnica	Chert		x	x	x	x				x	x	x
W-76	End scraper frag.	NIP	Unk.	1962	Warnica	Chert		x	x						x	x	x
W-134	End scraper	NIP	Unk.	1962	Warnica	Chert		x	x						x	x	x
W-132	End scraper	NIP	Unk.	1962	Warnica	Chert		x	x						x	x	x
W-91	End scraper frag.	NIP	Unk.	1962	Warnica	Ed. Chert		x	x						x	x	x
W-65	Flake scraper	NIP	Unk.	1962	Warnica	Ed. Chert		x	x	x					x	x	x
W-20	Flake scraper	NIP	Unk.	1962	Warnica	Chert		x	x						x	x	x
W-11	Flake scraper	NIP	Unk.	1962	Warnica	Chert		x	x			x			x	x	x
W-30	Flake scraper	NIP	Unk.	1962	Warnica	Alibates		x	x						x	x	x
W-105	Flake scraper	NIP	Unk.	1962	Warnica	Chert		x	x						x	x	x
W-116	Flake scraper	NIP	Unk.	1962	Warnica	Ed. Chert	P	x		x						x	x
W-64	Flake scraper	NIP	Unk.	1962	Warnica	Ed. Chert		x	x	x					x	x	x
W-131	Flake scraper	NIP	Unk.	1962	Warnica	Chert	x								x	x	x
W-5	Flake scraper	11A,D	Folsom	1962	Warnica	Ed. Chert		x	x					x	x	x	x
W-28	Flake scraper	NIP	Unk.	1962	Warnica	Alibates		x	x	x	x				x	x	x
W-61	Flake scraper	NIP	Unk.	1962	Warnica	Chert		x	x				x	x	x	x	x
W-128	Flake scraper	NIP	Unk.	1962	Warnica	Chert		x	x						x	x	x
W-96	Flake scraper	NIP	Unk.	1962	Warnica	Chert		x	x							x	x
W-3	Flake scraper	GS	Clovis	1962	Warnica	Quart.		x	x							x	x

Cat. No.	Nether Face Retouched	Modified by use	Transverse X Sec.	Anterior-Posterior X Sec.	Edge Angles	Expanding Stem	Shoulder Stem	Contracting Stem	Side Notches	Straight Base	Convex Base	Concave Base	Fluted	Parallel Flaking	Length of Grinding on Sides	Base Ground	Base Thinning	Blade Form	Tip Reworked	Portion of Edge Worked	Points on Perimeter	Median Ridge on Blade	Serrated Edge	Length	Width	Thickness	Length of Flute
W-135			LEN	LEN	40°	x				x					0.7	x	x	tri.		A				1.1	0.5	0.2	
W-79			LEN	LEN	40°	x	0.7													A				0.8	0.7	0.3	
W-39			LEN	LEN	10°-20°				x									tri.		A			x	1.0	0.7	0.2	
W-80			LEN	LEN	30°													leaf		A				1.2	0.9	0.2	
W-54			LEN	LEN	15°													tri.		A				0.6	0.8	0.1	
W-53			ST	ST	15°													leaf		1/3				1.4	1.0	0.2	
W-60			LEN	LEN	20°													leaf						1.2	0.7	0.2	
W-120		x	IT	PLCX	10°															2/3	2			1.0	0.7	0.1	
W-138			TRAP	TRAP	70°															1/2	2			0.4	0.7	0.1	
W-11			ST	ST	10°-45°															1/2	1			0.6	0.7	0.2	
W-24			TRAP	ST	70°															2/3				2.0	1.1	0.3	
W-35			IT	ST	30°															2/3				1.7	1.0	0.2	
W-62			ST	TRAP	50°-60°															3/4				2.0	1.2	0.3	
W-23			PLCX	PLCX	20°															7/8				2.0	1.3	0.3	
W-17			TRAP	PLCX	45°															1/3				2.0	1.3	0.3	
W-26			ST	ST	70°															2/3				2.1	0.9	0.5	
W-1			ST	PLCX	70°															1/2				2.0	1.6	0.5	
W-25	x		PA	BICV	65°															1/2				2.1	1.2	0.5	
W-16		x	TR	BICV	40°-70°															A				2.7	1.8	0.6	
W-42	x		BICV	PLCX	30°															1/2				2.5	1.2	0.4	
W-117			ST	ST	30°															1/3				0.7	0.8	0.1	
W-58			ST	TRAP	60°															1/3				0.9	0.5	0.2	
W-63			ST	PA	30°-60°															7/8	2			1.8	1.0	0.2	
W-56			TRAP	TRAP	40°															2/3	3			1.1	1.0	0.15	
W-104			ST	PLCX	60°-80°															3/4	4			1.2	1.4	0.2	
W-100			ST	PLCX	50°-80°																			1.3	1.1	0.2	
W-12		x	TRAP	ST	20°-70°															3/4				1.0	0.9	0.3	
W-141			PLCX	CC	40°-60°															7/8				1.0	1.0	0.2	
W-111			PLCX	ST	60°-80°															A	1			1.0	1.0	0.3	
W-15		x	TRAP	ST	60°															3/4				0.9	0.6	0.4	
W-69			ST	PLCX	60°-70°															7/8	1			1.1	1.0	0.2	
W-14			ST	ST	60°-80°															A	2			1.0	1.1	0.3	
W-82			PLCX	TRAP	45°-60°															A				1.6	1.2	0.5	
W-66			ST	ST	45°-70°															3/4	1			1.3	1.1	0.4	
W-37	x		IT	ST	35°-70°															A	1			1.4	1.0	0.4	
W-92			TRAP	TRAP	60°-80°															A	1			1.9	1.4	0.4	
W-43			TRAP	TRAP	50°-70°															A	1			1.6	1.1	0.2	
W-76			PA	TRAP	60°-80°															A	1			0.4	1.1	0.2	
W-134			TRAP	ST	70°-80°															A	1			0.9	0.7	0.2	
W-132			ST	TRAP	60°-80°															A	3			0.9	0.7	0.2	
W-91			ST	TRAP	50°-70°															2/3	1			0.8	0.7	0.1	
W-65			ST	ST	60°															2/3	1			2.0	2.8	0.3	
W-20			TRAP	PLCX	20°-60°															2/3				1.5	0.9	0.2	
W-11		x	PLCX	PLCX	20°															A				2.3	1.0	0.1	
W-30		x	ST	ST	35°															2/3				1.3	0.7	0.2	
W-105		x	PLCX	TRAP	20°															1/2				1.0	1.1	0.15	
W-116		x	ST	TRAP	15°															1/4				0.8	0.8	0.2	
W-64	x	x	ST	TRAP	20°-60°															2/3				2.0	1.5	0.4	
W-131	x		LEN	LEN	40°-50°															1/2				1.0	0.9	0.1	
W-5		x	PLCX	CC	30°-60°															A				3.3	1.3	0.3	
W-28		x	ST	CC	30°-40°															A				2.6	1.1	0.2	
W-61		x	CC	ST	20°-40°															A				2.4	2.0	0.2	
W-128		x	ST	CC	20°-30°															1/2				1.6	1.1	0.2	
W-96		x	TRAP	R	45°															1/2				0.9	1.1	0.2	
W-3		x	ST	CC	30°															1/2				1.6	0.6	0.1	

Cat. No.	Nether Face Retouched	Modified by use	Transverse X Sec.	Anterior-Posterior X Sec.	Edge Angles	Expanding Stem	Shoulder Stem	Contracting Stem	Side Notches	Straight Base	Convex Base	Concave Base	Fluted	Parallel Flaking	Length of Grinding on Sides	Base Ground	Base Thinning	Blade Form	Tip Reworked	Portion of Edge Worked	Points on Perimeter	Median Ridge on Blade	Serrated Edge	Length	Width	Thickness	Length of Flute
W-50		x	ST	ST	30°-40°															A				1.2	1.1	0.3	
W-10		x	PLCX	ST	20°															2/3				1.0	1.1	0.1	
W-45	x	x	TRAP	ST	15°-20°															2/3				1.4	1.0	0.15	
W-86	x		TRAP	R	15°															1/3				0.8	0.6	0.15	
W-87			ST	R	40°															1/3				0.8	0.7	0.1	
W-59	x		ST	PA	50°-60°															2/3				0.8	0.5	0.1	
W-40		x	ST	CC	50°															2/3				1.1	0.7	0.2	
W-51		x	ST	ST	10°-20°															1/3				1.5	1.1	0.5	
W-136			TRAP	TRAP	45°															1/4				1.0	0.6	0.1	
W-13			LEN	TRAP	30°															A				3.6	2.4	0.4	
W-24		x	LEN	LEN	30°-40°															A				2.1	1.4	0.4	
W-36			LEN	ST	40°															A				1.6	1.4	0.3	
W-107		x	CC	CC	35°-45°															A				2.0	1.1	0.3	
W-126			LEN	LEN	10°															A				0.6	0.4	0.1	
W-394			TRAP	PA	40°															1/2				0.7	0.4	0.1	
W-172	x		ST	TRAP	40°															1/4				1.0	0.7	0.2	
W-179		x	ST	TRAP	20°-30°															all				1.4	1.0	0.3	
W-238			LEN	ST	30°															all				1.0	1.0	0.2	
W-188			PLCV	CC	60°															all	2			0.8	0.9	0.2	
W-202			TRAP	LEN	60°															1/4	1			1.0	0.5	0.1	
W-166			TRAP	TRAP	20°																			0.4	1.1	0.2	
W-167		x	ST	ST	20°															1/2				1.2	0.9	0.1	
W-168		x	TRAP	TRAP	50°															1/8				0.8	0.7	0.1	
W-173			TRAP	TRAP	50°-60°																			0.8	0.5	0.3	
W-189			TRAP	TRAP	70°-90°																			0.9	0.5	0.1	
W-195		x	TRAP	TRAP	20°															1/4				0.6	0.6	0.1	
W-206	x	x	PLCV	CC	20°															1/3				0.9	0.8	0.2	
W-210		x	ST	R	10°															1/2				0.6	0.4	0.05	
W-215		x	ST	ST	10°															1/2				0.7	0.5	0.1	
W-230	x	x	ST	TRAP	20°															1/8				0.5	0.7	0.1	
W-231	x	x	TRAP	R	20°															1/8				0.6	0.7	0.1	
W-239		x	LEN	R	10°															1/2				1.0	0.8	0.1	
W-241		x	TRAP	TRAP	10°															1/4				0.5	0.7	0.2	
W-247			ST	TRAP	10°-20°																			1.0	0.9	0.2	
W-250			ST	TRAP	20°																			0.5	0.7	0.1	
W-297			LEN	TRAP	30°																			0.4	0.8	0.2	
W-298			ST	ST	40°-50°																			0.8	0.6	0.3	
W-313		x	TRAP	TRAP	20°															1/2				1.1	0.6	0.1	
W-316	x	x	ST	CC	10°															1/2				0.7	0.5	0.1	
W-324		x	ST	CC	10°															1/2				0.6	0.3	0.2	
W-340			PLCV	CC																				0.8	0.7	0.1	
W-341		x	CC	ST	10°															1/2				0.8	0.5	0.2	
W-342		x	LEN	ST	10°															1/4				0.7	0.8	0.1	
W-369			TRAP	TRAP	60°-80°																			0.8	0.3	0.2	
W-401			PLCV	R	20°																			0.9	0.7	0.1	
W-403			CC	R	20°-30°															1/2				1.3	0.6	0.2	
CO-25			ST	TRAP	60°-80°																			1.0	1.0	0.3	
CO-16		x	PLCV	TRAP	10°															1/3				0.7	0.7	0.1	
CO-14			ST	TRAP	10°-90°																			0.9	0.4	0.1	
CO-18		x	ST	R	10°															1/4				1.2	0.8	0.1	
CO-20		x	TRAP	TRAP	20°-50°															1/2				1.3	1.1	0.1	
CO-23		x	TRAP	TRAP	10°															1/4				0.5	0.6	0.1	
CO-26			ST	ST	20°-70°																			1.2	0.8	0.3	
CO-29			ST	ST	10°-90°																			0.6	0.4	0.1	
CO-28			ST	LEN	30°-70°																			2.3	1.5	0.6	

Cat. No.	Type	Locus	Culture	Date Found	Found By	Material	Core Tool	Secondary Flake	Prepared Core	Primary Flake	Bulb Trimmed	Billet Technique	Percussion Flaked	Pressure Chipped	Unifacially Retouched	Bifacially Retouched	Upper Face Retouched
W-50	Flake scraper	NIP	Clovis	1962	Warnica	Quart.		P	x						x		x
W-10	Flake scraper frag.	NIP	Clovis	1962	Warnica	Ed. Chert		x	x						x		x
W-45	Flake scraper	NIP	Clovis	1962	Warnica	Ed. Chert		x	x						x		x
W-86	Flake scraper	NIP	Clovis	1962	Warnica	Ed. Chert		x	x				x		x	x	
W-87	Flake scraper	NIP	Clovis	1962	Warnica	Chert		x	x						x	x	x
W-59	Flake scraper frag.	NIP	Clovis	1962	Warnica	Chert		x	x						x	x	x
W-40	Flake scraper frag.	NIP	Clovis	1962	Warnica	Alibates	x		x						x		x
W-51	Flake scraper	NIP	Clovis	1962	Warnica	Chert		P	x						x		x
W-136	Flake scraper frag.	NIP	Clovis	1962	Warnica	Jasper		x	x						x	x	x
W-13	Bifacial knife	NIP	Clovis	1962	Warnica	Chert		P	x				x	x		x	
W-29	Bifacial knife	NIP	Clovis	1962	Warnica	Alibates		x	x					x			
W-36	Bifacial knife frag.	NIP	Clovis	1962	Warnica	Alibates		x	x					x	x		
W-107	Bifacial knife	NIP	Clovis	1962	Warnica	Chert		x	x					x	x		
W-126	Projectile point frag.	NIP	Clovis	1962	Warnica	Chert			x							x	
W-394	Flake scraper frag.	20,SUR	Folsom	1962	Warnica	Ed. Chert		x	x						x	x	x
W-172	Flake scraper frag.	20,SUR	Folsom	1962	Warnica	Ed. Chert		x	x						x	x	
W-179	Flake knife	20,SUR	Folsom	1962	Warnica	Chert		x	x	x					x		x
W-238	Blade frag. bifacial	20,SUR	Folsom	1962	Warnica	Ed. Chert		x	x					x	x	x	
W-188	Graver	20,SUR	Folsom	1962	Warnica	Alibates		x	x			x			x	x	x
W-202	Graver	20,SUR	Folsom	1962	Warnica	Ed. Chert		x	x						x	x	x
W-166	Flake frag.	20,SUR	Folsom	1962	Warnica	Ed. Chert		P	x								
W-167	Flake frag.	20,SUR	Folsom	1962	Warnica	Alibates		x	x								
W-168	Flake frag.	20,SUR	Folsom	1962	Warnica	Ed. Chert		x	x	x							
W-173	Flake frag.	20,SUR	Folsom	1962	Warnica	Ed. Chert		P	x								
W-189	Flake frag.	20,SUR	Folsom	1962	Warnica	Ed. Chert		x	x								
W-195	Flake frag.	20,SUR	Folsom	1962	Warnica	Ed. Chert		x	x						x		x
W-206	Flake	20,SUR	Folsom	1962	Warnica	T. Jasper		x	x	x					x		
W-210	Flake	20,SUR	Folsom	1962	Warnica	Ed. Chert		x	x	x	x						
W-215	Flake	20,SUR	Folsom	1962	Warnica	Ed. Chert		x	x						x		x
W-230	Flake frag.	20,SUR	Folsom	1962	Warnica	Ed. Chert		x	x						x		
W-231	Flake frag.	20,SUR	Folsom	1962	Warnica	Ed. Chert		x	x	x					x		
W-239	Flake frag.	20,SUR	Folsom	1962	Warnica	Ed. Chert		x	x	x							
W-241	Flake frag.	20,SUR	Folsom	1962	Warnica	Ed. Chert		x	x						x		x
W-247	Flake frag.	20,SUR	Folsom	1962	Warnica	Quart.		x	x	x							
W-250	Flake frag.	20,SUR	Folsom	1962	Warnica	Alibates		x	x								
W-297	Flake frag.	20,SUR	Folsom	1962	Warnica	Ed. Chert		x	x	x							
W-298	Flake	20,SUR	Folsom	1962	Warnica	Alibates	x										
W-313	Flake frag.	20,SUR	Folsom	1962	Warnica	Ed. Chert		x	x						x		x
W-316	Flake	20,SUR	Folsom	1962	Warnica	Ed. Chert	x							x	x		
W-324	Flake	20,SUR	Folsom	1962	Warnica	Ed. Chert		P	x					x	x		x
W-340	Flake	20,SUR	Folsom	1962	Warnica	T. Jasper	x							x			
W-341	Flake	20,SUR	Folsom	1962	Warnica	Ed. Chert		x	x					x	x		x
W-342	Flake frag.	20,SUR	Folsom	1962	Warnica	Ed. Chert		x	x						x		x
W-369	Flake frag.	20,SUR	Folsom	1962	Warnica	Ed. Chert		x	x								
W-401	Flake frag.	20,SUR	Folsom	1962	Warnica	Ed. Chert	x										
W-403	Flake frag.	20,SUR	Folsom	1962	Warnica	T. Jasper		x	x	x							
CO-25	Flake	15E,BSW	Folsom	1962	Collins	Basalt		x	x								
CO-16	Flake	15E,BSW	Folsom	1962	Collins	Ed. Chert		x	x	x							
CP-14	Flake frag.	15E,BSW	Folsom	1962	Collins	Ed. Chert		x	x								
CO-18	Flake	15E,BSW	Folsom	1962	Collins	Ed. Chert		x	x								
CO-20	Flake	15E,BSW	Folsom	1962	Collins	Ed. Chert		x	x								
CO-23	Flake frag.	15E,BSW	Folsom	1962	Collins	Ed. Chert		x	x								
CO-26	Flake	15E,BSW	Folsom	1962	Collins	Quart.		x	x								
CO-29	Flake	15E,BSW	Folsom	1962	Collins	Ed. Chert	x	x									
CO-28	Flake	15E,BSW	Folsom	1962	Collins	Quart.	x	x									

Cat. No.	Type	Locus	Culture	Date Found	Found By	Material	Core Tool	Secondary Flake	Prepared Core	Primary Flake	Bulb Trimmed	Billet Technique	Percussion Flaked	Pressure Chipped	Unifacially Retouched	Bifacially Retouched	Upper Face Retouched
CO-31	Flake frag.	15E, BSW	Folsom	1962	Collins	Ed. Chert		x	x								
CO-32	Flake frag.	15E, BSW	Folsom	1962	Collins	Ed. Chert		x	x								
CO-33	Flake frag.	15E, BSW	Folsom	1962	Collins	Ed. Chert		x	x			x					
CO-34	Flake	15E, BSW	Folsom	1962	Collins	Alibates		x	x			x					
CO-39	Flake	15E, BSW	Folsom	1962	Collins	Alibates		x	x			x					
CO-40	Flake	15E, BSW	Folsom	1962	Collins	Ed. Chert		x	x								
CO-41	Flake frag.	15E, BSW	Folsom	1962	Collins	Ed. Chert		x	x								
CO-42	Flake frag.	15E, BSW		1962	Collins	Ed. Chert		x	x								
CO-43	Flake frag.	15E, BSW	Folsom	1962	Collins	Alibates		x	x								
CO-44	Flake	15E, BSW	Folsom	1962	Collins	Ed. Chert		x	x			x					
CO-45	Flake frag.	15E, BSW	Folsom	1962	Collins	Ed. Chert		x	x			x					
CO-46	Flake frag.	15E, BSW	Folsom	1962	Collins	Chert		x	x			x					
CO-47	Flake	15E, BSW	Folsom	1962	Collins	Chert		x	x			x					
CO-48	Flake frag.	15E, BSW	Folsom	1962	Collins	Ed. Chert		x	x								
CO-49	Flake frag.	15E, BSW	Folsom	1962	Collins	Ed. Chert		x	x								
CO-50	Flake frag.	15E, BSW	Folsom	1962	Collins	Ed. Chert		x	x								
CO-52	Flake frag.	15E, BSW	Folsom	1962	Collins	Ed. Chert		x	x								
CO-55	Flake	15E, BSW	Folsom	1962	Collins	Quart.											
CO-56	Flake	15E, BSW	Folsom	1962	Collins	Chert		x	x			x					
CO-57	Flake	15E, BSW	Folsom	1962	Collins	Ed. Chert		P	x	x							
CO-62	Flake	15E, BSW	Folsom	1962	Collins	Ed. Chert		x	x			x					
CO-63	Flake frag.	15E, BSW	Folsom	1962	Collins	T. Jasper		x	x								
CO-64	Flake frag.	15E, BSW	Folsom	1962	Collins	Alibates		x	x			x					
CO-64a	Flake frag.	15E, BSW	Folsom	1962	Collins	Ed. Chert		x	x								
CO-65	Flake frag.	15E, BSW	Folsom	1962	Collins	Ed. Chert		x	x								
CO-66	Flake frag.	15E, BSW	Folsom	1962	Collins	Ed. Chert		x	x								
CO-69	Flake	15E, BSW	Folsom	1962	Collins	Ed. Chert		x	x								
CO-71	Flake frag.	15E, BSW	Folsom	1962	Collins	Ed. Chert		x	x								
CO-72	Flake frag.	15E, BSW	Folsom	1962	Collins	Ed. Chert		x	x		x	x					
CO-74	Flake frag.	15E, BSW	Folsom	1962	Collins	Alibates		x	x								
CO-75	Flake frag.	15E, BSW	Folsom	1962	Collins	T. Jasper		x	x								
CO-77	Flake	15E, BSW	Folsom	1962	Collins	Ed. Chert		x	x			x					
CO-79	Flake	15E, BSW	Folsom	1962	Collins	Ed. Chert		x	x			x					
CO-79a	Flake frag.	15E, BSW	Folsom	1962	Collins	Ed. Chert		x	x								
CO-81	Flake frag.	15E, BSW	Folsom	1962	Collins	Chert		x	x								
CO-82	Flake frag.	15E, BSW	Folsom	1962	Collins	Chert		x	x								
CO-84	Flake frag.	15E, BSW	Folsom	1962	Collins	Chert		x	x			x					
CO-85	Flake frag.	15E, BSW	Folsom	1962	Collins	Quart.	x										
CO-21	Flake frag.	15E, BSW	Folsom	1962	Collins	Alibates	x								x	x	x
CO-15	Flake	15E, BSW	Folsom	1962	Collins	Chert	x										
CO-22	Flake	15E, BSW	Folsom	1962	Collins	Alibates	x			x							
CO-37	Flake	15E, BSW	Folsom	1962	Collins	Ed. Chert	x			x						x	
CO-53	Flake	15E, BSW	Folsom	1962	Collins	T. Jasper	x			x							
CO-58	Flake	15E, BSW	Folsom	1962	Collins	Ed. Chert	x			x							
CO-67	Flake	15E, BSW	Folsom	1962	Collins	Alibates	x										
CO-73	Flake	15E, BSW	Folsom	1962	Collins	T. Jasper	x			x							
CO-95	Folsom point base	15H, BSW	Folsom	1962	Collins	Ed. Chert										x	
CO-103	Folsom point base	15H, BSW	Folsom	1962	Collins	Ed. Chert		x	x							x	
CO-105	Folsom point base	15G, BSW	Folsom	1962	Collins	Ed. Chert										x	
CO-107	Folsom point base	15G, BSW	Folsom	1962	Collins	Ed. Chert										x	
CO-89	End scraper	15G, BSW	Folsom	1962	Collins	Ed. Chert		No	x	x			x	x	x		x
CO-100	End scraper	15G, BSW	Folsom	1962	Collins	Ed. Chert		x	x				x	x	x		x
CO-106	End scraper	15G, BSW	Folsom	1962	Collins	Chert		x	x	x			x	x	x		x
CO-97	Scraper frag.	15G, BSW	Folsom	1962	Collins	Quart.		x	x					x	x		x
CO-101	Unifacial knife	15G, BSW	Folsom	1962	Collins	Ed. Chert		x	x	x	x			x	x		x

Cat. No.	Nether Face Retouched	Modified by use	Transverse X Sec.	Anterior-Posterior X Sec.	Edge Angles	Expanding Stem	Shoulder Stem	Contracting Stem	Side Notches	Straight Base	Convex Base	Concave Base	Fluted	Parallel Flaking	Length of Grinding on Sides	Base Ground	Base Thinning	Blade Form	Tip Reworked	Portion of Edge Worked	Points on Perimeter	Median Ridge on Blade	Serrated Edge	Length	Width	Thickness	Length of Flute
CO-31			R	TRAP	70°-90°																			0.7	0.5	0.1	
CO-32		x	TRAP	TRAP	20°-90°															1/8				0.9	0.4	0.1	
CO-33		x	ST	TRAP	10°-50°															2/3				0.9	0.9	0.2	
CO-34			TRAP	ST	10°-20°																			0.8	0.5	0.1	
CO-39		x	PLCV	R	10°															2/3				0.5	0.3	0.05	
CO-40		x	TRAP	R	20°															3/4				0.8	0.4	0.1	
CO-41		x	ST	TRAP	10°															1/4				0.6	0.6	0.1	
CO-42		x	ST	R	10°															1/4				0.2	0.6	0.1	
CO-43		x	TRAP	ST	10°-30°															1/8				0.7	1.0	0.1	
CO-44		x	ST	CC	10°-20°															3/4				0.7	0.5	0.1	
CO-45		x	ST	TRAP	10°															1/2				0.6	0.2	0.1	
CO-46		x	ST	CC	20°															1/3				1.2	0.4	0.1	
CO-47		x	ST	TRAP	20°															1/2				1.1	1.0	0.2	
CO-48			TRAP	TRAP	70°-90°																			0.6	0.5	0.2	
CO-49		x	TRAP	CC	25°															1/4				0.6	1.0	0.2	
CO-50		x	ST	R	20°															1/3				0.7	0.7	0.1	
CO-52		x	TRAP	ST	10°-20°															1/3				1.0	0.7	0.1	
CO-55			PLCV	PLCV	40°																			1.1	0.9	0.2	
CO-56		x	ST	PLCV	40°															1/2				0.8	1.3	0.4	
CO-57		x	ST	PLCV	10°															2/3				1.7	1.0	0.1	
CO-62		x	PLCV	CC	10°															1/2				1.0	0.6	0.1	
CO-63		x	PA	ST	50°															1/2				1.2	1.0	0.2	
CO-64		x	ST	TRAP	20°															2/3				1.0	1.0	0.1	
CO-64a		x	LEN	R	10°															1/8				0.6	1.0	0.1	
CO-65		x	TRAP	R	10°															1/2				1.0	0.8	0.1	
CO-66		x	LEN	TRAP	10°															2/3				1.2	1.2	0.1	
CO-69		x	ST	TRAP	10°															1/4				0.6	0.7	0.1	
CO-71			R	TRAP	80°-90°																			1.3	0.5	0.1	
CO-72		x	ST	TRAP	10°															1/2				0.5	0.5	0.1	
CO-74			TRAP	TRAP	10°-30°																			0.6	0.6	0.1	
CO-75			R	ST	20°																			0.8	0.6	0.1	
CO-77		x	PLCV	CC	10°															1/3				1.1	1.0	0.1	
CO-79		x	PLCV	ST	10°															1/2				0.8	0.7	0.2	
CO-79a		x	TRAP	TRAP	30°-40°															2/3				1.0	0.7	0.2	
CO-81		x	ST	ST	10°															1/2				0.5	0.5	0.1	
CO-82		x	ST	PA	10°															1/4				0.7	1.0	0.1	
CO-84		x	ST	R	10°															1/2				0.9	1.0	0.1	
CO-85			PLCV	ST	60°																			0.5	1.0	0.2	
CO-21		x	ST	TRAP	30°															1/4				0.4	0.4	0.1	
CO-15		x	PLCV	PA	20°															1/4				0.5	0.5	0.1	
CO-22			PLCV	ST	10°																			0.4	0.4	0.1	
CO-37			ST	PLCV	40°															1/2				1.0	0.4	0.2	
CO-53			LEN	ST	20°																			0.4	0.6	0.2	
CO-58			PLCV	PLCV	30°																			0.6	0.7	0.2	
CO-67			ET	TRAP	60°																			0.7	0.4	0.3	
CO-73			ST	ST	10°																			0.4	0.4	0.1	
CO-95			BICV	LEN	25°			x		x	2			0.6		x	x	leaf		all				0.6	0.7	0.1	0.6+
CO-103			LEN	LEN	20°			x		x	0			0.8			x	leaf		all				1.0	0.7	0.1	
CO-105			BICV	LEN	20°			x		x	2			0.4+		x	x	leaf		all				0.4	0.7	0.1	
CO-107			LEN	LEN	20°			x			0			0.5+				leaf		all				0.9	0.6	0.1	
CO-89	x		PLCV	PLCV	30°-60°															all	2			1.2	1.5	0.3	
CO-100			ST	PA	40°-50°															2/3	2			1.2	1.2	0.3	
CO-106			TRAP	ST	20°-60°															all	1			1.1	1.3	0.4	
CO-97			ST	ST	30°-50°															2/3				0.7	0.5	0.2	
CO-101			ST	ST	20°-30°															2/3				1.5	1.2	0.2	

Cat. No.	Type	Locus	Culture	Date Found	Found By	Material	Core Tool	Secondary Flake	Prepared Core	Primary Flake	Bulb Trimmed	Billet Technique	Percussion Flaked	Pressure Chipped	Unifacially Retouched	Bifacially Retouched	Upper Face Retouched
CO-90	Flake frag	15G,BSW	Folsom	1962	Collins	Chalcedony		x	x								
CO-91	Flake frag.	15G,BSW	Folsom	1962	Collins	Ed. Chert		x	x								
CO-93	Flake frag.	15G,BSW	Folsom	1962	Collins	Alibates		x	x								
CO-94	Flake	15G,BSW	Folsom	1962	Collins	Ed. Chert		x	x	x							
CO-96	Flake frag.	15G,BSW	Folsom	1962	Collins	Ed. Chert		x	x								
CO-98	Flake frag.	15G,BSW	Folsom	1962	Collins	Ed. Chert		x	x								
CO-99	Flake	15G,BSW	Folsom	1962	Collins	Ed. Chert		x	x	x							
CO-102	Flake	15G,BSW	Folsom	1962	Collins	Ed. Chert		x	x	x							
CO-104	Flake frag.	15G,BSW	Folsom	1962	Collins	Ed. Chert		x	x								
CO-108	Unifacial knife	15F,BSW	Folsom	1962	Collins	Ed. Chert		x	x						x	x	x
CO-1	Flake frag.	15E,GS	Clovis	1962	Collins	Alibates		x	x								
CO-2	Flake	15E,GS	Clovis	1962	Collins	Alibates		x	x	x							
CO-3	Flake frag.	15E,GS	Clovis	1962	Collins	Alibates		x	x								
CO-4	End scraper	15E,GS	Clovis	1962	Collins	Alibates		x	x	x		x			x	x	x
CO-109	Flake frag.	15G,GS	Clovis	1962	Collins	Alibates		P	x								
CO-110	Flake	15G,GS	Clovis	1962	Collins	Alibates		x	x	x							
CO-8	Side scraper	NIP	Unk.	1962	Collins	Alibates		x	x	x					x	x	x
CO-9	End scraper	NIP	Unk.	1962	Collins	T. Jasper		x	x						x	x	x
CO-10	End scraper	NIP	Unk.	1962	Collins	Alibates		x	x						x	x	x
CO-11	Flake scraper frag.	NIP	Unk.	1962	Collins	Chert		x	x						x	x	x
CO-12	End scraper	NIP	Unk.	1962	Collins	Ed. Chert		x	x	x				x	x	x	x
CO-13	End scraper	NIP	Unk.	1962	Collins	Ed. Chert		x	x					x	x	x	x
W-158	End scraper	15E,BSW	Folsom	1962	Warnica	T. Jasper		x	x	x			x	x	x	x	x
W-160	Flake scraper	15E,BSW	Folsom	1962	Warnica	Ed. Chert		P	x	x					x	x	x
W-161	Flake frag.	15E,BSW	Folsom	1962	Warnica	Ed. Chert		x	x								
W-162	Blade frag. bifacial	15E,BSW	Folsom	1962	Warnica	Ed. Chert		P	x				x			x	
W-164	Flake	15E,BSW	Folsom	1962	Warnica	Ed. Chert		x	x	x							
W-159	Flake frag.	15E,BSW	Folsom	1962	Warnica	Ed. Chert		x	x								
W-165	Unifacial knife	15E,BSW	Clovis	1962	Warnica	T. Jasper		x	x						x	x	x
CH-19	Flake	17,BSW	Folsom	1962	Charboneau	Quart.		x	x	x							
CH-20	Flake	17,BSW	Folsom	1962	Charboneau	Chert		x	x							x	x
CH-15	Flake	17,BSW	Folsom	1962	Charboneau	T. Jasper	x		x				x				
CH-9	Flake	17,BSW	Folsom	1962	Charboneau	Quart.	x										
CH-10	Flake	17,BSW	Folsom	1962	Charboneau	Quart.	No	x									
CH-24	Flake	17,BSW	Folsom	1962	Charboneau	Ed. Chert	x										
CH-8	Flake	17,BSW	Folsom	1962	Charboneau	Quart.		x	x								
HA-1	Unifacial knife	15E,BSW	Folsom	1962	Harrison	Ed. Chert		x	x	x					x	x	x
HA-2	Flake	15E,BSW	Folsom	1962	Harrison	Ed. Chert		x	x	x							
HA-3	Flake scraper	15E,BSW	Folsom	1962	Harrison	Ed. Chert		x	x							x	x
HA-4	Flake	15E,BSW	Folsom	1962	Harrison	Ed. Chert		x	x								
HA-5	Flake	15E,BSW	Folsom	1962	Harrison	Quart.		x	x								
K-7	Unifacial knife	15E,BSW	Clovis	1962	Krieble	Alibates		x	x						x	x	x
K-8	Side scraper	15E,BSW	Clovis	1962	Krieble	Alibates		x	x	x						x	x
K-10	Flake	15E,BSW	Clovis	1962	Krieble	Alibates		P	x								
K-11	Flake	15E,BSW	Clovis	1962	Krieble	Chert		x	x								
K-12	Flake	15E,BSW	Clovis	1962	Krieble	Ed. Chert		x	x				x				
K-13	Bone tool	15E,BSW	Clovis	1962		Ed. Chert		x	x								
K-9	Flake	15E,BSW	Clovis	1962	Krieble	Chalcedony		P	x	x							
K-2	Folsom point	NIP	Folsom		Krieble	Ed. Chert								x	x	x	
K-1	Folsom point	NIP	Folsom		Krieble	Ed. Chert									x	x	
K-3	Folsom point base	NIP	Folsom		Krieble	Chert									x	x	
K-4	Plainview point base	NIP	Portales		Krieble	Ed. Chert									x	x	
K-5	Folsom point	NIP	Folsom		Krieble	Ed. Chert								x	x	x	
K-6	Parallel flaked point	NIP	Portales		Krieble	Alibates									x	x	
CO-5	Clovis point base frag.	15E,BSW	Clovis	1962	Collins	Alibates								x	x	x	

Cat. No.	Nether Face Retouched	Modified by use	Transverse X Sec.	Anterior-Posterior X Sec.	Edge Angles	Expanding Stem	Shoulder Stem	Contracting Stem	Side Notches	Straight Base	Convex Base	Concave Base	Fluted	Parallel Flaking	Length of Grinding on Sides	Base Ground	Base Thinning	Blade Form	Tip Reworked	Portion of Edge Worked	Points on Perimeter	Median Ridge on Blade	Serrated Edge	Length	Width	Thickness	Length of Flute
CO-90			ST	ST	10°-80°																			0.5	0.3	0.1	
CO-91		x	LEN	TRAP	10°															1/3				0.5	0.3	0.1	
CO-93		x	ST	ST	20°															1/4				1.2	1.2	0.2	
CO-94		x	PLCV	R	10°															2/3				1.1	0.8	0.1	
CO-96		x	TRAP	TRAP	40°															1/4				0.5	0.5	0.1	
CO-98		x	LEN	ST	10°															1/4				1.1	1.3	0.1	
CO-99		x	ST	CC	10°															1/2				0.8	0.7	0.1	
CO-102		x	ST	CC	10°															1/2				0.8	0.5	0.1	
CO-104		x	ST	R	10°-90°															1/3				0.8	0.5	0.1	
CO-108		x	PLCV	R	10°-20°															2/3				1.7	0.8	0.1	
CO-1			PLCV	R	10°																			0.6	0.4	0.1	
CO-2		x	PLCV	CC	10°															1/4				0.8	0.6	0.1	
CO-3		x	ST	TRAP	20°															1/2				0.5	0.6	0.2	
CO-4			PLCV	ST	40°-80°															all				1.5	1.0	0.3	
CO-109		x	ST	CC	20°															2/3				1.9	1.3	0.2	
CO-110		x	ST	PLCV	30°															all				3.0	1.0	0.3	
CO-8			PLCV	ST	30°-50°															2/3				1.7	1.5	0.3	
CO-9			TRAP	TRAP	40°-80°															3/4	2			0.9	0.9	0.2	
CO-10			ST	TRAP	20°-60°															3/4	2			1.0	1.0	0.3	
CO-11			TRAP	R	20°-40°															1/2				1.6	1.7	0.3	
CO-12	x		PLCV	ST	40°-70°															all				2.4	1.5	0.6	
CO-13			PLCV	TRAP	40°-80°															all	2			1.2	1.0	0.4	
W-158			PLCV	TRAP	30°-80°															2/3	2			1.5	1.0	0.5	
W-160			ST	CC	20°															1/2	1			2.1	0.8	0.2	
W-161		x	PLCV	ST	10°-20°															2/3				1.3	1.2	0.2	
W-162			LEN	ST	20°-40°															2/3				1.4	1.4	0.3	
W-164		x	R	CC	20°															1/4				1.3	1.2	0.2	
W-159		x	ST	TRAP	10°															1/4				1.3	1.1	0.2	
W-165			ST	TRAP	40°															1/2				2.2	1.0	0.3	
CH-19			ST	PLCV	60°																			1.6	2.2	0.4	
CH-20		x	PLCV	CC	10°															1/2				1.2	0.8	0.1	
CH-15			LEN	ST	10°																			0.4	0.4	0.1	
CH-9			LEN	ST	10°-30°																			0.9	0.9	0.2	
CH-10			PLCV	ST	30°-50°																			1.0	0.8	0.3	
CH-24			TRAP	TRAP	70°-90°																			0.8	0.4	0.2	
CH-8			ST	TRAP	20°-40°																			1.7	1.1	0.4	
HA-1		x	ST	PLCV	10°-20°															all				2.6	2.0	0.2	
HA-2		x	LEN	ST	10°															1/4				1.1	1.6	0.1	
HA-3		x	ST	TRAP	20°															1/2				1.2	0.6	0.1	
HA-4		x	ST	TRAP	20°															1/4				0.7	0.7	0.1	
HA-5		x	LEN	TRAP	10°															1/4				1.0	0.9	0.1	
K-7			TRAP	TRAP	40°															1/4				2.0	1.5	0.15	
K-8			LEN	LEN	30°-40°															3/4				1.5	2.3	0.4	
K-10		x	TRAP	TRAP	20°-70°															1/4				1.5	0.9	0.2	
K-11		x	ST	CC	10°-20°															1/2				1.4	0.6	0.2	
K-12		x	LEN	TRAP	10°															1/4				1.0	0.8	0.1	
K-13			LEN																					10.3	1.3	0.5	
K-9		x	LEN	TRAP	30°															1/4				0.9	0.8	0.2	
K-2			BICV	LEN	25°	x						x	2		0.6	x	x	leaf	x	all				1.0	0.8	0.1	
K-1			LEN	LEN	20°			x				x	0	x	0.9	x	x	leaf		all				1.4	0.7	0.1	
K-3			LEN	LEN	20°							x	0	x	0.4+	x	x			all				0.5	0.7	0.1	
K-4			LEN	LEN	25°			x				x		x	0.6	x	x			all				0.7	0.8	0.2	
K-5			BICV	LEN	25°			x				x	2		1.2	x	x	leaf		all				2.0	1.0	0.15	
K-6			LEN	LEN	25°							x		x				leaf		all		1		1.4	0.6	0.2	
CO-5			LEN	LEN	25°			x				x	1		1.0	x	x	leaf		all				1.2	1.6	0.2	

Cat. No.	Type	Locus	Culture	Date Found	Found By	Material	Core Tool	Secondary Flake	Prepared Core	Primary Flake	Bulb Trimmed	Billet Technique	Percussion Flaked	Pressure Chipped	Unifacially Retouched	Bifacially Retouched	Upper Face Retouched
CO-6	Folsom point	15E, BSW	Folsom	1962	Collins	Ed. Chert							x	x		x	
CO-7	Folsom point	15E, BSW	Folsom	1962	Collins	Ed. Chert							x	x		x	
CO-54	Point base	15, BSW	Folsom	1962	Collins	Alibates							x	x		x	
CO-86	Point frag.	15H, BSW	Folsom	1962	Collins	Ed. Chert							x			x	
CO-70	Unifacial knife	15H, BSW	Folsom	1962	Collins	T. Jasper		x	x					x	x		x
CO-61	Flake knife	15H, BSW	Folsom	1962	Collins	T. Jasper		x	x					x	x		x
CO-60	Bifacial knife	15H, BSW	Folsom	1962	Collins	Ed. Chert		x	x	x				x		x	
CO-80	Bifacial frag.	15H, BSW	Folsom	1962	Collins	Ed. Chert		x	x				x	x		x	
CO-59	Bifacial frag.	15H, BSW	Folsom	1962	Collins	Ed. Chert							x	x		x	
CO-38	Side scraper	15H, BSW	Folsom	1962	Collins	Alibates		x	x	x				x	x		x
CO-87	Side scraper	15H, BSW	Folsom	1962	Collins	Ed. Chert	P	x					x	x	x	x	x
CO-27	Side scraper	15H, BSW	Folsom	1962	Collins	Quart.		x	x					x	x	x	x
CO-17	Side scraper	15H, BSW	Folsom	1962	Collins	Ed. Chert		x	x	x				x	x		x
CO-78	Bifacial knife frag.	15H, BSW	Folsom	1962	Collins	Ed. Chert		x	x					x	x	x	
CO-36	Flake scraper	15H, BSW	Folsom	1962	Collins	Ed. Chert		x	x					x	x		x
CO-76	Flake scraper	15H, BSW	Folsom	1962	Collins	Alibates		x	x	x				x	x		x
CO-36a	Flake scraper frag.	15H, BSW	Folsom	1962	Collins	Ed. Chert		x	x					x	x		x
CO-68	Flake scraper frag.	15H, BSW	Folsom	1962	Collins	Chert		x	x					x	x		x
CO-51	Flake scraper	15H, BSW	Folsom	1962	Collins	Ed. Chert		x	x	x				x		x	
CO-83	Graver	15H, BSW	Folsom	1962	Collins	Ed. Chert		x	x					x	x		x
CO-30	Flake	15H, BSW	Folsom	1962	Collins	Chert		x	x	x							
CO-19	Flake	15H, BSW	Folsom	1962	Collins	Ed. Chert		x	x								
M-42	Flake	17, BSW	Clovis	1962	Murray	Chalcedony	x										
M-41	Flake	17, BSW	Clovis	1962	Murray	Alibates	x										
M-43,44,45	Pebble	17, BSW	Clovis	1962	Murray	Quart.	x										
M-26	Plainview point	15E, BSW	Folsom	1962	Murray	Chert								x		x	
M-25	Agate Basin point	15E, NIP	Portales	1962	Murray	Ed. Chert								x		x	
M-3	Scottsbluff point	NIP	Portales		Murray	Alibates								x		x	
M-9	Folsom point	NIP	Folsom		Murray	Ed. Chert								x		x	
M-20	Point frag.	NIP	Unk.		Murray	Chert								x		x	
M-16	End scraper	NIP	Unk.		Murray	Ed. Chert		x	x	x				x	x		x
M-10	Bifacial knife	NIP	Unk.		Murray	Quart.		x	x	x			x	x		x	
M-17	Bifacial knife frag.	NIP	Unk.		Murray	Quart.		x	x					x		x	
M-4	Unifacial knife	NIP	Unk.		Murray	T. Jasper		x	x					x	x		x
M-22	Flake knife	NIP	Unk.		Murray	Chert		x	x	x							
M-8	Side scraper	NIP	Unk.		Murray	Ed. Chert		x	x					x	x		x
M-7	Burin - bec de flute	NIP	Unk.		Murray	Quart.		x	x				x	x	x		x
M-23	Side scraper	NIP	Unk.		Murray	Ed. Chert		x	x					x	x		x
M-18	Scraper frag.	NIP	Unk.		Murray	Chert		x	x	x				x	x		x
M-6	Flake knife	NIP	Unk.		Murray	Chert		x	x					x		x	
M-5	Flake scraper	NIP	Unk.		Murray	Ed. Chert		x	x						x		x
M-11	Flake scraper	NIP	Unk.		Murray	Alibates		x	x	x	x			x	x		x
M-1	Core	NIP	Unk.		Murray	Ed. Chert	x						x			x	
M-19	Flake	NIP	Unk.		Murray	Ed. Chert		x	x								
M-2	Flake	NIP	Unk.		Murray	Alibates		x									
M-24	Flake	NIP	Unk.		Murray	Alibates	x			x							
M-12	Flake	NIP	Unk.		Murray	Ed. Chert		x	x	x							
M-13	Flake	NIP	Unk.		Murray	T. Jasper		x	x								
M-15	Flake	NIP	Unk.		Murray	Quart.		x	x								
M-21	Flake	NIP	Unk.		Murray	Quart.		x	x								
M-14	Flake	NIP	Unk.		Murray	Quart		x	x								
CH-12	Folsom point	17, BSW	Folsom		Charboneau	Ed. Chert								x		x	
CH-6	End scraper	17, BSW	Folsom		Charboneau	Ed. Chert		x	x					x	x		x
CH-22	Side scraper	17, BSW	Folsom		Charboneau	Ed. Chert		x	x	x				x	x		x
CH-4	Side scraper	17, BSW	Folsom		Charboneau	Ed. Chert	No	x						x	x		x

Cat. No.	Nether Face Retouched	Modified by use	Transverse X Sec.	Anterior-Posterior X Sec.	Edge Angles	Expanding Stem	Shoulder Stem	Contracting Stem	Side Notches	Straight Base	Convex Base	Concave Base	Fluted	Parallel Flaking	Length of Grinding on Sides	Base Ground	Base Thinning	Blade Form	Tip Reworked	Portion of Edge Worked	Points on Perimeter	Median Ridge on Blade	Serrated Edge	Length	Width	Thickness	Length of Flute
CO-6			BICV	LEN	20°			x					2		0.4	x	x	tri.	x	all				1.1	0.8	0.1	
CO-7			BICV	LEN	20°	x						x	2		0.5	x	x	tri.		all				1.2	0.8	0.1	
CO-54			LEN	LEN	20°	x						x					x	leaf		all				1.1	0.8	0.2	
CO-86			LEN	TRAP										x						all				0.8	0.5	0.1	
CO-70			TRAP	TRAP	25°															1/2				0.8	0.4	0.1	
CO-61			LEN	R	10°															1/2				1.3	1.6	0.2	
CO-60			ST	BICV	30°													tri.		3/4				2.1	1.2	0.2	
CO-80			LEN	LEN	25°													leaf		all				1.0	1.3	0.2	
CO-59			LEN	TRAP	20°															all				1.6	1.7	0.2	
CO-38	x		ST	ST	30°-50°															2/3				1.2	0.9	0.4	
CO-87			PA	ST	40°-60°															2/3				2.4	2.0	0.7	
CO-27			PLCV	ST	30°															1/2				2.0	2.5	0.5	
CO-17	x		ST	R	10°-40°															1/2				1.4	1.8	0.2	
CO-78			R	PA	30°															1/4				1.7	1.0	0.4	
CO-36			TRAP	PA	30°															1/4				0.5	0.7	0.1	
CO-76			ST	ST	20°															1/3				1.3	0.9	0.15	
CO-36a			ST	TRAP	70°															1/4				0.9	0.6	0.2	
CO-68			ST	R	50°															1/3				0.7	0.5	0.1	
CO-51			PLCV	LEN	40°-60°															all				1.0	0.6	0.1	
CO-83			TRAP	TRAP	60°-80°															1/3	2			1.0	0.6	0.1	
CO-30	x		ST	R	20°-60°															2/3				1.2	0.5	0.2	
CO-19	x		LEN	TRAP	10°															1/3				1.2	1.0	0.1	
M-42			PA	ST	60°																			0.5	0.4	0.1	
M-41			LEN	ST	35°-90°																			0.2	0.5	0.1	
M-43			OVAL	OVAL																				2.5	1.5	0.7	
M-26			LEN	LEN	25°						x			x	0.5		x	leaf		all		1		1.8	0.8	0.25	
M-25			LEN	LEN	40°				x					x	1.0	x	x	leaf	x	all				3.3	1.0	0.3	
M-3			LEN	LEN	25°	x			x						0.5	x	x	leaf		all		2		2.6	0.9	0.25	
M-9			LEN	LEN	20°-70°		x						x	0	0.8	x	x	leaf	x	all				1.2	0.9	0.15	
M-20			LEN	LEN	25°-80°									x					x	3/4				1.0	0.5	0.2	
M-16	x		ST	ST	20°-70°															all	2			0.8	0.6	0.2	
M-10			PLCV	PLCV	25°-40°					x								leaf		all				2.3	1.2	0.3	
M-17			LEN	ST	25°													leaf		all				1.1	1.4	0.3	
M-4			TRAP	R	10°-30°															1/2		1		2.2	2.5	0.25	
M-22	x		ST	CC	20°															all		1		2.3	0.9	0.2	
M-8			ST	TRAP	45°-70°															2/3	1	1		2.2	1.1	0.4	
M-7			PLCV	PLCV	70°															2/3	1			1.8	1.0	0.3	
M-23			PLCV	TRAP	45°-70°															1/2				0.8	1.0	0.2	
M-18			PLCV	ST	40°															all	1			0.9	0.6	0.2	
M-6			ST	CC	30°															1/2				1.8	0.7	0.2	
M-5	x		LEN	ST	20°															1/4				2.0	1.3	0.2	
M-11			LEN	ST	20°-40°															1/4				0.6	0.7	0.1	
M-1			LEN	TRAP	30°-70°															1/2				1.8	0.8	0.5	
M-19	x		IT	TRAP	20°															1/2				1.0	0.5	0.2	
M-2	x		ST	PA	20°-30°															1/2				1.0	0.5	0.2	
M-24	x		ST	ST	10°-20°															2/3				0.6	1.1	0.2	
M-12	x		ST	CC	10°															2/3				0.9	0.4	0.1	
M-13	x		ST	LEN	10°-20°															2/3				0.9	0.5	0.1	
M-15			TRAP	TRAP	30°-90°																			1.0	0.6	0.1	
M-21			ST	ST	60°-80°																			0.7	0.6	0.3	
M-14			ST	TRAP	25°-50°																			0.8	0.4	0.1	
CH-12			BICV	LEN	25°	x						x	2				x	leaf		all				0.7	1.0	0.1	
CH-6			ST	TRAP	20°-80°															all	1			1.3	1.3	0.4	
CH-22			ST	ST	30°-70°															all	1			1.8	1.3	0.5	
CH-4			PLCV	R	60°															1/4				1.0	1.0	0.2	

Cat. No.	Type	Locus	Culture	Date Found	Found By	Material	Core Tool	Secondary Flake	Prepared Core	Primary Flake	Bulb Trimmed	Billet Technique	Percussion Flaked	Pressure Chipped	Unifacially Retouched	Bifacially Retouched	Upper Face Retouched
CH-3	Unifacial knife	17,BSW	Folsom		Charboneau	Ed. Chert		x	x					x	x		x
CH-2	Unifacial knife	17,BSW	Folsom		Charboneau	Alibates		x	x					x	x		x
CH-14	Unifacial knife	17,BSW	Folsom		Charboneau	T. Jasper		x	x			x		x	x		x
CH-23	Unifacial knife	17,BSW	Folsom		Charboneau	Ed. Chert		x	x			x		x	x		x
CH-7	Flake	17,BSW	Folsom		Charboneau	Ed. Chert		x	x			x					
CH-18	Flake	17,BSW	Folsom		Charboneau	Ed. Chert		x	x								
CH-5	Flake	17,BSW	Folsom		Charboneau	Chalcedony		x	x								
CH-16	Flake	17,BSW	Folsom		Charboneau	Ed. Chert		x	x								
CH-21	Flake	17,BSW	Folsom		Charboneau	Alibates		x	x				x				
CH-11	Flake	17,BSW	Folsom		Charboneau	Ed. Chert		x	x				x				
CH-1	Flake	17,BSW	Folsom		Charboneau	Chert		x	x				x				
CH-17	Flake	17,BSW	Folsom		Charboneau	Chert		x	x				x				
CH-13	Flake	17,BSW	Folsom		Charboneau	Ed. Chert		x	x								
CH-25	Flake scraper frag.	17,BSW	Folsom		Charboneau	T. Jasper		x	x						x	x	x
M-73	Folsom point	17,BSW	Folsom	1962	Murray	Chert			x					x	x		x
M-72	Folsom point	17,BSW	Folsom	1962	Murray	Ed. Chert			x					x		x	
M-74	Folsom point	17,BSW	Folsom	1962	Murray	Chert			x					x		x	
M-66	Folsom point frag.	17,BSW	Folsom	1962	Murray	Ed. Chert			x				x	x		x	
M-78	Folsom point frag.	17,BSW	Folsom	1962	Murray	Ed. Chert			x				x	x		x	
M-64	End scraper	17,BSW	Folsom	1962	Murray	Ed. Chert	x	x	x					x	x		x
M-55	End scraper	17,BSW	Folsom	1962	Murray	Ed. Chert		x	x					x	x		x
M-48	Side scraper	17,BSW	Folsom	1962	Murray	Chert		x	x					x	x		x
M-47	Side scraper	17,BSW	Folsom	1962	Murray	Ed. Chert		x	x	x				x	x		x
M-59	Side scraper	17,BSW	Folsom	1962	Murray	T. Jasper		x	x					x	x		x
M-52	Side scraper frag.	17,BSW	Folsom	1962	Murray	Ed. Chert		x	x					x	x		x
M-68	Side scraper	17,BSW	Folsom	1962	Murray	T. Jasper		x	x	x				x	x		x
M-77	Flake scraper	17,BSW	Folsom	1962	Murray	Ed. Chert		x	x					x	x		x
M-79	Unifacial knife	17,BSW	Folsom	1962	Murray	Ed. Chert		x	x				x	x	x		x
M-46	Flake knife	17,BSW	Folsom	1962	Murray	Ed. Chert		x	x							x	
M-69	Knife, bifacial frag.	17,BSW	Folsom	1962	Murray	Ed. Chert								x		x	
M-56	Knife frag.	17,BSW	Folsom	1962	Murray	T. Jasper								x		x	
M-67	Knife frag.	17,BSW	Folsom	1962	Murray	Ed. Chert		x	x					x		x	
M-70	Flake	17,BSW	Folsom	1962	Murray	Ed. Chert		x	x	x							
M-60	Flake	17,BSW	Folsom	1962	Murray	Ed. Chert	x										
M-65	Flake	17,BSW	Folsom	1962	Murray	Ed. Chert		x	x	x							
M-76	Flake	17,BSW	Folsom	1962	Murray	Ed. Chert		x	x								
M-71	Flake	17,BSW	Folsom	1962	Murray	Ed. Chert		x	x	x							
M-54	Flake	17,BSW	Folsom	1962	Murray	Ed. Chert		x	x								
M-61	Flake	17,BSW	Folsom	1962	Murray	Ed. Chert		x	x	x							
M-75	Flake	17,BSW	Folsom	1962	Murray	Ed. Chert	x			x							
M-58	Flake	17,BSW	Folsom	1962	Murray	T. Jasper		x	x	x							
M-60	Flake	17,BSW	Folsom	1962	Murray	Quart.		x	x								
M-51	Flake	17,BSW	Folsom	1962	Murray	Ed. Chert		x	x	x							
M-53	Flake	17,BSW	Folsom	1962	Murray	Ed. Chert		x	x								
M-63	Flake	17,BSW	Folsom	1962	Murray	T. Jasper	x										
M-62	Flake	17,BSW	Folsom	1962	Murray	T. Jasper		x	x								
M-49	Flake	17,BSW	Folsom	1962	Murray	Ed. Chert		x	x								
M-57	Flake	17,BSW	Folsom	1962	Murray	Chert	x										
M-36	Side scraper	17,BSW	Clovis	1962	Murray	Alibates		x	x					x	x		x
M-37	Side scraper frag.	17,BSW	Clovis	1962	Murray	Chert		x	x					x	x		x
M-30	Flake scraper	17,BSW	Clovis	1962	Murray	Alibates		x	x	x				x	x		x
M-31	Flake scraper frag.	17,BSW	Clovis	1962	Murray	Chalcedony		x	x					x	x		x
M-34	Flake scraper frag.	17,BSW	Clovis	1962	Murray	Chalcedony		x	x					x	x		x
M-40	Knife frag.	17,BSW	Clovis	1962	Murray	Alibates		x	x	x				x	x	x	
M-27	Flake knife	17,BSW	Clovis	1962	Murray	Quart.		x	x								

Cat. No.	Nether Face Retouched	Modified by use	Transverse X Sec.	Anterior-Posterior X Sec.	Edge Angles	Expanding Stem	Shoulder Stem	Contracting Stem	Side Notches	Straight Base	Convex Base	Concave Base	Fluted	Parallel Flaking	Length of Grinding on Sides	Base Ground	Base Thinning	Blade Form	Tip Reworked	Portion of Edge Worked	Points on Perimeter	Median Ridge on Blade	Serrated Edge	Length	Width	Thickness	Length of Flute
CH-3	x		PLCV	ST	20°															3/4				0.9	0.7	0.1	
CH-2	x		LEN	R	20°															3/4				2.6	1.3	0.2	
CH-14			ST	PLCV	30°															3/4				2.7	1.1	0.25	
CH-23			PLCV	R	20°-40°															1/2				1.5	1.0	0.1	
CH-7		x	ST	CC	10°															1/2				1.5	1.2	0.1	
CH-18		x	ST	TRAP	10°-90°															1/4				0.8	0.8	0.1	
CH-5		x	ST	PLCV	10°-80°															1/4				1.4	0.7	0.2	
CH-16			ST	R	10°-80°																			0.5	0.6	0.1	
CH-21		x	PLCV	PLCV	10°															1/4				0.8	0.7	0.1	
CH-11		x	ST	R	10°-35°															1/2				0.7	0.8	0.1	
CH-1		x	ST	LEN	10°-20°															3/4				1.2	1.0	0.2	
CH-17		x	PLCV	TRAP	10°															1/2				0.8	1.0	0.1	
CH-13		x	PLCV	TRAP	10°-20°															2/3				0.8	0.7	0.1	
CH-25			ST	ST	40°															1/3				0.7	0.6	0.2	
M-73			LEN	LEN	25°													leaf		all				1.3	0.8	0.15	
M-72			LEN	LEN	20°		x								0.5			leaf		all				1.5	0.7	0.1	
M-74			LEN	LEN	25°	x					x				0.4	x	x	leaf	x	all				1.4	0.6	0.2	
M-66			CC	LEN	20°			x				x	1		0.0		x			all				0.5	0.5	0.1	
M-78			BICV	LEN	30°			x					2					leaf		all				1.2	0.7	0.1	
M-64			TRAP	PLCV	35°-70°															7/8	1			1.2	0.8	0.4	
M-55			PLCV	PLCV	35°-80°															all				1.3	1.4	0.3	
M-48			ST	TRAP	70°															1/4				1.5	1.2	0.2	
M-47	x		PLCV	CC	30°-80°															all				2.1	1.5	0.4	
M-59			ET	TRAP	20°-40°															1/4				1.8	1.3	0.5	
M-52			ST	ST	50°															1/2				1.1	0.7	0.3	
M-68			ST	PLCV	30°-60°															all	1	x		1.4	0.9	0.4	
M-77		x	R	TRAP	70°															1/3				0.9	1.1	0.1	
M-79			PLCV	CC	20°-40°															3/4				2.9	1.8	0.3	
M-46		x	ST	TRAP	10°-20°															2/3		x		1.9	1.1	0.2	
M-69			LEN	LEN	25°															all				1.2	1.5	0.2	
M-56			ST	R	20°															all				0.9	1.4	0.1	
M-67			ST	ST	25°															1/3				1.7	0.8	0.2	
M-70		x	ST	R	10°															2/3				1.3	0.7	0.1	
M-60			TRAP	ST	20°-80°																			1.1	0.3	0.2	
M-65		x	ST	PLCV	10°-20°															1/2				0.9	0.7	0.1	
M-76		x	TRAP	TRAP	50°-90°															1/2				1.1	0.8	0.1	
M-71		x	PLCV	CC	10°-30°															1/2				1.3	1.0	0.1	
M-54		x	IT	R	10°															1/3		x		0.9	0.9	0.1	
M-61		x	ST	TRAP	10°-90°															1/4				1.1	0.8	0.2	
M-75		x	PLCV	CC	10°															1/2				1.2	0.8	0.1	
M-58		x	PLCV	ST	10°															1/2				0.9	0.9	0.2	
M-60			ST	ST	10°-90°																			0.9	0.6	0.1	
M-51			PLCV	ST	10°-20°																			0.6	0.8	0.2	
M-53			ST	TRAP	15°																			0.6	0.6	0.2	
M-63			ST	CC	10°-20°																			0.7	0.5	0.1	
M-62		x	ST	TRAP	10°-20°															1/3				0.6	0.7	0.1	
M-49		x	RT	R	10°-90°															1/3				0.6	0.5	0.1	
M-57			ST	TRAP	10°-60°																			0.9	0.5	0.2	
M-36	x		ST	CC	35°-70°															all				2.1	1.0	0.5	
M-37			PA	ST	80°															1/2				1.2	0.5	0.2	
M-30			ST	PLCV	10°-40°															1/2				1.9	1.3	0.1	
M-31			R	TRAP	40°															1/2				0.5	0.3	0.1	
M-34			RT	R	30°															1/2				0.9	0.3	0.1	
M-40			PLCV	PLCV	40°-60°															all				1.8	1.5	0.3	
M-27		x	ET	TRAP	30°-40°															1/2		x		1.5	1.0	0.5	

Cat. No.	Type	Locus	Culture	Date Found	Found By	Material	Core Tool	Secondary Flake	Prepared Core	Primary Flake	Bulb Trimmed	Billet Technique	Percussion Flaked	Pressure Chipped	Unifacially Retouched	Bifacially Retouched	Upper Face Retouched
M-28	Flake knife	17,BSW	Clovis	1962	Murray	Ed. Chert		x	x	x						x	x
M-35	Flake	17,BSW	Clovis	1962	Murray	Alibates		x	x	x						x	x
M-38	Flake	17,BSW	Clovis	1962	Murray	Ed. Chert		x	x	x							
M-39	Flake	17,BSW	Clovis	1962	Murray	Alibates		x	x	x							
M-33	Flake	17,BSW	Clovis	1962	Murray	Ed. Chert		x	x								
M-32	Flake	17,BSW	Clovis	1962	Murray	Chert	x										
EL-1	Unifacial knife	18,GS	Clovis	1962	Burdine	Alibates		x	x						x	x	x
EL-2	Flake	18,GS	Clovis	1962	Collins	Quart.		x	x								
EL-3	Side & end scraper	18,GS	Clovis	1962	Collins	Alibates		x	x	x				x	x	x	x
EL-4	Scraper frag.(see EL-35)	18,GS	Clovis	1962	Warnica	Chert			P	x						x	x
EL-5	Side scraper	18,GS	Clovis	1962	Duran	Quart.	x							x	x	x	x
EL-6	Flake frag.	18,GS	Clovis	1962	Duran	Chalcedony		x	x	x	x						x
EL-7	Flake scraper knife	18,GS	Clovis	1962	Bradley	Ed. Chert		x	x	x					x	x	x
EL-8	Chopper	18,GS	Clovis	1962	Simnacher	Chert	x						x			x	x
EL-9	Flake scraper	18,GS	Clovis	1962	Duran	Ed. Chert		x	x						x	x	x
EL-10	Clovis point frag.	18,GS	Clovis	1962	Duran	Ed. Chert								x	x	x	x
EL-11	Small chip	18,GS	Clovis	1962	Durreti	Alibates		x		x							
EL-12	Flake scraper	18,GS	Clovis	1962	Duran	Quart.		x	x	x					x	x	x
EL-13	Flake scraper knife	18,GS	Clovis	1962	Simnacher	Ed. Chert		x	x					x	x	x	x
EL-14	Flake scraper	18,GS	Clovis	1962	Graves	Quart.			x	x	x				x	x	x
EL-15	See EL 12	18,GS	Clovis	1962	Collins												
EL-16	Side scraper	18,GS	Clovis	1962	Collins	Ed. Chert		x	x	x				x	x	x	x
EL-17	Side scraper	18,GS	Clovis	1962	Duran	Alibates		x	x						x	x	x
EL-18	Flake knife frag.	18,GS	Clovis	1962	Duran	Alibates		x	x							x	x
EL-19	Chip	18,GS	Clovis	1962	Simnacher	Chalcedony	x							x			
EL-20	Grinding stone	18,GS	Clovis	1962	Brown	Sandstone											
EL-21	Side scraper	18,GS	Clovis	1962	Duran	Alibates			P	x					x	x	x
EL-22	Chip	18,GS	Clovis	1962	Bradley	Alibates		x		x							
EL-23	End & side scraper	18,GS	Clovis	1962	Jones	Alibates			P	x					x	x	x
EL-24	Graver & flake knife frag.	18,GS	Clovis	1962	Mrs. Place	Alibates		x	x				x	x	x	x	x
EL-25	Blade frag.	18,GS	Clovis	1962	Collins	Ed. Chert			x								
EL-26	Flake	18,GS	Clovis	1962	Duran	Chert		x	x	x						x	x
EL-27	End & side scraper	18,GS	Clovis	1962	Warnica	Chert		x	x						x	x	x
EL-28	Flake	18,GS	Clovis	1962	Duran	Ed. Chert	x						x				
EL-29	Flake frag.	18,BSW	Folsom	1962	Collins	Ed. Chert		x	x	x							
EL-30	Clovis point Type 2	18,GS	Clovis	1962	Warnica	Alibates									x	x	x x
EL-31	Flake frag.	18,GS	Clovis	1962	Warnica	Ed. Chert		x	x								
EL-32	Flake knife frag.	18,GS	Clovis	1962	Warnica	Quart.		x	x	x					x	x	
EL-33	Clovis point frag. Type 1	18,GS	Clovis	1962	Warnica	Ed. Chert											
EL-34	Flake	18,GS	Clovis	1962	Duran	Quart.		x	x	x						x	x
EL-35	Hollow edge scraper frag.	18,GS	Clovis	1962	Duran												
EL-36	Flake scraper	18,GS	Clovis	1962	Turner	Chert		x	x		x				x	x	x
EL-37	Flake	18,GS	Clovis	1962	Greaves	Quart.		x	x								
EL-38	Bifacial knife frag.	18,GS	Clovis	1962	Duran	Alibates		x	x				x			x	x
EL-39	Flake frag.	18,GS	Clovis	1962	Warnica	Alibates		x	x	x							
EL-40	Core	18,BSW	Folsom	1962	Collins	Chert	x										
EL-41	Bone artifact	18,BSW	Folsom	1962	Crew	Bone											
EL-42	Flake	18,BSW	Folsom	1962	Collins	Quart.	x										
EL-43	Shell artifact	18,CS	Portales	1962	Crew	Shell											
EL-44	Flake frag.	18,BSW	Folsom	1962	Duran	Alibates			P	x						x	x
EL-45	Possible artifact	18,GS	Clovis	1962	Collins	Bone											
EL-46	Bone artifact	18,GS	Clovis	1962	Collins	Bone											
EL-47	Clovis point Type 2	18,GS	Clovis	1962	Gallegos	Alibates									x	x	x x
EL-48	End scraper	18,BSW	Folsom	1962	Crew	Alibates		x	x	x						x	x
EL-49	End & side scraper	NIP	Clovis	1962	Collins	Quitaque		x	x						x	x	x

Cat. No.	Nether Face Retouched	Modified by use	Transverse X Sec.	Anterior-Posterior X Sec.	Edge Angles	Expanding Stem	Shoulder Stem	Contracting Stem	Side Notches	Straight Base	Convex Base	Concave Base	Fluted	Parallel Flaking	Length of Grinding on Sides	Base Ground	Base Thinning	Blade Form	Tip Reworked	Portion of Edge Worked	Points on Perimeter	Median Ridge on Blade	Serrated Edge	Length	Width	Thickness	Length of Flute
M-28	x	x	ST	LEN	20°															3/4			x	1.6	0.8	0.3	
M-35	x	x	ST	CC	10°-20°															all				1.0	1.5	0.2	
M-38		x	LEN	R	10°															2/3				0.6	0.9	0.1	
M-39			PLCV	ST	10°																			0.5	0.7	0.1	
M-33		x	PLCV	PLCV	10°															2/3				1.4	0.8	0.1	
M-32			TRAP	TRAP	80°-90°																			0.3	0.3	0.1	
EL-1			TRAP	TRAP	25°															1/4				1.0	0.9	0.1	
EL-2			LEN	ST	10°																			0.8	1.1	0.15	
EL-3	x		PLCX	R	60°-80°															all	1			2.4	1.9	0.4	
EL-4	x	x	LEN	ST	10°-20°															1/8				1.3	1.1	0.1	
EL-5					30°-70°															2/3				1.3	1.2	0.5	
EL-6			ST	TRAP	20°-40°																			0.9	0.7	0.2	
EL-7			TRAP	PLCX	20°-50°															1/2				1.9	1.0	0.2	
EL-8	x		PLCX	TRAP	30°-70°															all				1.7	2.2	0.7	
EL-9			ST	CC	30°-80°															7/8				1.85	0.7	3.5	0.8
EL-10	x		LEN	LEN	25°							x	2		1.5	x	x	leaf		all				3.6	1.0	0.3	1.3
EL-11			PLCX	ST	20°																			0.3	0.2	0.5	
EL-12		x	PLCX	ST	80°															2/3				1.8	0.9	0.2	
EL-13		x	ST	CC	25°-50°															all			x	7.2	2.1	0.45	
EL-14			PLCX	PLCX	35°															all				2.3	1.4	0.3	
EL-15																											
EL-16			TRAP	PA	60°-90°															2/3				3.1	1.7	0.3	
EL-17			PLCX	PLCX	40°-80°															1/2				2.0	1.7	0.35	
EL-18		x	PLCX	TRAP	20°															1/2				1.3	1.5	0.2	
EL-19			LEN	ST	10°																			0.6	0.5	0.02	
EL-20																								2.9	1.9	1.6	
EL-21			ST	CC	60°															2/3				2.1	1.5	0.35	
EL-22			PLCX	CC	10°																			0.3	0.25	0.01	
EL-23			TRAP	PA	60°															2/3	1	x		2.1	0.9	0.45	
EL-24			LEN	ST	40°-60°															1/8	1			1.8	1.4	0.3	
EL-25		x	ST	TRAP	20°-60°															1/2			x	1.4	0.4	0.15	
EL-26		x	TRAP	PLCX	20°															2/3				1.9	0.8	0.1	
EL-27		x	ST	ST	40°-70°															all	2		x	1.9	0.8	0.3	
EL-28			ST	ST	10°																			0.7	0.6	0.06	
EL-29			R	ST	40°																			0.6	0.7	0.1	0.4
EL-30	x		LEN	LEN	25°							x	2		0.6	x	x	tri.		all				1.3	0.7	0.2	0.6
EL-31	x	x	ST	TRAP	70°															1/8				0.8	0.5	0.1	
EL-32	x		ST	TRAP	30°															1/2				1.7	0.9	0.25	
EL-33					30°							x	0		x	x	x							0.4	0.3	0.15	
EL-34		x	TRAP	TRAP	25°															1/4				1.7	1.3	0.5	
EL-35																											
EL-36			ST	ST	40°-60°															1/3				2.0	1.15	0.2	
EL-37			ST	TRAP	30°															1/4				1.6	0.8	0.3	
EL-38	x		LEN	ST	30°-50°															all				1.4	1.2	0.3	
EL-39			LEN	R	20°																			0.7	1.1	0.1	
EL-40			PA	TRAP	70°																			1.0	1.0	0.5	
EL-41																											
EL-42			LEN	CC	20°																			0.3	0.2	0.1	
EL-43																											
EL-44		x	LEN	R	20°															1/4				1.0	1.0	0.1	
EL-45																								2.3	0.6	0.6	
EL-46																								2.4	0.8	0.7	
EL-47	x		BICV	LEN	30°-40°							x	2		0.5	x	x	tri.		all				1.5	0.7	0.2	0.7,1.0
EL-48			LEN	ST	25°-80°															all	2			1.7	1.7	0.3	
EL-49	x	x	PA	TRAP	30°-60°															3/4				2.2	1.0	0.2	

Cat. No.	Type	Locus	Culture	Date Found	Found By	Material	Core Tool	Secondary Flake	Prepared Core	Primary Flake	Bulb Trimmed	Billet Technique	Percussion Flaked	Pressure Chipped	Unifacially Retouched	Bifacially Retouched	Upper Face Retouched
EL-50	Flake knife	18,GS	Clovis	1962	Roberts	Alibates			x	x		x		x	x		x
EL-51	Unifacial knife frag.	18,BSW	Folsom	1962	Crew	Ed. Chert			x	x	x		x	x	x		x
EL-52	Flake	18,BSW	Folsom	1962	Crew	Ed. Chert			x	x	x				x		x
EL-53	Flake	NIP	Clovis	1962	Collins	Ed. Chert			x	x							
EL-54	Flake scraper	18,GS	Clovis	1962	Powell	Alibates			x	x					x	x	x
EL-55	Flake	18,GS	Clovis	1962	McKnight	Alibates			x	x	x				x		x
EL-56	Flake	18,GS	Clovis	1962	McKnight	?			x	x					x		
EL-57	Possible hammer stone	NIP	Clovis	1962	Greaves	Quart.											
EL-58	Bifacial knife frag.	18,GS	Clovis	1962	Bradley	Alibates			x	x					x	x	x
EL-59	Possible hammer stone	18,GS	Clovis	1962	Place	Basalt											
EL-60	Flake frag.	18,GS	Clovis	1962	Bradley				x	x					x		x
EL-61,78	Flake frag.	18,GS	Clovis	1962	Bradley	Alibates			x	x	x				x		x
EL-62	Side scraper	18,GS	Clovis	1962	Bradley	Ed. Chert			x	x		x			x	x	x
EL-63	End & Side scraper	18,GS	Clovis	1962	Shay	Ed. Chert			P	x			x		x		x
EL-64	Bifacial knife frag.	18,GS	Clovis	1962	Latham	Quart.			x	x			x			x	x
EL-65	Flake frag.	18,BSW	Folsom	1962	St. Museum	Chert			x	x					x		x
EL-66	Flake frag.	18,BSW	Folsom	1962	St. Museum	Ed. Chert			P	x					x		x
EL-67	Flake	18,GS	Clovis	1962	St. Museum	Ed. Chert			x	x	x						
EL-68	Flake	18,BSW	Folsom	1962	St. Museum	Ed. Chert			x	x	x						
EL-69	End & side scraper	NIP	?	1962	St. Museum	Alibates			x	x				x	x	x	x
EL-70	Flake frag.	18,BSW	Folsom	1962	St. Museum	Alibates			x	x							
EL-71	Flake frag.	18,BSW	Folsom	1962	St. Museum	Alibates			P	x		x			x		
EL-72	Flake frag.	18,BSW	Folsom	1962	St. Museum	Ed. Chert			x	x							
EL-73	Folsom point base	18,BSW	Folsom	1962	St. Museum	Ed. Chert			x	x				x	x	x	x
EL-74	Flake frag.	NIP	?	1962	St. Museum	Ed. Chert			x	x							
EL-75	Bifacial knife frag.	18,GS	Clovis	1962	St. Museum	Alibates			x	x			x			x	x
EL-76	Flake	18,GS	Clovis	1962	St. Museum	Alibates			x	x					x		
EL-77	Flake	18,GS	Clovis	1962	St. Museum	Ed. Chert			x	x	x						
EL-78	Flake frag.	18,GS	Clovis	1962	Collins	Alibates											
EL-79	Bone tool	18,GS	Clovis	1962		Bone											
EL-80	Chip	18,GS	Clovis	1963	Collins	Alibates		x				x					
EL-81	Core	18,BSW	Folsom	1962	St. Museum	Chert	x					x			x		
EL-82	Possible bone tool	18,GS	Clovis	1962	Bradley	Bone											
EL-83	End scraper	18,GS	Clovis	1962	Warnica	Ed. Chert			x	x				x	x		x
EL-84	Flake	18,CSE	Portales	1963	Collins	Alibates			P	x					x		x
EL-85	Flake	18,GS	Clovis	1962	Williamson	Alibates		x							x		
EL-86	Flake frag.	18,GS	Clovis	1962	Harrison	Quart.			x	x							
EL-87	Flake frag.	18,GS	Clovis	1962	Williamson	Alibates			x	x							
EL-88	Flake frag.	18,GS	Clovis	1962	Harrison	Alibates			x	x							
EL-89	Bone tool	18,GS	Clovis	1962	Harrison	Bone											
EL-90	Burin on Clovis point	18,GS	Clovis	1962	Brown	Ed. Chert								x	x	x	x
EL-91	Flake	18,GS	Clovis	1962	Warnica	Alibates			x	x					x		x
EL-92	Flake frag.	18,GS	Clovis	1962	Collins	Alibates			x	x	x						
EL-93	Flake	18,GS	Clovis	1962	Harrison	Ed. Chert			x	x	x						
EL-94	Graver frag.	18,GS	Clovis	1962	Harrison	Alibates			x	x					x		x
EL-95	Side scraper	NIP	Clovis	1962	Bradley	Alibates			x	x	x		x	x		x	x
EL-96	Flake knife/graver frag.	18,GS	Clovis	1962	St. Museum	Alibates											
EL-97	Flake scraper frag.	18,BSW	Folsom	1962	St. Museum	Ed. Chert			x	x					x		x
EL-98	Flake knife frag.	NIP	?	1962	St. Museum	Ed. Chert			x	x	x			x	x		x
EL-99	Caliche nodule	NIP	?	1962	St. Museum	Caliche	x										
EL-100	Flake	NIP	?	1962	St. Museum	Alibates			x	x							
EL-101	Flake	18,BSW	Folsom	1962	Duran				x	x							
EL-102	Flake	18,GS	Clovis	1962	Duran	Alibates			x	x					x	x	x
EL-103	Side scraper	18,GS	Clovis	1962	Duran				x	x	x				x	x	x
EL-104	Flake knife	18,GS	Clovis	1962	Place	Quart.			x	x	x				x	x	x

Cat. No.	Nether Face Retouched	Modified by use	Transverse X Sec.	Anterior-Posterior X Sec.	Edge Angles	Expanding Stem	Shoulder Stem	Contracting Stem	Side Notches	Straight Base	Convex Base	Concave Base	Fluted	Parallel Flaking	Length of Grinding on Sides	Base Ground	Base Thinning	Blade Form	Tip Reworked	Portion of Edge Worked	Points on Perimeter	Median Ridge on Blade	Serrated Edge	Length	Width	Thickness	Length of Flute
EL-50			TRAP	PLCX	30°															1/3				1.4	0.9	0.1	
EL-51			LEN	ST	30°															2/3				1.9	2.0	0.3	
EL-52		x	PLCX	CC	20°															1/4				1.7	1.3	0.2	
EL-53		x	TRAP	ST	20°															1/2				1.4	0.8	0.2	
EL-54	x	x	ST	PLCX	25°-40°															7/8	x			1.7	0.8	0.3	
EL-55		x	ST	PLCX	10°															1/2				1.2	0.7	0.1	
EL-56		x	PLCX	LEN	20°															1/2				2.2	1.0	0.15	
EL-57			TRAP	TRAP																				2.4	2.4	0.2	
EL-58	x	x	ST	ST	30°-40°															1/4				0.9	1.0	0.15	
EL-59			PA	PA																				2.8	2.2	1.4	
EL-60		x	TRAP	R	20°-70°															1/2				3.0	2.05	0.25	
EL-61		x	PLCX	CC	20°															1/3				1.4	1.9	0.1	
EL-62			TRAP	TRAP	60°															2/3				1.9	0.1	0.25	
EL-63	x	x	TRAP	CC	40°-70°															7/8				2.2	1.9	0.4	
EL-64	x		PLCX	R	40°															all				2.0	1.3	0.3	
EL-65		x	LEN	ST	20°															1/4				1.3	1.3	0.1	
EL-66		x	TRAP	TRAP	40°															1/10				1.3	1.8	0.3	
EL-67			PLCX	CC	10°																			1.6	1.1	0.15	
EL-68			ST	TRAP	10°																			0.9	0.7	0.1	
EL-69	x		IT	TRAP	40°-70°															all	1			3.2	2.0	0.9	
EL-70			TRAP	TRAP	20°																			0.4	0.5	0.1	
EL-71	x	x	LEN	TRAP	20°															1/4				0.4	0.7	0.2	
EL-72			TRAP	TRAP	70°-90°																			0.7	0.4	0.1	
EL-73	x		BICV	LEN					x			x	2				x	leaf		all				1.3	1.2	0.2	
EL-74			TRAP	CC	20°-30°																			2.2	1.8	0.2	
EL-75	x		LEN	R	30°-40°															all				2.2	1.7	0.4	
EL-76	x	x	ST	ST	20°															1/3				1.7	1.1	0.25	
EL-77			PLCX	CC	10°																			1.8	0.8	0.1	
EL-78																											
EL-79																								3.9	0.7	0.55	
EL-80			PLCX	R	10°																			0.6	0.4	0.05	
EL-81			CC	PLCX	30°-60°																			3.2	2.2	0.7	
EL-82																								3.9	1.1	0.4	
EL-83		x	TRAP	ST	40°															all		x		1.5	1.1	0.3	
EL-84		x	ST	ST	20°															1/4				1.0	2.0	0.2	
EL-85	x	x	PLCX	CC	10°															1/2				0.8	0.6	0.1	
EL-86		x	TRAP	TRAP	20°															1/4				0.8	1.5	0.3	
EL-87		x	TRAP	TRAP	20°															1/8				0.6	1.7	0.15	
EL-88			TRAP	TRAP	20°																			1.1	0.7	0.1	
EL-89																								11.2	1.5	0.7	
EL-90	x		LEN	LEN	25°						x	x					x	leaf		all				1.9	1.15	0.3	0.9,1.6
EL-91		x	PLCX	CC	10°															1/4				1.1	0.7	0.05	
EL-92		x	LEN	R	10°															1/2				1.15	0.8	0.05	
EL-93		x	LEN	ST	10°															1/2				1.2	1.0	0.1	
EL-94		x	PLCX	TRAP	10°															1/4				1.5	1.1	0.1	
EL-95	x		PLCX	PLCX	60°															all				1.9	1.1	0.4	
EL-96																											
EL-97			TRAP	TRAP	40°															1/3				1.2	1.6	0.1	
EL-98			PLCX	ST	20°															1/4				1.5	0.9	0.1	
EL-99			ET	ST	60°																			2.0	1.3	0.1	
EL-100			LEN	ST	10°																			1.2	0.7	0.1	
EL-101			TRAP	CC	20°																			2.2	0.8	0.2	
EL-102			IT	TRAP	40°															1/20				1.8	1.3	0.4	
EL-103			TRAP	CC	50°															1/2				2.1	1.2	0.4	
EL-104			LEN	TRAP	25°															1/3				2.0	2.0	0.25	

Cat. No.	Type	Locus	Culture	Date Found	Found By	Material	Core Tool	Secondary Flake	Prepared Core	Primary Flake	Bulb Trimmed	Billet Technique	Percussion Flaked	Pressure Chipped	Unifacially Retouched	Bifacially Retouched	Upper Face Retouched
EL-105	Side scraper	18,GS	Clovis	1962	Collins	Alibates			x	x			x	x	x	x		x
EL-106	Unifacial knife frag.	18,GS	Clovis	1962	Place	Chalcedony			x	x				x		x		
EL-107	Graver	18,GS	Clovis	1962	Warnica	Alibates			x	x					x	x		x
EL-108	Broken pebble	18,GS	Clovis	1962	Collins	Quart.							x					
EL-109	Flake frag.	18,GS	Clovis	1962	Bradley	Chalcedony			x	x		x				x		x
EL-110	Burin and scraper	18,GS	Clovis	1962	Duran	Quitaque			x	x				x			x	x
EL-111	Unifacial knife	18,GS	Clovis	1962	Duran	Alibates			x	x					x	x		x
EL-112	Flake frag.	18,GS	Clovis	1963	Place	Alibates			x	x								
EL-113	Flake frag.	18,GS	Clovis	1963	Collins	Alibates			x	x		x						
EL-114	Bifacial knife	18,GS	Clovis	1963	Place	Quart.			x	x	x			x	x		x	x
EL-115	Flake frag.	18,GS	Clovis	1963	Place													
EL-116	End scraper	18,GS	Clovis	1963	Simnacher	Ed. Chert			x	x	x			x	x			x
EL-117	Flake	18,GS	Clovis	1963	Simnacher	Chalcedony			x	x		x		x	x			x
EL-118	Flake knife	18,GS	Clovis	1963	Simnacher	Quart.			x	x		x		x	x			x
EL-119	Flake frag.	18,CSE	Portales	1963	Collins	Alibates			x	x		x						
EL-120	Bifacial knife	18,CSE	Portales	1963	Collins	Alibates			x	x	x		x				x	x
EL-121	Projec. frag.	18,CSE	Portales	1963	Collins	Chert			x	x				x			x	x
EL-122	Side scraper	18,CSE	Portales	1963	Collins	Alibates	P		x		x			x	x			x
EL-123	Flake	18,CSE	Portales	1963	Collins	Ed. Chert			x	x					1			
EL-124	Flake	18,CSE	Portales	1963	Collins	Chert			x	x								
EL-125	Flake	18,CSE	Portales	1963	Collins	Ed. Chert	x					x						
EL-126	Flake	18,CSE	Portales	1963	Collins	Ed. Chert			x	x	x							x
EL-127	Flake	18,CSE	Portales	1963	Collins	Alibates			x	x								
EL-128	Unifacial knife	18,CSE	Portales	1963	Collins	Alibates			x	x					x	x		x
EL-129	Flake frag.	18,CSE	Portales	1963	Collins	Ed. Chert	P		x									
EL-130	Flake frag.	18,CSE	Portales	1963	Collins	Ed. Chert			x	x					x	x		x
EL-131	Flake	18,CSE	Portales	1963	Collins	Alibates	P		x									
EL-132	Flake frag.	18,CSE	Portales	1963	Collins	Alibates			x	x		x						
EL-133	Parallel flaked point frag.	18,CSE	Portales	1963	Collins	Alibates								x			x	x
EL-134	Flake frag.	18,CSE	Portales	1963	Collins	Ed. Chert			x	x								
EL-135	Flake	18,CSE	Portales	1963	Collins	Obsidian	x											
EL-136	Flake	18,CSE	Portales	1963	Collins	Alibates			x	x	x				x			x
EL-137	Flake	NIP	?	1963	Collins	Alibates			x	x					x	x		x
EL-138	Flake	18,CSE	Portales	1963	Collins	Chert			x	x								
EL-139	Flake	18,CSE	Portales	1963	Collins	Alibates			x	x								
EL-140	Flake	18,GS	Clovis	1963	Bandy	Quart.			x	x	x							
EL-141	Flake	18,CSE	Portales	1963	Collins	Alibates	x											
EL-142	Flake frag.	18,CSE	Portales	1963	Brown	Alibates			x	x								
EL-143	Possible graver frag.	18,GS	Clovis	1963	Collins													
EL-144	Flake	18,GS	Clovis	1963	Collins	Alibates			x	x								
EL-145	Side & end scraper	18,GS	Clovis	1963	Collins	Alibates			x	x				x	x	x		x
EL-146	Flake knife	18,GS	Clovis	1963	Collins	Quart.			x	x					x	x		x
EL-147	Bone tool	18,GS	Clovis	1963	Collins	Bone												
EL-148	Flake	18,NIP	Clovis	1963	Warnica	Alibates			x	x	x							
EL-149	Possible hammer stone	18,GS	Clovis	1963	Warnica	Sandstone												
EL-150	Scraper	18,GS	Clovis	1963	Bandy	Quart.	x								x	x		
EL-151	Hammer stone	18,GS	Clovis	1963	McWilliams	Shale	x							x			x	
EL-152	Broken pebble	18,GS	Clovis	1963	Warnica	Chert	x							x				
EL-153	Flake	18,GS	Clovis	1963	Bradley	Chert		x										
EL-154	Flake frag.	18,GS	Clovis	1963	Warnica	Quart.			x	x								
EL-155	Broken pebble	18,GS	Clovis	1963	Warnica	Basalt								x				
EL-156	Unifacial knife frag.	18,GS	Clovis	1963	Warnica	Alibates			x	x					x	x		x
EL-157	Core	18,JS	Archaic	1963	Simnacher	Quart.	x		x					x			x	
EL-158	Flake frag.	18,GS	Clovis	1963	Collins	Quart.			x	x								
EL-159	See EL-105	18,GS	Clovis	1963	Collins													

Cat. No.	Nether Face Retouched	Modified by use	Transverse X Sec.	Anterior-Posterior X Sec.	Edge Angles	Expanding Stem	Shoulder Stem	Contracting Stem	Side Notches	Straight Base	Convex Base	Concave Base	Fluted	Parallel Flaking	Length of Grinding on Sides	Base Ground	Base Thinning	Blade Form	Tip Reworked	Portion of Edge Worked	Points on Perimeter	Median Ridge on Blade	Serrated Edge	Length	Width	Thickness	Length of Flute
EL-105			PLCX	CC	45°															all				3.1	0.8	0.75	
EL-106	x		ST	TRAP	35°															1/3				1.9	2.1	0.4	
EL-107			ST	PLCX	60°															1/20	3			1.2	1.2	0.15	
EL-108					70°																			1.7	0.9	0.8	
EL-109		x	ST	TRAP	20°															2/3				0.7	0.5	0.1	
EL-110	x	x	TRAP	TRAP	50°															1/2				1.6	1.0	0.4	
EL-111			ST	PLCX	35°															1/2				3.9	1.1	0.3	
EL-112			ST	R	20°																			0.9	0.6	0.15	
EL-113			ST	TRAP	30°																			1.0	0.6	0.2	
EL-114	x		LEN	ST	35°															all				2.3	1.3	0.35	
EL-115																											
EL-116			TRAP	ST	50°-80°															all	2			1.3	0.8	0.25	
EL-117			ST	ST	50°															1/8				1.0	0.8	0.1	
EL-118			PLCX	PLCX	20°															1/2				1.9	1.5	0.2	
EL-119			LEN	TRAP	20°																			0.5	0.5	0.1	
EL-120	x		TRAP	CC	30°-60°															all				3.1	0.9	0.4	
EL-121	x		LEN	LEN	25°															all				1.1	0.6	0.2	
EL-122			ST	ST	40°															2/3				1.9	1.0	0.3	
EL-123		x	LEN	ST	20°															3/4				1.0	0.8	0.2	
EL-124			ST	ST	10°																			0.6	0.7	0.1	
EL-125			LEN	TRAP	20°-70°																			0.6	0.7	0.1	
EL-126		x	TRAP	TRAP	20°-90°															1/2				0.7	0.9	0.1	
EL-127			CC	TRAP	40°-70°																			0.7	1.0	0.2	
EL-128			PLCX	ST	20°															7/8				2.2	0.7	0.2	
EL-129			LEN	TRAP	20°																			0.8	1.1	0.2	
EL-130			TRAP	TRAP	20°															1/4				0.8	0.8	0.2	
EL-131			CC	ST	10°																			0.8	1.2	0.1	
EL-132			LEN	TRAP	10°																			0.6	0.7	0.1	
EL-133	x		LEN	ST	25°													tri.		all				2.4	1.0	0.3	
EL-134			R	R	90°																			0.7	0.6	0.1	
EL-135			ST	TRAP	30°-90°																			1.0	0.9	0.2	
EL-136		x	CC	ST	20°															1/8				2.0	1.5	0.2	
EL-137			ST	CC	40°															1/8				1.5	1.1	0.2	
EL-138			ST	ST	10°																			0.8	0.9	0.1	
EL-139			ST	ST	20°-90°																			0.6	0.5	0.1	
EL-140			ST	PLCX	20°																			1.3	0.7	0.1	
EL-141			PLCX	CC	10°																			1.1	0.6	0.1	
EL-142			PLCX	ST	20°																			0.7	0.5	0.1	
EL-143																						x					
EL-144			LEN	TRAP	20°																			1.7	0.8	0.15	
EL-145			ST	TRAP	65°															3/4	3	x		1.5	0.9	0.35	
EL-146			PLCX	PLCX	35°															1/2				2.2	1.3	0.2	
EL-147																								1.7	0.6	0.35	
EL-148			TRAP	CC	30°																			1.2	0.7	0.2	
EL-149		x																						3.0	1.4	1.8	
EL-150	x	x	PA	TRAP	70°															1/4				1.6	1.3	0.6	
EL-151		x	ST	TRAP	70°															1/2				2.3	1.7	1.6	
EL-152			TRAP	TRAP	70°-80°																			1.3	0.8	0.3	
EL-153			LEN	ST	10°																			0.35	0.3	0.05	
EL-154			LEN	PA	30°																			0.8	1.0	0.4	
EL-155																								1.5	0.9	0.7	
EL-156			ST	TRAP	30°															1/4				0.8	1.5	0.2	
EL-157			LEN	TRAP	40°-80°																			1.7	1.5	0.8	
EL-158			LEN	TRAP	20°																			1.9	0.8	0.2	
EL-159																											

Cat. No.	Type	Locus	Culture	Date Found	Found By	Material	Core Tool	Secondary Flake	Prepared Core	Primary Flake	Bulb Trimmed	Billet Technique	Percussion Flaked	Pressure Chipped	Unifacially Retouched	Bifacially Retouched	Upper Face Retouched
EL-160	Knife frag.	18,GS	Clovis	1963	Bandy	Alibates		x	x				x				
EL-161	Broken pebble	18,GS	Clovis	1963	Trout	Chert											
EL-162	Hollow edge scraper	18,GS	Clovis	1963	Trout	Quart.		x	x	x	x			x	x		x
EL-163	Graver & side scraper frag.	18,GS	Clovis	1963	Warnica	Alibates		x	x					x	x		x
EL-164	Side scraper frag.	18,GS	Clovis	1963	Bradley	Quart.		x	x					x			x
EL-165	Bifacial knife frag.	18,GS	Clovis	1963	Bradley	Alibates		x	x					x	x	x	x
EL-166	Graver	18,GS	Clovis	1963	Bradley	Alibates		x	x					x	x		x

Cat. No.	Nether Face Retouched	Modified by use	Transverse X Sec.	Anterior-Posterior X Sec.	Edge Angles	Expanding Stem	Shoulder Stem	Contracting Stem	Side Notches	Straight Base	Convex Base	Concave Base	Fluted	Parallel Flaking	Length of Grinding on Sides	Base Ground	Base Thinning	Blade Form	Tip Reworked	Portion of Edge Worked	Points on Perimeter	Median Ridge on Blade	Serrated Edge	Length	Width	Thickness	Length of Flute
EL-160			LEN	ST	25°-30°																			2.6	1.6	0.3	
EL-161		x	IT	SC	40°																			1.8	1.3	0.5	
EL-162	x		ST	LEN	20°-60°															2/3				2.1	1.7	0.4	
EL-163			TRAP	ST	30°-60°															2/3	3			1.3	1.0	0.25	
EL-164			TRAP	TRAP	50°															1/3				1.7	1.3	0.2	
EL-165	x		ST	ST	40°															all				1.5	1.2	0.01	
EL-166			TRAP	ST	50°															1/8	2			1.3	0.7	0.2	

APPENDIX II

SUMMARY OF ARTIFACTS RECOVERED BY EXCAVATION

TABLE I

ARTIFACTS RECOVERED BY
THE UNIVERSITY MUSEUM-PHILADELPHIA ACADEMY INVESTIGATIONS,
1932-1937

Cat. No.	Type	Locus	Association	Date Found	Reference
33-36-11	Bifacial knife	Blue Sand W. side pit	With mammoth tooth	1932	Howard 1935, Pl. XXIX, pp. 92
	Unfluted Folsom pt?	Blue Sand		Fall 1933	Howard 1935, Pl. XXX, no. 6 p. 93
33-36-5	Knife-like-scraper	Blue Sand E. side pit	In situ, w/ bison bones	Summer 1933	Howard 1935, Pl. XXXI, no. 4 pp. 93, Pl. XVIII
33-36-8	Knife-like scraper	Blue Sand E. side pit	In situ, w/ bison bones	Summer 1933	Howard 1935, Pl. XXXI no. 2 p. 94, Pl. XVIII
33-36-7	Flake knife or scraper	Bottom Blue Sand, E. side of pit			Howard 1935, pp. 94
9-1	Clovis point	Dump		1936	Cotter 1937
9-4	Clovis point	GS	Mammoth bones	1936	1937
9-7	Side scraper	D	Mammoth tusk	1936	1937
9-8	Flake knife or point frag.	GS	Mammoth tusk	1936	1937
9-9	Bone artifact	GS	Mammoth ulna	1936	1937
9-10	Bone artifact	GS	Mammoth tusk	1936	1937
9-12	Milnesand? point	Dump		1936	1937
9-14	Flake	GS	Mammoth tooth	1936	1937
9-15	Side scraper	N.E. corner S. pit Blue clay		1936	1937
9-16	Point frag.	S. side S. pit Blue clay		1936	1937
9-17	Clovis point	Dump		1936	1937
9-18	Folsom point	Dump		1936	1937
9-21	Point frag.	GS	Mammoth scapula	1936	1937
9-22	Clovis point	GS	Mammoth ulna	1936	1937
9-23	Folsom point	Dump		1936	1937
9-26	Flake	GS	Mammoth vert.	1936	1937
9-27	Flake	GS	Bison scapula	1936	1937
9-28	Knife frag.	Dump		1936	1937
9-29	Side scraper	Dump		1936	1937
9-30	Point frag.	Dump		1936	1937
9-32	Side scraper frag.	Dump		1936	1937
9-33	Clovis point	GS	Mammoth scapula	1936	1937

Cat. No.	Type	Locus	Association	Date Found	Reference
9-34	Scraper	D		1936	1937
	Unfluted Folsom point	D(?)	Bison bones	1937	Cotter 1938
	Knife	CS(?)		1937	1938
	Folsom point		Bison bones	1937	1938
	Clovis point	NIP		1937	1938
	Yuma point	NIP		1937	1938
	Small Clovis?	GS	Mammoth	1937	1938

*All specimens from the mammoth pit excavations unless otherwise stated.

TABLE II

TEXAS MEMORIAL MUSEUM ARTIFACTS FROM STATIONS A, B, AND C,
APRIL-MAY 1954*

Cat. No.	Type	Locus	Association	Found By	Date
937-281	Eden point frag.	NIP (not in place)	----	Oscar Shay	April 1954
937-282	Flake scraper	Brown sand interval (sic)	----	E.H. Sellards	April 1954
937-283	Base of Folsom pt.	NIP	----	Otto Schoen	April 1954
937-284	Unfluted Folsom point frag.	NIP, Station B	----		April 1954
937-285	Possible worked rib	Station C BSW	----	Oscar Shay	April 1954
937-286	Flake scraper	16" from top Station B of BSW	----	Otto Schoen	April 1954
937-287	Base of Folsom point	NIP Station B	----	Otto Schoen	April 1954
937-288	Chip	D, Station B	----	Oscar Shay	April 1954
937-289	Angostura point	Station C, Unk	With bones	Oscar Shay	April 1954
937-290	Knife	Station A, BSW	----	Oscar Shay	April 1954
937-291	Scraper	Station A, D	----	Oscar Shay	April 1954
937-292	Graver	NIP, Station B	----	Don Krieble	April 1954
937-293	Flake	BSW, Station C	With bison skull & wolf	Otto Schoen	April 1954
937-294	Scraper	6" from base, BS, Station A	----	Otto Schoen	April 1954
937-295	Flake	JS, 8" above D, Station B	----	Adolph Witte	May 1954
937-296	Flake	6" from top of D, Station B	----	Adolph Witte	May 1954
937-297	Scraper	4" below D in sand, GS or BSW, Station A	----	Adolph Witte	May 1954
937-298	Parallel point fragment	8" above D, JS, Station C	----	Adolph Witte	May 1954
937-299	Flake	12" below top of D, Station B	Bison bones	Jim Warnica	May 1954
937-300	Core burin	JS, 5" Station B	----	Jim Warnica	May 1954
937-301	Flake	Near bottom of D, Station B	----	Adolph Witte	May 1954
937-302	Parallel point fragment	JS? Station B	----		May 1954
937-304	Worked bone?	D, Station B	----		May 1954
937-305	Flake	14" above D, JS, N. end Station C	----		May 1954
937-306	Scraper fragment	14" above D, JS, N. end Station C	----		May 1954
937-307	Flake	D, Station C	----	Oscar Shay	May 1954
937-308	Flake scraper-graver	GS or D, Station B	----	Adolph Witte	May 1954

Cat. No.	Type	Locus	Association	Found By	Date
937-309	Flake	Basal D, Station B	----	E.H. Sellards	May 1954
937-310	Hammerstone	In well west side of north pit	----	Adolph Witte	May 1954
937-312	Worked bone?	Basal D, Station B	----	Oscar Shay	May 1954
937-313	Flake scraper-graver	4" from top of unit, probably C silt, Station B	----	Don Krieble	May 1954
937-314	Flake scraper	Near base of D, Station C	----	Don Krieble	May 1954
937-316	Hammerstone	Believed to be from GS, Station C	----	Adolph Witte	May 1954
937-531	Chopper & flake	D in ditch between N & S pits			
937-532	Worked? bone	GS (?) ditch between N & S pits			

*Data from TMM accession record for Tables 2,3,4,5,6,8.

TABLE III

WARNICA AND SHAY FINDS, STATIONS B AND C,
JULY-AUGUST 1954

Cat. No.	Type	Locus	Association	Found By	Date
937-326	Archaic point	JS - E extension of Station B		Jim Warnica	July 1954
937-327	Archaic point	Same as 326		Jim Warnica	July 1954
937-328	Archaic point	Same as 326		Jim Warnica	July 1954
937-329	Archaic point	10 steps NE of locus of 3 points above		Jim Warnica	July 1954
937-333	Plainview point	Same as 326	Bison bones	Oscar Shay	July 1954
937-334	Bone tool	E. extension of Station B, Portales horizon		Oscar Shay	July 1954
937-398	Millstone	JS Station B	Bison kill level	Shay & Warnica	July 1954
937-399	Scraper	JS Station B	Bison kill level	Shay & Warnica	July 1954
937-400-401	Scraper fragments	JS Station B	Bison kill level	Shay & Warnica	July 1954
937-402	Spalls & artifact fragments (36)	JS Station B	Bison kill level	Shay & Warnica	July 1954
937-403	Knife	JS Station B	Bison kill level	Shay & Warnica	July 1954
937-404	Indeterminant object	JS Station B	Bison kill level	Shay & Warnica	July 1954
937-406	Stones (10)	JS Station B	Bison kill level	Shay & Warnica	July 1954
937-407	Stone	JS Station B	Bison kill level	Shay & Warnica	July 1954
937-408	Chopper	JS Station B	Bison kill level	Shay & Warnica	July 1954
937-409	Stone	JS Station B	Bison kill level	Shay & Warnica	July 1954
937-412	Stones (22)	JS Station B	Bison kill level	Shay & Warnica	July 1954
937-413	Carved stone	Hole in bedrock		Shay & Warnica	July 1954
937-414	Beads (2)	JS Station B		Shay & Warnica	July 1954
937-415	Scraper	JS Station B		Shay & Warnica	July 1954
937-416	Ellis type point	JS Station B		Shay & Warnica	July 1954
937-417	Scraper	JS Station B		Shay & Warnica	July 1954
937-418	Scraper-graver	JS Station B		Shay & Warnica	July 1954
937-419	Scraper	JS Station B		Shay & Warnica	July 1954
937-420	Scraper	JS Station B		Shay & Warnica	July 1954
937-421	Chips (2)	JS Station B		Shay & Warnica	July 1954
937-422	Worked flints (2)	JS Station B		Shay & Warnica	July 1954

Cat. No.	Type	Locus	Association	Found By	Date
937-423-428	Projectile points (6)	JS Station B		Shay & Warnica	July 1954
937-429	Point fragments	JS Station B		Shay & Warnica	July 1954
937-430	Scraper	JS Station B		Shay & Warnica	July 1954
937-431	Possible scraper	JS Station B		Shay & Warnica	July 1954
937-432	Scraper	JS Station B	Bison kill level	Shay & Warnica	July 1954
937-433	Worked flint	JS Station B	Bison kill level	Shay & Warnica	July 1954
937-434	Small stone	JS Station B	Bison kill level	Shay & Warnica	July 1954
937-435	Unused stone	JS Station B	Bison kill level	Shay & Warnica	July 1954
937-436	Chips (17)	JS Station B	Bison kill level	Shay & Warnica	July 1954
937-437	Hematite nodule	JS Station B	Bison kill level	Shay & Warnica	July 1954
937-439	Marked hematite	JS Station B	Bison kill level	Shay & Warnica	July 1954
937-440	Hematite (2)	JS Station B	Bison kill level	Shay & Warnica	July 1954
937-441	Used stone	JS Station B	Bison kill level	Shay & Warnica	July 1954
937-460	7 artifacts	Dump		Jim Warnica	Aug. 1954
486-488	No data				

TABLE IV

ARTIFACTS FROM SELLARD'S CLOVIS <u>BISON</u> DIG, MAY 1955

Cat. No.	Type	Locus	Association
937-601	Atlatl weight (?)	Screen from GS	
937-602	Flake knife	Screen from GS	
937-603	Pebble	Surface	
937-604	Atlatl weight (?)	GS	
937-679	Flake	GS	
937-680	Ornament (?)	GS	
937-683	Projectile point	Dump	
937-684	Artifacts (19)	Dump	
	3--end scraper; 6--point frag., parallel flaked; 7--knife; 8--end scraper; --point frag.; 5--end scraper; 4--end scraper; 2--scraper; 0--Archaic point; M--point; I--scraper; K--point, prob. parallel flaked, reused as scraper; F--unfluted Folsom point; C--Archaic point; B--Archaic point; A--Neo Indian point; -- drill; --Plainview point; --potsherd;		
937-686	Bone implement	GS	
937-688 (a)	Bone implement	GS	
937-729	Clovis point	GS	Bison scapula 937-726
937-739	Projectile point	GS	Near bison
937-740	Projectile point	GS	Bison radius
937-741	Projectile point	GS	
937-743	Flake knife	GS	
937-744	Flake knife		

(a) Found by Gordon Brown.

TABLE V

ARTIFACTS FROM WARNICA AND BROWN PECCARY DIG., AUGUST 1955

Cat. No.	Type	Locus	Association	Found By
937-745	Worked bone	GS	Peccary	Warnica Brown
937-747	Worked (?) bone	GS	Peccary	Warnica Brown
927-748-749	Worked bones (2)	GS	Peccary	Warnica Brown
937-751-753	Worked bones (2)	GS	Peccary	Warnica Brown
937-755-757	Worked bones (3)	GS	Peccary	Warnica Brown
937-761	Scraper-knife	GS	Peccary	Warnica Brown

TABLE VI

ARTIFACTS FROM SELLARDS' EXCAVATIONS, OCTOBER-NOVEMBER 1955

Cat. No.	Type	Locus	Association
937-776 (a)	Unfluted Folsom point	Dump	
937-777	Atlatl weight (?)	GS SE corner of Pit	
937-778	Scraper fragment	SE corner Pit 2	Plainview (?)
937-783	Worked bones (3)	SW corner Pit 2 GS	
937-784	Worked bone	SW corner Pit 2 GS	
937-785	Polishing stone	JS-CS contact East Ditch dig	Near C-14 samples dated by Humble
937-787	Hammer stone	GS	
937-798	Worked bone	GS SW part Pit 2	
937-821	Hammer stone	Pit 1	
937-828	Bone implement	West ditch	

(a) Found by O. Schoen.

TABLE VII

ARTIFACTS FROM DITTERT AND WENDORF EXCAVATIONS
MAY 1956

Cat. No.	Type	Locus	Association	Found By	Date
30/3211	Grinding stone, frag.	Trench A, Sec. 3	Portales	Dittert & Wendorf	May 1956
30/3212	Worked bone	Trench B, GS		Dittert & Wendorf	May 1956
30/3213	Worked bone	Trench B, GS		Dittert & Wendorf	May 1956
30/3214	Worked bone	Trench B, GS		Dittert & Wendorf	May 1956
30/3215	Worked bone	Trench B, GS		Dittert & Wendorf	May 1956
30/3216	Flake	Trench A	Archaic-Portales contact	Dittert & Wendorf	May 1956
30/3217	Graver, frag.	Trench A, Sec. 6	Archaic	Dittert & Wendorf	May 1956
30/3218	Side scraper, frag.	Trench A, Sec. 1	Archaic-Portales contact	Dittert & Wendorf	May 1956
30/3219	Graver	Trench A, Sec. 4	Archaic-Portales contact	Dittert & Wendorf	May 1956
30/3220	Hammerstone	Trench A, Sec. 6	Archaic	Dittert & Wendorf	May 1956
30/3221	24 flakes	Trench A, Sec. 1	Archaic	Dittert & Wendorf	May 1956
30/3222	2 flakes	Trench A, Sec. 2	Archaic	Dittert & Wendorf	May 1956
30/3223	4 flakes	Trench A, Sec. 6	Archaic	Dittert & Wendorf	May 1956

TABLE VIII

ARTIFACTS ASSOCIATED WITH MAMMOTH EXCAVATED
BY OSCAR SHAY, AUGUST 1956

Cat. No.	Type	Locus	Association	Found By
937-862	Clovis point	Probably BSW (notes say "stratum next above Clovis Horizon")	Elephant vertebrae	O. Shay
937-863	Flake		Elephant vertebrae	O. Shay
937-864	Flake	"stratum next above Clovis Horizon"	Elephant vertebrae	O. Shay

APPENDIX III

SUMMARY OF VERTEBRATE FOSSILS COLLECTED BY EXCAVATION

TABLE I

VERTEBRATE FOSSILS COLLECTED BY THE CALIFORNIA INSTITUTE OF
TECHNOLOGY-PHILADELPHIA ACADEMY EXPEDITIONS
1932-1937

Cat. No.	Species	Specimens	Locus	Associ- ation	Date Found	Text & Fig- ure Ref.	Map Ref.
	Cynomys near ludo- vicianus	A left mandi- bular incisor, and a left P- 4-M3	Pink sands, east wall of pit		Summer 1933	Stock and Bode 1937, pp. 234- 5	
Cal. Tech. No. 1941	Parelephas? cf. columbi (Falconer)	Front limb bones	Blue sands, west side of pit		Summer 1933	Stock & Bode 1937, pp. 235- 6, Pl. 8, Figs. 2, 2a, 2b; Pl. 6b	Stock & Bode 1937 Figs. 1 & 3
Cal. Tech. Nos. 13670, 13765, 13683, 13690, 13694	Equus cf. excelsus Leidy	Individual teeth, both upper and lo- wer dentition	Top of yellow sands		Summer 1933	Stock & Bode 1937, p. 237 Fig. 4, c, e, f, h, i, & k	
A.N.S.P. No. 13804	Platygo- nus spe- cies	One upper premolar probably P3	Top of yellow sands	With teeth of Equus	Summer 1933	Stock & Bode 1937, p. 238 Fig. 6	
	Bison, extinct species or subspecies	Skeletal elements	Blue sands		Summer 1933	Stock & Bode 1937, pp. 221; 238-9, Pl. 7b	
	Bison species	Numerous skeletal elements	Speckled sand (bed B blue sands (beds E,D,B, A) 1936 exca- vation pit	With arti- facts, (all levels) & mammoth (speckled sand & blue sands)	Summer 1936	Cotter 1937, pp. 9-10	Cotter 1937, Text Pl. 2,3, Pl. 6, Fig. 3
	Mammoth	Skeletons of 2 individuals	Top of speckled sand extend- ing into blue sand	With arti- facts and rare bison	Summer 1936	Cotter 1937, pp. 3-9	Cotter 1937, Text Pl. 2, 3 Pl. 5
	Mammoth	Skeletal ele- ments of 3 individuals	In blue sands		Summer 1933	Howard, 1935 pp. 91, 95	Howard 1935, Pl. XVIII
	Bison	Numerous skeletons	Blue sands and yellow sand	With arti- facts in blue sand	Summer 1933	Howard, 1935 pp. 92- 3	
	Cervus, species indet.		Mammoth pit		Summer 1936	Cotter 1937, p. 11	
	Rodent, species indet.		Mammoth pit		Summer 1936	Cotter 1937, p. 11	
	Terrapene ornata agassiz		Mammoth pit		Summer 1936	Cotter 1937, p. 11	

TABLE II

VERTEBRATE FOSSILS COLLECTED BY THE TEXAS MEMORIAL MUSEUM,
1949-50

(Identifications by Ernest L. Lundelius, Jr.)

Cat. No.	Species	Specimens	Locus	Cat. No.	Species	Specimens	Locus
937-35	Bison	Metapodial	BSW Station B	937-150	Bison	Astragalus	D Station G.
937-36	Equus (?)	Lower molar	BSW-GS contact NE end South Pit	937-151- 152	Bison	Phalanges (2)	D or CS E. Side, S. Pit
937-37 (Folsom association)	Bison	Jaw	Station No. 1* Base of diatomite	937-153	Bison	Astragalus	D Station G
				937-154	Bison	Phalanx	D Station G
937-38 (Folsom association)	Bison	Teeth	D Probably Station E	937-155	Bison	Navicular	D Station G
				937-156- 157	Bison	Phalanges (2)	D or CS. E. Side, S. Pit
937-39 (Folsom association)	Bison	Teeth	D Probably Station E	937-158	Terrapene canaliculata	Skull	GS Station E
937-44	Bison	Distal end of humerus	BSW Station B	937-159	Similodon calfironicus	Right mandible	GS Station E
937-45	Equus (?)	Scapula	Station No. 1 white sand N. pit	937-160	Ondatra zibetheca	Mandible	GS Station E
937-46	Elephant	Molar	Base of white sand E. side, N. Pit	937-161	Turtle	Limb bone	GS Station E
				937-162	Ondatra zibetheca	Left M$_1$	GS Station E
937-47	Wolf canis lupus	Jaw	BSW W. Side, S. Pit	937-164	Bison	Articulated foot (13 bones)	D Station B
937-48	Equus	Molar	Station No. 1 GS	937-165 (Folsom association)	Bison	Metapodial & articulated toe bone (4)	D Station E
937-49	Turtle	Portion of carapace	Station No. 1 GS				
937-108	Elephant	Foot bone	GS-D contact NW corner S. Pit	937-166	Bison	Metapodial & articulated ankle bones (5)	D Station E
937-109	Bison	Metapodial	D NW Corner S. Pit	937-167- 168	Bison	Calcanei (2)	BSW Station B
937-110	Bison	Metapodial	D NW Corner S. Pit	937-169	Equus scotti	Lower tooth	GS Station A
937-111	Bison	Proximal end of scapula	D NW Corner S. Pit	937-170- 173	Equus scotti	Left P^3-M^2	GS Station A
937-112	Bison	Phalanx	D NW Corner S. Pit	937-174	Equus scotti	Left astragalus	GS Station A
937-113 to 118	Bison	Phalanges	D NW Corner S. Pit	937-175- 176	Bison	Astragali (2)	BSW Station B
937-119 to 125	Equus	Molars	Base of GS S.W. Corner, S. Pit	937-177	Bison	Articulated foot (11 bones)	D Station E
937-126	Elephant	Molar plate	Base of GS S.W. Corner S. Pit	937-178	Bison	Calcaneum	BSW Station B
937-129	Bison	Radius	D Station B	937-179	Bison	Astragalus	BSW Station B
937-130	Bison	Radius	D E Side W. Pit (?)	937-180	Bison	Phalanx	BSW Station B
				937-181	Bison	Calcaneus	BSW Station B
937-131	Bison	Radius	D W Trench, Station E	937-182	Bison	Articulated toe bones (3)	D Station E
937-132	Bison	Rear metapodial	BSW Station B	937-183	Bison	Articulated toe bones (3)	D Station E
937-133	Bison	Calcaneum	D W. Side, S. Pit				
937-134- 135	Bison	Axis vertebrae	BSW Station B	937-184	Bison	Associated ankle bones (7)	D Station E
937-136	Bison	Front metapodial	GS Station B	937-185	Equus conversidens	Right astragalus	GS Station E
937-137	Bison	Front metapodial	Station B GS				
937-138	Bison	Front metapodial	D or CS (?) E Side, S. Pit	937-186	Equus	Ankle bone	GS Station E
				937-187	Bison	Tibia	CS W. End S. Pit
937-139	Bison	Associated foot bones (8)	D , W. Trench Station E	937-188	Bison	Radius	CS W. End S. Pit
937-140	Bison	Calcaneum	CS W Side, N. Pit	937-189- 190	Bison	Jaws (2)	D Station G
937-41	Bison	Hoof	D or CS (?) E Side, S. Pit	937-191	Equus niobrarensis	Tooth	GS NW Corner S. Pit
937-142	Bison	Hoof	CS W Side, N. Pit	937-192	Equus niobrarensis	Tooth	GS NW Corner S. Pit
937-143	Bison	Hoof	D W Side, N. Pit	937-193	Equus niobrarensis	Tooth	GS NW Corner S. Pit
937-144	Bison	Calcaneum	CS W Side, S. Pit	937-194*	Equus conversidens	Upper molar	GS NW Corner S. Pit
937-145	Bison	Toebone and hoof	D or CS. (?) E Side, S. Pit	937-195*	Equus conversidens	Upper molar	GS NW Corner S. Pit
937-146	Bison	Atlas vertebrae	SW Side, N. Pit	937-196	Equus	Tooth	GS NW Corner S. Pit
937-147	Bison	Calcaneum	D W. Side, S. Pit	937-197	Equus	Tooth	GS NW Corner S. Pit
937-148	Bison	Phalanx	D W. Side, S. Pit	937-198	Equus	Unidentified bone	GS NW Corner S. Pit
937-149	Bison	Calcaneum	D W. Side, N. Pit	937-199	Turtle	Carapace fragment	GS NW Corner S. Pit
				937-200	Platygonus sp.	M$_3$	GS NW Corner S. Pit
				937-201	Turtle	Partial carapace	Well M Station E

* Station No. 1 is not mentioned elsewhere in the field notes but is
assumed to be Station A. The west side, S. Pit location is assumed
to be Station E. The W. Side, N. Pit is Station G.

Cat. No.	Species	Specimens	Locus
937-202	Turtle	Partial carapace	D - GS contact S side N Pit
937-203	*Equus conversidens*	Upper molar	GS Station E
937-204	*Equus*	Molar	GS Station B
937-205		Unidentified bone	Well M Station E
937-206	*Terrapene canaliculata*	Partial carapace & plastron	GS Station E
937-207	*Equus con-versidens*	Upper molar	GS Station E
937-208	Turtle	Fragments of plastron	GS Station E
937-209		Small animal ulna (?)	GS Station E
937-210 (Elephant association)	*Equus*	Incisor	GS Station A (?)
937-211- 214	*Equus*	Teeth (4)	GS Station A (?)
937-215 (Elephant association)		Unidentified bone	GS Station A (?)
937-216	Turtle	Plastron (1/2)	D Station E
937-217	*Microtus pennsylvanicus*	Jaw	D Station E
937-219 (Elephant association)	Carnivore	Canine	GS Station A (?)
937-220 (Elephant association)		Tibia	GS Station A (?)
937-221 (Elephant association)		Caudal vertebrae	GS Station A (?)
937-222 (Elephant association)		Tooth fragments	GS Station A (?)
937-223- 225	*Equus*	Molars (3)	GS
937-226 (Folsom association)	*Bison*	Astragalus	D Station E
937-227- 229	*Equus conversidens*	Articulated toe bones	GS Station E
937-230	Bird	Carpus	GS Station A
937-231	*Bison*	Metapodial & associated foot bones (3?)	D Station E
937-232- 235	*Bison*	Phalanges (4)	D Station E
937-236	*Bison*	Front metapodial	D
937-237	*Bison*	Phalanx & 6 associated ankle bones	D Station E
937-238	*Bison*	Front metapodial & associated foot bones (3?)	D Station E
937-239	*Bison*	Humerus	D Station E
937-240	*Equus*	Radius-ulna	GS Station E
937-241	Turtle	Carapace fragment	GS Station A (?)
937-242	Turtle	Carapace (partial)	GS Station E
937-243	*Bison*	Front metapodial	GS?
937-244- 247	*Equus*	Molars (4)	GS Station E
937-248	Turtle	Plastron fragment	GS Station E
937-249	Elephant	Rib	GS Station A
937-250	*Equus scotti*	Molars	GS
937-251	*Equus scotti*	Molars	GS
937-252	*Equus niobrarensis*	Left molar	GS Station A
937-253	*Equus scotti*	Molars	GS
937-254	*Equus*	Molar	GS
937-255	*Mammuthus*	Molar fragments (2)	GS
937-256- 260	*Bison*	Phalanges (5)	D Station A
937-261- 262	*Bison*	Sesamoids (2)	D Station A
937-264- 265	*Bison*	Rear metapodials (2)	D Station G

Cat. No.	Species	Specimens	Locus
937-266- 267	*Bison*	Rear metapodials (2)	D Station E
937-268	*Bison*	Rear metapodial	D Station B
937-269	*Bison*	Rear metapodial	D Station E
937-270- 271	*Bison*	Front metapodials (2)	D Station E
937-272	*Bison*	Front metapodials	D Station G
937-273- 275	*Bison*	Front metapodials (3)	D Station E
937-276- 277	*Bison*	Rear metapodials (2)	CS Station E
937-278	*Bison*	Front metapodial	CS Station E
937-279	*Bison*	Front metapodial	D Station G
937-280	*Mammuthus*	Vertebrae	GS Station A?
937-474- 478	*Bison* sp?	Astragali (5)	D (?) Station B

TABLE III

VERTEBRATE FOSSILS COLLECTED BY THE TEXAS MEMORIAL MUSEUM
STATIONS B AND C, APRIL 1954

Cat. No.	Species	Specimens	Locus	Association
937-317		Astragalus	GS (brown sand lens)	
937-318		Astragalus	BSW-D contact	
937-319		Astragalus	Brown Sand lense (probably BSW)	
937-320		Astragalus	GS	
937-321- 325		Astragali (5)	Unknown	Folsom?
937-465		Femur	BSW-D Contact Station C	
937-466		Head of scapula	BSW-D Contact Station C	
937-467		Metatarsals (2) phalanges (2)	CS? Station C	
937-468		Phalanges	CS Station C	
937-469		Metacarpal	CS Station C	
937-470		Mandible	CS Station C	
937-471	*Bison*	Cervical vertebrae	GS Station C	
937-472		Astragalus	Dump	
937-473		Calcaneus	GS Station C	
937-479		Astragalus	D N Side S Pit	With knife 937-313
937-516	*Bison*	Vertebrae	BSW	
937-517	*Bison*	Vertebrae	D	
937-518	*Bison*	Phalanx	Dump	
937-519	*Bison*	Vertebrae	BSW	
937-520		Rib	BSW	
937-521	*Canis lupus*	Skull	BSW	
937-522	*Bison*	Metapodial	BSW or D	
937-523	*Bison*	Jaw	GS	
937-524	*Bison*	Astragalus	JS Station B	
937-525	*Bison*	Calcaneus	GS West of N Pit	
937-526	*Bison*	Phalanges (3)	JS	
937-527	*Bison* & *Equus*	Teeth (2)	Pink & White sand	
937-528	*Bison*	Astragalus		
937-529	*Bison*	Astragalus	CS NW Corner S Pit	
937-530		Limb bone fragment	D ditch between N & S Pits	
937-534		Bone	JS	
937-535	Turtle	Carapace fragment	GS NE Corner N Pit	
937-536- 540	*Bison*	Bones	JS Station A	
937-541	*Bison*	Humerus	NE side of N Pit beneath D	Bison Skull
937-542		Small bone	NE Corner N Pit	
937-543		Phalanges (2) limb bones (2)	Basal diatomite (BSW?) NE Corner N Pit	Bison skull
937-544	*Equus*	Tooth		
937-549		Portion of skull	D N Side N Pit	
937-551	*Bison*	Astragalus	GS NE Side N Pit	Bison skull
937-552	*Bison*	Scapula	D Station A	
937-554		Bone fragments	Station A GS	Wolf skull
937-555	Elephant	Vertebrae	GS N Side N Pit	

TABLE IV

VERTEBRATE FOSSILS COLLECTED BY WARNICA AND SHAY STATIONS B & C, JULY-AUGUST 1954

Cat. No.	Species	Specimens	Locus
937-331		Astragalus	JS Station B
937-332		Calcaneus	JS Station B
937-335-336		Astragali (2)	JS Station B
937-337-338		Foot bones (2)	JS Station B
937-339		Astragalus	JS Station B
937-340		Calcaneus	JS Station B
937-344		Scapula	JS Station B
937-345	Bison	Radius	JS Station B
937-346-348		Astragali (3)	JS Station B
937-349		Calcaneus	JS Station B
937-350-370		Astragali (21)	JS Station B
937-371-379		Calcaneus (9)	JS Station B
937-380-381		Phalanges (2)	JS Station B
937-382		Horn core	JS Station B
937-383		Unidentified bone	JS Station B
937-384-385		Limb bones (2)	JS Station B
937-386		Miscellaneous bones	JS Station B
937-387		Rib	JS Station B
937-389		Small bones (8)	JS Station B
937-390		Unidentified bone	JS Station B
937-391		Skull fragment	JS Station B
937-392	Bison	Jaw	D or CS Station C
937-393		Limb bone	D or CS Station C
937-394	Bison	Vertebrae	D or CS Station C
937-395 (Elephant association)	Bison	Limb bone	D or CS Probably Station A
937-396	Bison	Limb bone	D or CS Station C
937-397	Bison	Limb bone	D or CS Station C
937-405		Unidentified bones	JS Station C
937-410		Astragali (8)	JS Station C
937-438 (Bison kill level association)		Small bone	JS Station C
937-447	Elephant	Tooth	GS
937-445		Small rib	
937-456	Horse and Bison	Teeth	
937-457		Astragalus	CS Station B
937-458		Astragali (3)	CS Station B
937-459		Gnawed bone	JS Station B
937-461	Bison	Astragalus	JS - CS Station B

TABLE V

VERTEBRATE FOSSILS COLLECTED FROM SELLARDS' CLOVIS BISON DIG, MAY 1955

Cat. No.	Species	Specimens	Locus	Association
937-585	Mammuthus	Head of femur	D West of N Pit	
937-586	Bison	Vertebrae spine	GS	
937-587		Bone	GS	
937-588	Bison	Skull		
937-589	Bison	Jaws	GS	
937-595		Tibia	GS	Bison skulls
937-596-598		Cut bones (3)	GS	
937-599	Bison	Tooth	GS	
937-600		Tooth	GS	
937-607	Bison	Tooth		
937-608	Deer	Teeth		
937-610	Bison	Scapula	GS	
937-614	Bison	Horn core	GS	Bison skulls
937-615		Cut bone	Screen	
937-616	Bison	Calcaneus	GS	
937-617	Bison	Vertebrae	GS	
937-618		Phalanges (2)	GS	
937-619	Bison	Tibia	GS	Bison skulls
937-620	Wolf	Jaw	GS	
937-634		Phalanges (2?)	GS	
937-635	Bison	Leg bones (2?)	GS	Bison skulls
937-636	Bison	Phalanges (2?)	GS	
937-637		Cut bone	GS	
937-638	Bison	Metapodial	GS	
937-639	Bison	Bone	GS	
937-640		Cut bone	GS	
937-641	Bison	Vertebrae	GS	Projectile points
937-642	Bison	Astragalus	GS	Bison skulls
937-643		Cut bone	GS	
937-644	Camelops	Tooth	GS	
937-645		Foot bone		
937-645		Cut bone	GS	
937-647	Bison	Astragalus	GS	
937-648	Bison	Tibia		
937-649	Bison	Tibiae (3 packages)		
937-650	Bison	Astragalus	D	
937-651	Bison or horse	Rib	GS	
937-652		Cut bone	GS	
937-653	Bison	Tibia		
937-654		Metapodial	GS	
937-655		Tooth, foot bone	GS	
937-656		Calcaneus	GS	
937-657		Cut bone	GS	
937-658	Bison	Jaw	GS	
937-659		Ulna	GS	
937-660		Astragalus	D	
937-661	Camel	Tooth	GS	
937-662	Bison	Calcaneus	GS	
937-663	Bison	Astragalus	D	
937-664	Camel	Tooth	GS	
937-665		Small teeth		
937-667	Bison	Jaw	GS	Bison skulls
937-669		Vertebrae	GS	
937-670		Phalanx		
937-671		Vertebrae	GS	
937-672	Bison		GS	
937-673	Bison	Jaw	GS	Bison skulls
937-674	Bison	Tibia (3 packages)		
937-675-676		Vertebrae	GS	
937-677		Cut bone	GS	
937-678A	Equus niobrarensis	Tooth	GS	
937-678	Equus scotti	Tooth	GS	
937-681	Equus	Teeth & bone	GS	
937-682	Deer	Antler tine	GS	
937-687		Cut bone	GS	
937-689-690	Camel	Teeth (2)		
937-691	Equus	Tooth		
937-692		Teeth	GS	
937-693		Bones (2?)	GS	
937-694		Skull		
937-695		Skull bones	GS	

Cat. No.	Species	Specimens	Locus	Association
937-724		Bone artifacts? (4)	GS	
937-725	Equus	Teeth (2?)	GS	
937-726	Bison	Scapula	GS	With Clovis point
937-727	Bison	Scapula	GS	Same animal as 937-726
937-728		Rib	GS	With 937-726, 937-727
937-730	Mammuthus	Patella	GS	937-726
937-731	Bison	Vertebrae	GS	937-726
937-732	Bison	Astragalus	GS	
937-733	Equus scotti	Metapodial	GS	
937-734	Bison	Calcaneus	GS	
937-735	Turtle	Carapace fragment	GS	
937-736	Camelops	Teeth (3)	GS	
937-737	Camelops	Teeth	GS	
937-738	Equus scotti	Tooth	GS	
937-738A	Equus niobrarensis	Tooth	GS	
937-740	Bison	Radius		Projectile point
937-762	Bison	Skull	GS	
937-763	Bison	Skull	GS	
937-764	Bison antiquus	Skull	GS	

TABLE VI

VERTEBRATE FOSSILS COLLECTED FROM WARNICA AND BROWN
PECCARY DIG, AUGUST 1955

Cat. No.	Species	Specimens	Locus
937-746	Equus scotti	Astragalus	Base of GS
937-750		Fragmentary bone	Base of GS
937-754		Fragmentary bone	Base of GS
937-758		Undetermined bone	Base of GS
937-759	Elephant	Foot bone	Base of GS
937-760	Equus scotti	Molar	Base of GS
937-760	Camel	Lower molar	Base of GS
937-760	Equus	Lower molar	Base of GS
937-760	Equus	Upper incisor	Base of GS
Not assigned	Peccary	Jaw	Base of GS

TABLE VII

VERTEBRATE FOSSILS COLLECTED FROM SELLARDS' EXCAVATIONS,
OCTOBER-NOVEMBER 1955

Cat. No.	Species	Specimens	Locus	Association
937-780	Mammuthus	Tusk	GS NW Corner Pit 2	
937-781	Equus	Tooth	GS SW Corner Pit 2	
937-782	Equus & camel	Teeth (2)	GS SW Corner Pit 2	
937-786		Sesamoid	GS SW Corner Pit 2	
937-789	Bison	Bone		Folsom level
937-790		Split bone	GS SW Corner Pit 2	
937-791	Bison	Astragalus	GS SW Corner Pit 2	
937-792	Equus & camel	Teeth	GS SW Corner Pit 2	
937-795		Bones	JS-CS Contact East Ditch	C-14 samples dated by Humble
937-796		Astragali (2)	JS-CS Contact East Ditch	C-14 samples dated by Humble
937-797		Foot bone	JS East Ditch	
937-799	Equus	Tooth	GS SW part Pit 2	

Cat. No.	Species	Specimens	Locus
937-818	Mammuthus	Tooth	GS NW Corner Pit 2
937-820	Bison	Metacarpal	Pit 1
937-822*	Equus conversidens	Tooth	GS Pit 1
937-823	Bison	Bones & teeth	GS Pit 1
937-824	Mammuthus	Bone	GS Pit 1
937-825		Foot bone	GS Pit 1
937-826		Teeth & hoof bones	GS Pit 1
937-827	Mammuthus	Bone	GS Pit 1

* Identification by Ernest L. Lundelius, Jr.

TABLE VIII

VERTEBRATE FOSSILS COLLECTED FROM SELLARDS' EXCAVATIONS,
MAY 1956

Cat. No.	Species	Specimens	Locus	Association
937-857	Equus	Tooth	GS	
937-858		Bone	SE corner Pit 2	Portales level
937-859	Equus scotti	Tooth	GS	
937-860		Charred bone	East Ditch	

TABLE IX

VERTEBRATE FOSSILS COLLECTED FROM DITTERT AND WENDORF
EXCAVATIONS, MAY 1956

Cat. No.	Species	Specimens	Locus	Association
3324-1	Unidentified	Mostly teeth	Trench B, GS	
3324-2	Unidentified		Trench A, Sec. 1	Archaic
3324-3	Bison*	Jaw	Trench A, Sec. 5	Archaic
3324-4	Bison*		Trench A, Sec. 5	Portales
3324-5	Bison*		Trench A, Sec. 6	Archaic
3324-6	Unidentified		Trench A, Sec. 6	Archaic-Portales contact
3324-7	Unidentified		Face W of Trench A	Portales
3324-8	Unidentified		Trench A, Sec. 5	Archaic-Portales contact
3324-9	Unidentified		Trench B, GS	
3324-10	Unidentified	Teeth (2)	Trench B, GS	
3324-11	Unidentified		SW Corner, N Pit BSW	

* Field identification by Dittert and Wendorf

BIBLIOGRAPHY

Agogino, G.A. and J.J. Hester
n.d.

Excavations at the Clovis Site 1963-4
Eastern New Mexico University Publications in Paleo-Indian Studies, (In Press).

Anonymous
1936

Literary Digest, Vol. 122, p. 20.

Antevs, E.
1936

The Occurrence of Flints and Extinct Animals in Pluvial Deposits near Clovis, New Mexico, Pt. II, Age of Clovis Lake Beds. Proceedings Philadelphia Academy of Natural Sciences, Vol. LXXXVII, pp. 304-311.

1949

Geology of the Clovis Sites. Appendix in "Ancient Man in North America" by H.M. Wormington. Denver Museum of Natural History Popular Series No. 4. 3rd Edition.

1953

Artifacts with Mammoth Remains, Naco, Arizona, II: Age of Clovis Fluted Points with the Naco Mammoth. American Antiquity, Vol. XIX, No. 1, pp. 15-18.

Aveleyra, Luis
1962

Antiguedad del Hombre en Mexico Y Centroamerica: Catalogo Razonado de Localidades Y Bibliografia Selecta (1867-1961). Cuadernos Del Instituto De Historia, Serie Anthropologica No. 14. Mexico, D. F.

Brannon, H.R., Jr.,
Daughtry, A.C., Perry, D.,
Simons, L.H., Whitaker,
W.W., and Williams, M.
1957

Humble Oil Company Radiocarbon Dates I: Science, V. 125, No. 3239, pp. 147-150.

Bryan, F.
1938

A Review of the Geology of the Clovis Finds Reported by Howard and Cotter. American Antiquity, Vol. IV, pp. 113-130.

Byers, D.
1954

Bull Brook - A Fluted Point Site in Ipswich, Massachusetts. American Antiquity, Vol. XIX, No. 4, pp. 343-51.

1959

Radiocarbon Dates for the Bull Brook Site, Massachusetts, American Antiquity, Vol. 24, pp. 427-9.

Clarke, W.T., Jr.
1938

List of Molluscs from Drift Debris of Paladora Creek, Texas. <u>Nautilus</u>, Vol. 52, pp. 14-15.

Cotter, J.L.
1938a

The Occurrence of Flints and Extinct Animals in Pluvial Deposits near Clovis, New Mexico, pt IV. Report on the Excavations at the Gravel Pit in 1936. <u>Proceedings of the Philadelphia Academy of Natural Sciences</u>, Vol. LXXXIX, pp. 2-16.

1938b

The Occurrence of Flints and Extinct Animals in Pluvial Deposits near Clovis, New Mexico. Part VI - Report on Field Season of 1937. <u>Proceedings of the Philadelphia Academy of Natural Sciences</u>, Vol. XC, pp. 113-17.

1954

Indications of a Paleo-Indian Co-Tradition for North America. <u>American Antiquity</u>, Vol. XX, No. 1, pp. 64-67. Salt Lake.

1962

Comments on Mason's "The Paleo-Indian Tradition in Eastern North America," <u>Current Anthropology</u>, Vol. 3, No. 3, pp. 250-52.

Dalquest, Walter and
J.T. Hughes
1965

The Pleistocene Horse, <u>Equus conversidens</u>. <u>American Midland Naturalist</u>, Vol. 75, No. 2, pp. 408-17.

Damon, P.E., C.V. Haynes,
Jr., and A. Long
1967

Arizona Radiocarbon Dates V, <u>Radiocarbon</u>, Vol. 6, pp. 91-107.

Davis, E.M.
1962

Archeology of the Lime Creek Site in Southwestern Nebraska. <u>Special Publication of the Nebraska State Museum</u>, No. 3.

Dick, H.W., and
B. Mountain
1960

The Claypool Site: a Cody complex Site in Northeastern Colorado, <u>American Antiquity</u>, Vol. 26, No. 2, pp. 223-35.

Dittert, A.E., Jr.
1957

Salvage Excavations at Blackwater No. 1 Locality near Portales, New Mexico, <u>Highway Salvage Archeology</u>, Vol. III, Edited by Stewart Peckham, pp. 1-9.

Evans, G.L.
1951

Prehistoric Wells in Eastern New Mexico, <u>American Antiquity</u>, Vol. XVII, No. 1, pt. 1, pp. 1-8.

Fitting, James E.
1965

A Study of Natural Radioactivity in Osteological Materials from the Black-water Draw Number 1 Locality, Roosevelt County, New Mexico. In "Studies in the Natural Radioactivity of Prehistoric Materials" edited by A.J. Jelinek and J.E. Fitting. Anthro. Pap. Univ. of Mich. No. 24, pp. 64-76.

Flint, R.F.
1963

Status of the Pleistocene Wisconsin Stage in Central North America, Science, Vol. 139, No. 3553, pp. 402-4, Washington.

Green, F.E.
1962

Additional Notes on Prehistoric Wells At the Clovis Site. American Antiquity, Vol. 28, No. 2, pp. 230-4.

1963

The Clovis Blades: An Important Addition to the Llano Complex. American Antiquity, Vol. 29, No. 2, pp. 145-165.

Greenman, E.F.
1962

The Upper Paleolithic and the New World. Current Anthropology, Vol. 4, No. 1, pp. 4-91.

Griffin, J.B.
1960

Some Prehistoric Connections between Siberia and America, Science, Vol. 131, pp. 801-12.

Hall, E.R., and
Kelson, K.R.
1959

The Mammals of North America, New York, Ronald Press, 1084 pp.

Harbour, J.
n.d.

Geology of the Tahoka Age Sediments, in "Paleoecology of the Llano Estacado, Vol. 2", assembled by Fred Wendorf, and J.J. Hester. Papers of the Fort Burgwin Research Center, (in press).

Haury, E.W.
1953

Artifacts with Mammoth Remains, Naco, Arizona. Discovery of the Naco Mammoth and the Associated Projectile Points. American Antiquity, Vol. XIX, No. 1 pp. 1-14.

Haury, E.W., E.B. Sayles,
and W.W. Wasley
1959

The Lehner Mammoth Site, Southeastern Arizona, American Antiquity, Vol. 25, No. 1, pp. 2-30.

Hay, O.P.
1913A

Notes on some fossil horses with descriptions of four new species. Proceedings of the U.S. National Museum. Vol. 44, pp. 569-594.

1913B

Camels of the fossil genus Camelops. Proceedings of the U.S. National Museum. Vol. 46, pp. 267-77.

Haynes, C.V., Jr.
1964

Fluted Projectile Points: Their Age and Dispersion. Science, Vol. 145, No. 3639, pp. 1408-13.

n.d.

Geology of Blackwater Draw, in "Paleoecology of the Llano Estacado, Vol. 2" Assembled by Fred Wendorf and J.J. Hester. Papers of the Fort Burgwin Research Center, (in press).

Haynes, C.V., Jr., P.E. Damon, and D.C. Grey
1966

Arizona Radiocarbon Dates VI, Radiocarbon, Vol. 8, pp. 1-21.

Haynes, C.V., Jr., D.C. Grey, P.E. Damon, and R. Bennett
1967

Arizona Radiocarbon Dates VII, Radiocarbon, Vol. 9, pp. 1-14.

1965

Carbon - 14 Dates and Early Man in the New World. Interim Research Report No. 9, Geochronology Laboratories, University of Arizona.

Haynes, C.V., Jr., and George Agogino
1966

Prehistoric springs and Geochronology of the Clovis Site, New Mexico. American Antiquity, Vol. 31, pp. 812-21.

Haynes, C.V., Jr., and E.T. Hemmings
1968

Mammoth-Bone Shaft Wrench from Murray Springs, Arizona. Science, Vol. 159, pp. 186-187.

Hester, J.J.
1960

Late Pleistocene Extinction and Radiocarbon Dating. American Antiquity, Vol. 26, pp. 58-77.

1962

A Folsom Lithic Complex from the Elida Site, Roosevelt County, New Mexico; El Palacio, Vol. 69, No. 2, pp. 92-113.

1966

Origins of the Clovis Culture. Proceedings of the XXXVI International Congress of Americanists, pp. 127-38.

Hibbard, C.W. and W.W. Dalquest
1962

Artiodactyls from the Seymour Formation of Knox County, Texas, Michigan Academy of Science Papers, Vol. 47, pp. 83-99.

Hopkins, D.M.
1962

Comment to Mason's "The Paleo-Indian Tradition in Eastern North America," Current Anthropology, Vol. 3, No. 3, p. 254.

Howard, E.B.
1935

Evidence of Early Man in North America. The Museum Journal, University of Pennsylvania Museum, Vol. XXIV, Nos. 2-3.

Jelinek, A.J.
1960

An Archaeological Survey of the Middle Pecos River Valley and the Adjacent Llano Estacado, Doctoral Dissertation, University of Michigan, Ann Arbor.

1962

Comment to Mason's "The Paleo-Indian Tradition in Eastern North America," Current Anthropology, Vol. 3, No. 3, pp. 255-56.

Jennings, J.D.
1955

The Archeology of the Plains: An Assessment. Salt Lake City: Department of Anthropology. University of Utah, and the National Park Service.

Jepsen, G.L.
1 51

Ancient Buffalo Hunters of Northwestern Wyoming. Southwestern Lore, Vol. 19, No. 2, pp. 19-25, Boulder.

Jordan, D.F.
1960

The Bull Brook Site in Relation to "Fluted Point" Manifestations in Eastern North America. PhD. Dissertation, Department of Anthropology. Harvard University, Cambridge.

Krieger, A.D.
1954

A comment on "Fluted Point Relationships" by John Witthoft. American Antiquity, Vol. XIX, No. 3, pp. 273-5.

Lance, J.F.
1953

Artifacts with Mammoth Remains, Naco, Arizona III: Description of the Naco Mammoth. American Antiquity, Vol. XIX, No. 1, pp. 19-22.

1959

Faunal Remains from the Lehner Mammoth Site. American Antiquity, Vol. 25, pp. 35-39.

Lull, R.S.
1921

The Fauna of the Dallas Sand Pits. American Journal of Science, 5th Series, Vol. 2, pp. 159-76.

Lundelius, E.L.
1960

Mylohylus nasutus, long nosed peccary of the Texas Pleistocene. Texas Memorial Museum Bulletin, No. 1, pp. 9-40.

Marshack, A.
1964

Lunar Notations on Upper Paleolithic Remains. Science, Vol. 146, pp. 743-745.

Mason, R.J.
1958

Late Pleistocene Geochronology and the Paleo-Indian Penetration into the Lower Michigan Peninsula. Anthropological Papers, Museum of Anthropology, University of Michigan, No. 11, Ann Arbor.

1962

The Paleo-Indian Tradition in Eastern North America. Current Anthropology, Vol. 3, No. 3, pp. 227-278.

Merriam, J.C.
1913

The Skull and Dentition of a Camel from the Pleistocene of Rancho La Brea. University of California Publications in Geology, Vol. 7, pp. 305-23.

Merriam, J.C. and
C. Stock
1932

The Felidae of Rancho La Brea, Carnegie Institution of Washington Publication 422.

Milstead, W.W.
1956

Fossil Turtles of Friesenhahn Cave, Texas, with the Description of a new species of Testudo. Copeia, No. 3, pp. 162-71.

Müller-Beck, H.
1962

Comment to Mason's "The Paleo-Indian Tradition in Eastern North America," Current Anthropology, Vol. 3, No. 3, pp. 259-61.

1966

Paleohunters in America: Origins and Diffusion, Science, Vol. 152, pp. 1191-1210.

Osborn, H.F.
1942

Proboscidea, Volume 2, Stegodontoidea, Elephantoidea. New York, American Museum Press, 1675 pages.

Patrick, R.
1938

The Occurrence of Flints and Extinct Animals in Pluvial Deposits near Clovis, New Mexico. Part V-Diatom Evidence from the Mammoth Pit. Proceedings, Philadelphia Academy of Natural Sciences, Vol. 90, pp. 15-24.

Price, W.A.
1944

The Clovis Site: Regional Physiography and Geology. American Antiquity, Vol. X, pp. 401-7.

Quimby, G.
1958

Fluted Points and Geochronology of Lake Michigan Basin. American Antiquity, Vol. XXIII, pp. 247-54.

Quinn, J.H.
1957

Pleistocene Equidae of Texas, Bureau of Economic Geology, University of Texas, Report of Investigations, No. 33, pp. 5-55.

Ritchie, W.A.
1957

Traces of Early Man in the Northeast. New York State Museum and Science Service, Bulletin 358. Albany.

Schuster, C.
1963

Speculations on the Similarity of Some Notched Artifacts in the Folsom Culture and in the Old World Paleolithic. Paper presented at the Cleveland Meeting of the American Association for the Advancement of Science, Section H, December 30, 1963.

Sellards, E.H.
1940

Early Man in America: Index to Localities and Selected Bibliography. <u>Bulletin</u> <u>Geo-</u> <u>logical</u> <u>Society</u> <u>of</u> <u>America</u>. Vol. 51, pp. 373-432.

1952

<u>Early</u> <u>Man</u> <u>in</u> <u>America</u>. University of Texas Press.

1955

Fossil Bison and Associated Artifacts from Milnesand, New Mexico, <u>American</u> <u>Antiquity</u>, Vol. XX, No. 4, pp. 336-344.

Sellards, E.H. and
G.L. Evans
1960

The Paleo-Indian Culture Succession in the Central High Plains of Texas and New Mexico. In "<u>Men</u> <u>and</u> <u>Cultures</u>," pp. 639-49, selected papers of the 5th International Congress of Anthropological and Ethnological Sciences, Philadelphia University of Pennsylvania Press.

Simpson, G.G.
1949

A Fossil Deposit in a cave in St. Louis. <u>American</u> <u>Museum</u> <u>Novitiates</u>, No. 1408, pp. 1-46.

Skinner, M.F.
1942

The Fauna of Papago Springs Cave, Arizona, and a study of <u>Stockoceros</u>; with three new antilocaprinea from Nebraska and Arizona. <u>Bulletin</u>, <u>American</u> <u>Museum</u> <u>of</u> <u>Natural</u> <u>History</u>, Vol. 80, pp. 143-270.

Skinner, M.F., and
O.C. Kaisen
1947

The Fossil <u>Bison</u> of Alaska and Prelimi-mary Revision of the Genus. <u>American</u> <u>Museum</u> <u>of</u> <u>Natural</u> <u>History</u>, <u>Bulletin</u>, Vol. 89, pp. 131-256.

Slaughter, Bob, W.W. Crook,
R.K. Harris, D.C. Allen,
and Martin Seifert
1962

The Hill-Shuler local faunas of the Trinity River, Dallas and Denton Counties, Texas. <u>University</u> <u>of</u> <u>Texas</u>, <u>Bur</u>. <u>Econ</u>. <u>Geol</u>. <u>Report</u> <u>Inv</u>. 48, 75 pp.

Spaulding, A.C.
1946

Northeastern Archaeology and General Trends in the Northern Forest Zone. <u>Papers</u> <u>of</u> <u>the</u> <u>Robert</u> <u>S</u>. <u>Peabody</u> <u>Foundation</u> <u>for</u> <u>Archaeology</u>, Vol. 3, pp. 143-167. Andover.

Stock, C.
1928

<u>Tanupolama</u>, New Genus of Llama from the Pleistocene of California, <u>Carnegie</u> <u>Institu-</u> <u>tion</u> <u>of</u> <u>Washington</u>, <u>Publication</u> 393, pp. 29-37.

Stock, C. and F.D. Bode
1937

The Occurrence of Flints and Extinct Animals in Pluvial Deposits near Clovis, New Mexico: Part III, Geology and Vertebrate Paleontology of the Late Quaternary near Clovis, New Mexico. <u>Proceedings</u> <u>Philadelphia</u> <u>Academy</u> <u>of</u> <u>Natural</u> <u>Sciences</u>, Vol. LXXXVIII, pp. 219-241.

Suhm, Dee Ann, A.D. Krieger, and E. Jelks
1954

An Introductory Handbook of Texas Archaeology, <u>Bulletin</u> <u>Texas</u> <u>Archaeo-logical</u> <u>Society</u>, Vol. 25. Austin.

Troxell, E.L.
1915

The Vertebrate Fossils of Rock Creek, Texas. <u>American</u> <u>Journal</u> <u>Science</u>, Vol. 39, pp. 613-638.

Vertes, L.
1965

"Lunar Calendar" from the Hungarian Upper Paleolithic. <u>Science</u>, Vol. 149, pp. 855-856.

Wallis, George A.
1936

Exploring Antiquity. <u>New</u> <u>Mexico</u> <u>Magazine</u>, Vol. XIV, No. 10. pp. 18-19. Santa Fe.

Warnica, J.M.
1961

The Elida Site: Evidence of a Folsom occupation in Roosevelt County, Eastern New Mexico. <u>Bulletin</u> <u>of</u> <u>the</u> <u>Texas</u> <u>Archaeological</u> <u>Society</u>, Vol. 30, pp. 209-15. Austin.

1966

New Discoveries at the Clovis Site, <u>American</u> <u>Antiquity</u>, Vol. 31, No. 3, Part I, pp. 345-357.

Wendorf, D.F.
(assembler)

Paleoecology of the Llano Estacado. <u>Papers</u> <u>of</u> <u>the</u> <u>Fort</u>. <u>Burgwin</u> <u>Research</u> <u>Center</u>, No. 1.

Witthoft, J.
1952

A Paleo-Indian Site in Eastern Pennsylvania, An Early Hunting Culture. <u>Proceedings</u> <u>of</u> <u>the</u> <u>American</u> <u>Philosoph-ical</u> <u>Society</u>, Vol. 96, No. 4, pp. 464-495. Philadelphia.

Wormington, H.M.
1957

Ancient Man in North America, 4th Edition. <u>Denver</u> <u>Museum</u> <u>of</u> <u>Natural</u> <u>History</u>, <u>Popu-lar</u> <u>Series</u>, No. 4.

1962

A Survey of Early American Prehistory. <u>American</u> <u>Scientist</u>, Vol. 50, No. 1, pp. 230-242. Easton, Pennsylvania.

Wright, F.B.
1903

The Mastodon and Mammoth Contemporary with Man. <u>Records</u> <u>of</u> <u>the</u> <u>Past</u>, Vol. II, pp. 243-253. Records of the Past Explor-ation Society, Washington.

Young, S.P. and E.A. Goldman
1944

<u>The</u> <u>Wolves</u> <u>of</u> <u>North</u> <u>America</u>. The American Wildlife Institute, Washington, D.C.

Errata

1. Clovis pts., type 2 – from Gray Sand at Location 4, W-135, W-154 are not illustrated, and W-154 is not in Appendix I.
2. Artifacts 2B and Q from Loc. 5, BSW were excavated but exact provenience of 2B has been lost and neither is described in Appendix I.
3. Artifact W-147 from base of BSW at Loc. 4 is not in Appendix I.
4. Artifacts not shown on any map: 937-7, 937-9, 937-15, 937-25-25a-25a2, 937-28, 937-68, 937-88.
5. Artifacts not on Chart – Appendix I – 937-50, 937-57, 4 E, E, 4 A, D.
6. Artifact M, plate 109, illustrates the same side of the artifact as plate 108, a mistake in plate layout.

On Loan to IISER Library

DATE DUE

DEMCO 38-297